ALVIN B. KERNAN

Yale University

Modern Satire

HARBRACE SOURCEBOOKS

under the general editorship of
David Levin
Stanford University

Harcourt, Brace & World, Inc.   *New York* · *Chicago* · *Burlingame*

CONTENTS

Satire has never had the best of reputations. Readers may admire it, but at the same time they find it embarrassingly ungenerous in its depiction of man, particularly when its harshness is contrasted with the kindly tolerance of comedy or the profound sympathy of tragedy for the failings of human nature. While lamenting this situation, the satirist has always stoutly defended the necessity for his savage art in a world where vulgarity and pride constantly threaten civilization. Alexander Pope's expression of the divine mission of satire in a world grown totally corrupt and *almost* incurably idiotic, states perfectly the sense of urgency and dedication which satirists have always felt:

O sacred weapon! left for Truth's defence,
Sole dread of Folly, Vice, and Insolence!
To all but Heaven-directed hands denied,
The Muse may give thee, but the Gods must guide.

Whenever nonsense has threatened to overwhelm sense, a satirist has appeared to strip away the solemn pretenses of dignity and worth with which the vulgar and foolish cover themselves, and to make clear the chaos toward which the world is tending. The prophet Jeremiah exposed the stiff-necked pride and worldliness of the Jews; Aristophanes the dangerous reliance on human reason of the fifth-century Athenians; Horace and Juvenal the power-seeking and self-indulgence of the Romans of the early Empire; Erasmus and Rabelais the pomposity and muddledom of the scholastics; John Skelton and Ben Jonson the proud boast of Renaissance man to make of himself and his world whatever he willed; Dryden, Pope, Swift, and Voltaire the Enlightenment's unexamined belief in the inherent goodness of man and society; Byron

the Romantic identification of man as a purely noble and spiritual creature for whom the body was only unimportant baggage.

After a lapse during the Victorian period— the Victorian optimism and concern for manners caused such satirists as Thomas Love Peacock, Samuel Butler, and Lewis Carroll to mute and soften their criticism of society— satire has had a revival in our own century in tne woɪk oɪ such writers as Waugh, Nathanael West, Aldous Huxley, Orwell, Auden, and Wyndham Lewis. Great satire is usually written, we are told, in periods when there is general agreement on morals, when the majority of men define right and wrong in the same way. But this has certainly not been the case in the relativistic twentieth century, and probably not at any time. Apparently our satirists have been brought into being by a suitable target for their attacks, a target so large and obvious—and so dangerous—that the potential satirist has been unable to resist. "Fools rush into my head, and so I write" is Pope's way of declaring that the foolishness of the world, not the venom of the satirist, creates satire. In our time the particular form that this tempting foolishness has taken is a specious and fatuously simple belief in progress, progress based on some form of material improvement, on scientific achievements, and on wildly optimistic assumptions about human nature and history. Our satirists do not, of course, necessarily deny that man can improve himself and his lot in life—if they did they wouldn't bother to write—but they are harsh critics of unreasoned and unearned views of progress which conveniently neglect the awkward facts of human existence.

All satires appearing in this volume attack some variety of the modern belief that man and his institutions are better than they were in the past and that our morals, our social institutions, our technology, and our wisdom are all approaching perfection. In each work the satirist has contrived some clever technique for confronting these beliefs with the inescapable facts of existence which make simple views of progress ridiculous and untenable. It should perhaps be added that the history of our century seems to have produced the same kind of rude shocks for our characteristic hope that every day, in every way, we are getting better and better. Total war, concentration camps, overpopulation, nuclear bombs, brainwashing, advertising, overproduction, and persistent, widespread anxiety are all either the unwelcome by-products of discoveries that were once thought to be evidence for the progress of civilization, or manifestations of the unchanging facts of human nature.

The volume is arranged so that the satires reprinted here not only form a series of attacks on various kinds of "progress," but offer, as well, an outline of the range and the major techniques of satire. The first items, Wylie's battering of the American educational system and Twain's mocking treatment of missionaries, lie on the very boundary of satire. Some critics might, in fact, prefer to term them "invective" and exclude them from the category of satire altogether. My own opinion is that works of this type are a definite form of satire, more sophisticated varieties of the primitive satires described by Robert Elliott in the essay "The Satirist and Society," printed in the critical section of this volume. At any rate, attacks like Wylie's and Twain's are closely related to the type of work we normally call "satire," and, whether they are included in that category or not, they will provide the basis for interesting and illuminating comparisons with the other more traditional types of satire. The contents are ordered to facilitate this kind of comparison: we begin with Philip Wylie's direct attack on contemporary education and pass on to works in which the satire becomes increasingly more indirect and shielded. By the time we reach the short stories and *Animal Farm* the satirists pretend to attack nothing at all, maintaining the fiction that they are simply telling amusing little tales. At the same time the satires provide an example from each of the principal modes of literature: essay, poem, play, short story, and novel, demonstrating that the satiric spirit, like the tragic or comic spirit, may find expression in all of the principal kinds of writing. This arrangement will permit the teacher, if he desires, to discuss the differences among the major literary modes.

As satire revived in this century, and as first-rate authors began to work again in this genre, critics responded by attempting to define the formal characteristics of this kind of writing and by suggesting ways of reading it. The three critical selections included here approach these tasks in different ways. Robert C. Elliott's "The Satirist and Society" explores the activities of primitive satirists and their relation to the tribes for whom, or on whom, they employed their magical arts. By coming at satire from the direction of the primitive, Elliott provides both a theory of the origins of satire and an illuminating explanation of its fundamental values and dangers. Northrop Frye's "The Mythos of Winter: Irony and Satire" and my own "Theory of Satire" attempt to extract from the satire written in historical times the standard difficulties involved in reading satire, the nature of the satiric vision of life, and the patterns or "configurations" in which this vision is invariably expressed. The extracts from David Worcester's *The Art of Satire* bring us closer to the verbal texture of satire by focusing on the rhetorical figures regularly employed in this type of writing. Because of the broad historical range of these critical essays they provide the reader with a history of satire at the same time that they raise a variety of specific questions relevant to the satires included in this book: the relation of the author to his work, the interaction of moral standards and the form of satire, the question of exaggeration and truthfulness. While helping the student to read these satires, the critical essays should also lead him to some general understanding of the nature of satire as a literary genre different from such other genres as tragedy and comedy.

The supplementary material makes available to the student some information which will help him to understand the satires. For example, Lewis Mumford's discussion of the

"Doctrine of Progress" as it developed in the late eighteenth and the nineteenth centuries provides a good description of the conditions which made for a belief in progress and the objections which have been raised to it. These supplementary materials allow for a variety of exercises, such as a comparison of the use Byron makes of *ottava rima* and the ways in which Auden employs his approximation of this stanza form. Three pieces bearing directly on Orwell's *Animal Farm* have been grouped together to provide some help in reading and understanding the novel and to raise certain questions about its purpose, its effectiveness, and its value. Short introductions have been provided for each piece of writing, and some suggestions for papers of various lengths and types have been placed either directly after the work they bear on or at the end of the volume.

ALVIN B. KERNAN

December 1961
New Haven, Connecticut

I. Selections

PHILIP WYLIE

A Specimen American Institution

When Philip Wylie's *Generation of Vipers,* from which this attack on American education is taken, first appeared during World War II (1943), the reviewers had a number of unpleasant things to say about the book. It was, they said, an "embarrassing vulgarity," "a tub-thumping diatribe," "uninterrupted, violent, and petulant complaint," "magnificent arrogance coupled with ignorance." The book, we were told, was written by Wylie "at the top of his voice as if he were shouting," and the "rudimentary" perceptions of the troubles in American society were deliberately "meant to shock." About the best that was said of the book was that it was a candid display of "honest and utter confusion."

This is about par for the course for any satirist, who can, if he is effective, always expect to be charged with sadism, pruriency, misanthropy, and envy. But despite the bad press and the characteristic American distaste for criticism—"Boost, Don't Knock"—*Generation of Vipers* has persisted sturdily through twenty editions and one revision, and has recently come out in a paper-bound edition. It is perhaps the best modern American example of the ancient and honorable art of direct attack, of going at your antagonist with every available rhetorical weapon in order to overwhelm him. Some readers may prefer not to call this kind of writing "satire," arguing that it is simply a display of bad temper and a release of frustrations, while true satire is a more artful, a more indirect indictment of men and their institutions. Mr. Wylie does appear in this piece to be writing in the white heat of anger, simply pouring out onto the page his naked feelings about the mess of modern American education, without stopping to shape or control his statements. But a careful examination of "A Specimen American Institution" will reveal that Wylie's prose is very artful indeed, and that one of the most skillful effects is, in fact, the carefully maintained fiction that the author is simply an artless and honest man who says what he thinks without fear of consequences. Wylie's writing offers a good opportunity to analyze the techniques and effectiveness of first-person satire, that standard type of satire in which the author pretends to speak in his own person, denouncing iniquity in good, plain terms. The prophet Jeremiah, the Roman satirist Juvenal, the English satirists Pope and Swift, and many others have all pretended, along with Philip Wylie, that, as Juvenal puts it, *si natura negat, facit indignatio versum;* that though they are not endowed with poetic gifts by nature, their indignation at the foolishness of the world has made writers of them.

Philip Wylie (b. 1902) is the author of a number of novels and general philosophical works, and of a great many popular fishing stories. "A Specimen American Institution" forms Chapter 7 of *Generation of Vipers*. The version printed here is from the revised edition (1955). The footnotes were added in this latest edition by Wylie to meet objections to the first version of the book and to show that his predictions had been proven true.

Lux et veritas. Light and truth.

The school, excepting for its sedulous care in teaching the basic principles of the physical sciences—interesting, necessary, and pertinent though they are—is the instrument of stupidity and lies. Just as the church is the repository of man's instinct, including by fiat his sex instinct, which neither man nor the church knows what to do with, so the school is the organ for promulgating the secular traditions by which man has tried to compass and codify his instinct. He has always made the attempt, so far, through organizations rather than through individual effort. It is a pity.

The school is an organism which teaches reading, writing, and arithmetic. It does that so the pupil can communicate. These accomplishments should also be taught so the pupil can *think,* but few schools have stumbled upon that notion of education. A thinking child would not think much of school—which would upset the system. The next step in school procedure is to teach the child political geography. A notion that political geography is permanent is imbued in the pupil—though how that can be done these days is more than I know.

Thus, to the average product of the little red schoolhouse, or the big cement one in the city, the boundaries of Oregon are important and permanent—congruent, approximately, to the Atlas Mountains.

Here the sinister process unfolds. The Atlas Mountains are real. Only the ages will change them—by erosion. But Oregon is a myth. It does not exist. Temporary posts mark its border—but even its border was once uncertain. Its size was once different. Oregon is only an idea. It is in no scientific sense a reality.

Revolution, a referendum, or enemy action could change the shape of Oregon, the color of the people in it, its name, and its nationality. There will only be an Oregon—just as there will only be an England, in spite of the song—so long as a group of people are agreed to keep in mind that the name of a certain arbitrary area on the surface of the earth is Oregon, or England.

In Oregon (and Massachusetts, and Texas, for that matter) they will tell you that Oregon is a lot more. They will say it is a tradition, a way of life, a kind of people, an accent, or apples in the midst of a dank west coast morning. They will give you all sorts of arguments to prove that Oregon is *something*—besides an idea. But it isn't. You could replace all the people and still call it Oregon and all but the people who were dispossessed would agree it still *was* Oregon. Oregon, then, is a dream.

So, for another example, is a dollar bill. A dollar bill is nothing in itself. The idea of a "dollar," in fact, is nothing. Once, it stood for a certain part of an ounce of gold. Then the rules changed and you could no longer get gold for it. Its value was recently decreased from one hundred cents to fifty-nine cents. The "worth" of a dollar is, therefore, unstable and subject to change. The dollar itself is a piece of paper with silk threads in it and ink on it. No more, as such, than the wrapping of a cigarette package. A Confederate dollar, which once bought things, won't any more. A dollar is also a dream—one that exists only so long as men agree that it exists. If men even argue about the value of a dollar, its value changes.

It is not necessary further to elaborate that idea. But *how many* similar concepts have you, as a school-taught American, misidentified in your mind? You do not know.

A few years ago the American "intellectuals" (again a dream—this one, their own) turning from a futile bout with what they called "humanism" fell with glad cries upon semantics. Semantics deals with meanings. It is no wonder that the intellectuals, having thought so hard and written so much only to find tenet after tenet as carefully explained by themselves collapse in the face of reality, should suddenly decide to delve into the meaning of meaning. It is no wonder, either, that, having exhausted the superficial illumination which flows from the study of semantics, they did not pursue it back to the origin of all meaning, and find it in their own internal struggles. Such a step would have demonstrated that, in the real meaning of "intellectual," they were using *their* intellects for nothing more than antique theological rhetoric, dressed up as "science." The intellectuals have a spiritual wall against that shock which is easily as thick as the wall in the minds of the godly.

But even a superficial understanding of the meanings of words is a help toward thought. This applies, especially, to words like "state" and "dollar."[1]

Children should be taught above all else to make the simple distinction between real objects and arbitrary ideas, between real laws and mere opinions, between facts and mere rules or prejudices. They are not, of course, so it is almost impossible to find an adult whose mind has escaped from the vise of the institutional method of our schools. You may not find it hard to apperceive that Oregon is nothing, outside the heads of men. It will probably be more difficult for you to accept the fact that a dollar, too, is nothing except a loose agreement between people. You will be likely to quibble about it. (A dollar may change in value, but there has to be *some*

[1] It was obvious to numerous readers of this discussion that I had not made myself familiar with semantics, that I was ignorant of Korzybski and Hayakawa and the rest. At their suggestion, I have made my way through some dozen or so books on the subject and so become aware that this field of "meaning" has been explored by men better qualified than I. And, while I emerged from my perusal with an assurance that semantics does not, as Korzybski thought, connote a philosophical system, I do appreciate it as a great, new instrument for reasoning. It will be a long while, however, before many people—even many teachers—come to see how badly their rigid symbols have bolted their brains together.

standard; there has been money, even for exchange between savages, for ages; etc.) But if I were to suggest to you that no fact whatever was *necessarily* described by the following words, you might be even harder put: murder, vice, holiness, courage.

Nevertheless, that is the case. Your idea of each is, in fact, your own. You have not added much to them; perhaps you have taken a good deal from those concepts as they were originally given to you. But the original gift was crummy, for nobody told you those things were all opinions.

The little red schoolhouse would scarcely hand out for a school lunch an allotment of sandwiches, half of which were poisoned and none of which was labeled. Of course, owing to greedy boards of education and stingy or stupid lunchroom managers, school children are often served sandwiches which contain metallic poisons, botulus bacilli, and so on, and the tots die. But the schoolhouse *is* engaged in the steady business of passing out information, part of which is poison and part food, but all unlabeled. Half the people in hospitals are insane—the people who got the poisoned sandwiches. The rest of the people, sick from lighter doses of the red schoolhouse toxins, are trying to carry on the affairs of a great republic. A pretty sight, you must admit.

The kids are dosed and overdosed not only with opinions stated as fact but with opinions that are cockeyed and fact that is deliberately made into falsehood.

The teaching of history, for instance, which begins in the sixth or seventh grade, is a shoddy performance and all educators now alive should, in fairness, be given the noose and faggot for it. I don't mean, merely, such rubbish as George-Washington-couldn't-tell-a-lie, but the whole subject. Ancient history, dehumanized and fumigated, is proffered as a rote exercise in place and ruin identification, simplified battle plan, and old law. One long look at the murals of Pompeii would teach more ancient history than fifty years in such a classroom.

American history of the school brand is a disgrace to the human cerebrum. It is taught as if America, an infallible nation, rose through heroism from dire persecution, with a shining and untarnished escutcheon. This is not the stuff to give drips, because it compounds drippery. In the first place, its inhuman excess of virtue makes it unreal and thus very dull. In the second, it in no way educates. To the mind of a future voter, the contents of a school history book are about as valuable as a knowledge of all the formulas for all the emetics in Christendom. Think, for a moment, of a few of the facts.

America was founded by a multitude of discontented colonists and a handful of well-intentioned men and women who took advantage of a European war to free themselves of taxation. It was partly a godly land, but in larger part, a slave-trading, rum-tippling, whoring melee of lawless opportunists who couldn't get along in a more conventionally organized society. It stuck together because a few men with a few ideals, wily compromisers who failed to compromise, were backed in a civil war by the industrial half of the union against the agricultural South. In the American Revolution, our book-vaunted militia broke and ran a dozen times from Hessian mercenaries and British regulars. In the civil war, our record of graft and bad generalship, of draft rioting and governmental mismanagement was unparalleled.

The conquest of the West was, again, the most brutal, brawling page of exploitatious and irresponsible rapine yet written by any nation upon its own population. Just in the process, a whole cross section of ethnology was pushed off the map: the Indians.

Our part in the First World War might have been considerable—and costly in human lives. It was not, many though our monuments may be, and the multitudes of men who came back brought from the whole of Europe one idea that topped all others in spread and repetition: that the French were sexually perverse.

We, who high-hat the British for their Empire, have already taken the empire of a hundred whole nations of red men, together with assorted chunks of sod we lifted from Spain, Canada, France, and Mexico.

Such are a few of the nonglorious pages of history. Taught truthfully, they might startle the moppets into an effort to improve a society plainly in bad shape. They would give no smug sense of national grandeur and security. We need leaders to reform our world —but reform begins with evil seen—and not where the teacher and the book point only with perfect pride.

In these days of war, patriots are busy saying that the "debunking" which has been modestly attempted in the last few decades has so soured and spoiled the souls of the young that they have no patriotism at all, no eagerness to die for their land, and no earnest will to fight for freedom. Of the young now soldiers, there is no use to speak. They no longer have any choice. But the indictment squarely fits millions of civilians. It fits not because of honest iconoclasm, however, but because of the failure of everybody—the educators, the intellectuals, the debunkers, and the sleazy people themselves—to hunt up and substitute real values for the false ones which were taken away by the debunking.

Such, of course, is the "practical" danger of teaching history as our schools teach it: somebody will come along and kick the props out of every lesson, leaving a vacuous lot of routed thumb-suckers.

Somebody has proved that Washington chased women and Grant was a drunk, that Lincoln told dirty jokes and that there was no Betsy Ross. Where, then, are the young minds? Busy in war—without reason, anchor, philosophy, introspection, knowledge, integrity, faith, hope, code, or even sanity—fighting because Mr. Whiskers makes them do it—with a vague and moody hope that somehow, someday, things will be better—and everybody will be Cinderella or the Prince and eat candy always.

The most Lethean error of the eunuch moms who operate the little red schoolhouse for the politicians has been to forget death. Death is implicit in what I call integrity and what others call honor or even just responsibility. Death is not merely an industrial hazard or the result of careless driving. During the first half of our national existence it was apparent that demise in war was a social function and the sterner schools of that period taught the fact. Custard-like thinking, quibble, and the nature of momism have wiped the bold and bloody axioms from the slates of the youngsters. Japs, Germans and Russians are taught they may die for their respective countries. The Chinese are always decently aware of the imminence of death. The English, even lately, have entertained a dim realization that extinction was possible.

Not we. Dying for liberty, for an ideal, or for any other sound reason has no place in our curriculum. It is, to American moppets, the romantic, exhilarating and obsolete activity of a group of ill-housed, ill-fed and ill-clad people who once lived in this country, fought amid its unlumbered regions, and were called patriots. No teacher, for the past generation, has greeted her roomful of fresh young morning faces with the words: "It is almost inevitable that a goodly proportion of you will die for your country; arrange your thinking to suit that fact." Such a greeting would have done wonders in sobering the radio-movie-comic-strip minds and helping them to put first things first. A kid who grows up thinking he may be knocked off to maintain the public franchise maintains that franchise while alive—or is likely to try to.

But the Americans who went to the last war didn't consider dying. They sang about coming back. And those who are girding themselves for this one still hope and believe that by some miracle it will be over before any large-scale perishing takes place. Moreover, since they were reared without the background of necessary risk, they lack the emotional foundation necessary for the maintenance of ideals in the face of confusions, arguments, treacheries and follies. No effort has yet been made either by the government or the schools to re-establish that foundation; the churches have made an opposite effort; science is still too rudimentary to comprehend the need of it.

The result is that we are asking our men to fight for what they regard as antipathetic attitudes, in hundreds of thousands of individual cases. They believe they are being forced to fight to maintain the New Deal, or to pave the way for socialism, or to keep Roosevelt in office, or to create a militaristic nucleus which will later become a political bloc, or to save the British Empire, or to settle remote and irrelevant European quarrels, or to establish new and arbitrary rights for labor, or for any other of a dozen such ideas. The grisly corruption of labor, the indeterminate international outlook of numerous European squabbles, the occasionally rancid political history of army veterans, the many sophistries and casuistries of Roosevelt, and the unrealistic diaperism of much of the New Deal are not, and will never be adequate reasons for dying. They are merely fine reasons for political argument and heavy balloting.

None of them, unfortunately, has anything to do with the reasons for which we are fighting—reasons which ought to make every American ready to risk his life without hesitation. We are fighting because we have the best way of life yet learned by mankind and we want to preserve it. We are fighting because a couple of hundred million mechanized atavars have sworn to murder and enslave us. Those are the two existing reasons. There should be another: we should be fighting because we have the intelligence, will and dignity to sacrifice ourselves whenever mass retrogression threatens numbers of our human fellows. The little red schoolhouse never taught the last thesis and it has overlooked the preceding two for so long that our adults cannot discern their own interests any more. They will have to learn the hard way, now: by doing.

Small wonder we have no battle-cry or battle song—for this one![2]

Our history is every human history: a black and gory business, with more scoundrels than wise men at the lead, and more louts than both put together to cheer and follow. This is the most moral war men ever engaged in; and we have not enough moral sense left to see it.

I might say here, before we get deeper into this deep business, and while we are on an erudite subject like education, that I could fill this opus with asterisks; under the as-

[2] Although World War II continued for more than three years, no noteworthy songs ever emerged. The ballads of World War I are, today, more frequently heard. The songs of the Second War were weak and dependent (God Bless America), fatuous (Praise the Lord and Pass the Ammunition), feeble-minded (There'll Be Bluebirds over the White Cliffs of Dover) or childish in an effort to be martial (Off We Go into the Wild Blue Yonder). People frequently think that *postwar* songs were written earlier; they tend to identify the lovely, romantic music of "South Pacific" with the unlovely facts of, say, Guadalcanal. As the evils of Europe have been expunged and we have become friends with the Germans—so the dreadful combat in the Pacific has been Michenerized. Korea produced no music I ever heard of.

terisks in small type I could quote a slew of cross references and supply recondite confirmation for each fact. That kind of business, a literary loading of the dice, is not germane to my method. If names come in, they will appear in the large print.

This aside on source references will serve, in connection with the discussion of schools, to introduce the name of Dorothy Thompson, one of the great she-sachems of the intellectuals. She has the virtue of being exceedingly earnest. She has had several sound, workable ideas, mostly of a retributive nature. She has the additional nuance of knowing always, in a superficial way, what she is talking about, and even that is rare in women. But she has the handicap, like any average product of modern educational methods, of not knowing *why* she talks about anything at all, or why anybody does what anybody does. She can answer the routine questions of who, where, what, when, and how. But when you ask why, she talks gibberish from the book.

"The three main props of western civilization," writes this precious example of what I'm discussing . . . "Christianity, Rationality, and Organized Law." There, forsooth, is the little red schoolhouse talking! If these are, in truth, the props of Western society, then Western society is done for. They *could* be. They aren't.

I have pointed out that not half the population belongs to a church. I shall later show why not one church member in ten thousand has the faintest idea of what Christ was talking about. Our civilization, as this book is designed to demonstrate, suffers from *not* being rational and from not knowing that it is *irrational*. As for "organized law," whatever that is, there is no longer much relationship between our law and what we already admit about ourselves and there is no organization of the law, to speak of, whatever. Besides, law, in point of usefulness, exists only in so far as it is enforced. If American law or any other sort is enforced here, then, all these years, my nine senses have betrayed me.

The little muckers dawdle through school, getting such ideas as that our society is Christian, rational, and our law organized. They grow up and believe them. Then, whatever happens, they assume it is divine. Such

is the teaching of fact and morality. Consider the teaching of art.

English literature (an art) is rubbed into the human American hide by the school as if it were a hormone salve. The friction continues after the grease has disappeared and the hard palm of the teacher goes on chafing until not one graduate in ten thousand, to employ again a useful and conservative figure, gives a damn for reading all the rest of his life. Pulp fiction, yes. But real reading—no.

We are a "literate" nation. But there are not a million adults in America today who could comprehend even this casual treatise. There are hardly a million who voluntarily read nonfiction books.

That is a satisfactory comment on the educational system, from the standpoint of the essayist. It shows that, in the matter of teaching English, either our schools are incompetent to deal with our moppets or else society has produced a gaggle of Dodger fans, impervious to any literary schooling.

English, it happens, is our only common means of communication. A recent scientific study of "successful" business and professional men has shown that the graph of their vocabulary parallels the graph of their success, but bears no relation to the amount of their formal schooling. From that and other abundant evidence it may be assumed that the English a person knows will have a very direct relationship to his success as a person, his usefulness to the state, and his peace of mind and pride of being.

The way to teach English would be to divide pupils by aptitude rather than by age, to insist on grammatical precision from the start, and to see to it that errors in grammar and in usage, as well as vocabulary failures, brought punitive deprivations. Rewards would not be made. To reward a child for the performance of a duty is to corrupt it with Cinderellaism. Life holds no such rewards. The first gold star a child gets in school for the mere performance of a needful task is its first lesson in graft. Discipline is essential. A man clumsy in syntax cannot express himself. A man ignorant of terms cannot learn anything.

Children who are unable to learn or who will not learn the exact use of the only tongue in which, probably, they will ever try to articulate their ideas should not be permitted to listen to radios, go to movies, or otherwise amuse themselves with the ideo-onanisms of our society. If this restraining practice is instituted early enough and sternly enough—if it is attended to at school and followed up at home—most youngsters will by the age of twelve have a sufficient sense of ease and confidence with their native tongue to proceed more or less of their own momentum in the employment of reading as a means of self-advancement, an augmentation of consciousness, and an interesting pleasure. The rest will behave foolishly all their lives, vote badly, risk wars, aid the unscrupulous, and so menace your peace, health, safety, and life.

There is no way to pound such an exacting skill as reading into the brain of the yapping barbarian which a ten-year-old is—save by physical deprivation or punishment. No motive but the physical will make sense to his undeveloped brain. Any pretensions on his part to loftier ideals, such as religious ones, are sheer fatuity, sly purchase, or the remembrance of racial ceremony, largely orgy, associated in his young but by no means tender consciousness with mayhem rather than manners.

Since there flows in our veins largely the blood of generations of people who have managed to survive by the low cunning and treachery necessitated by the unnatural aspect of all past society, some kids will be unamenable even to the physical system of compulsory education. Taking away their desserts or knocking them on the head will not enliven them to any effectual effort at serious learning, even of their own language. These people should not be permitted to continue their schooling along general lines. An effort might be made to reclaim some of them after they reach maturity. But most should be prepared at once for the sedentary handicrafts—work in the trades, in the factories, in the iron seats of farm machines, and at the pump handles of filling stations. They have no aptitude for learning, make no use of what they do manage to be taught, and are a waste of tax money. A group of that group, the least stable and reasonable, should be politically disenfranchised. No one in the entire multitude should

ever be permitted to hold public office. And a certain small percentage of this dreadful offal, much of which regularly accumulates in the bleachers of our ball parks, should be quietly put to sleep.[3]

That is, of course, real democracy. That is the true application of the plan to give every man an equal opportunity. Any other is a fascism of sentimentality, forever handicapping the abler majority with an incompetent minority, artificially made equal—the feeble-minded, warped, stupid, cruel, mean, perverse, deluded, hysterical, dull, depraved, and silly. There must be reason in our collective behavior soon, as all can perceive. There must be an end to a government of boobs, by boobs, for boobs. Because there are already more boobs in our society than wise men, or even than scrupulous men, and the machines devised by science are so exact, so productive, and so powerful that a government which is in the hands of boobs will as surely commit national suicide as a sixteen-year-old kid,

[3] There is now much ado concerning all these matters and especially juvenile delinquency—though no one else, so far as I am aware, has even ironically suggested that the most hopeless of the lot be put to sleep. The "home" is blamed for the misbehavior of youth—and then it is found that some of the nastiest assassins come from "good" homes. So the "school" is blamed, as if personality were formed there—rather than at home, well before any child reached school.

No one seems willing to confess that "juvenile delinquency" as it occurs these days is, quite plainly, proof that the "American way of life" itself is sick. The teachers, whom I have rather harshly treated here, are not to blame for their own lack of education, incompetence, genetic inadequacy, and so on. The goals of our society are such that only the less attractive and the less aggressive remain to teach—the social leftovers; and our general population is so well satisfied (consciously) with its cheesy objectives that it is content to have its youth "taught" by bevies of suggestible, spineless dimwits. That amounts in essence to one more scramble for short-range, private gain at the certain cost—if the attitude persists—of national suicide.

To pretend to educate people—which we do—to "pass" every student (for the presumed sake of "personality") is to give all USA a gradual lobotomy, destined finally to produce vegetables, not men. By such means we are not even keeping abreast of the prejudicial system called "education" in Russia.

What is remarkable is that, here and there, a few able people still elect to teach; what is lucky is that even one good teacher in a lifetime may sometimes change a delinquent into a solid citizen.

blind drunk on a blind curve, doing eighty in a twelve-cylinder sedan.

The idea of universal education sounded sensible to the founding fathers. Universal education consisted, then, in teaching everybody the language, simple arithmetic, and the structure of eighteenth century society. Science was elementary. Industry was nil, as we know it. There is no such society today. Only a third of contemporary people, at a generous guess, are even potentially educable to the degree at which their judgment would be of any value to the rest of man, politically, socially, morally, economically, or any other way. There should be an equal opportunity to have this higher education. But those competent to profit by it should not be held for one day to the standards of the whole. To do so is to impose slavery of the mind in the name of national mental emancipation.

An educated man does *not* go on all his life believing American history was hearts and flowers. He does *not* go on thinking that the Romans were purely ornamental people who wore togas and spoke ponderously in their senate. He does *not* learn his native tongue so badly that he makes errors in the use of it, does not know the main words in it, and has no adult wish, ever, to read any book printed in it except such stuff as wet dreams are made of.

Above everything, perhaps, an educated man can tell at once the difference between a fact and an opinion. He knows whether a subject is established or debatable. He knows, for example, that you can argue forever on what mistakes Spinoza may have made—but that it is foolish to argue at all about the height of the Sphinx or the weight of Mars.

The schools give pupils no such approach to life. Because universal education is a national law, they do not dare to. Nine-year-olds, backed by political drag, money, prejudice, and other blackmail power, make it impossible for schools to teach anything but gibberish. That reason, plus the sheer inability of two-thirds of every class to stay in the same mental games with the other, together with the peewee caliber of teachers as a class, has reduced our education to a public swindle, an assassination of sanity.

A teacher who said Washington was a whoremaster would be confronted by the D.A.R. A teacher who said that there was no scientific evidence of the existence of the Holy Ghost would be confronted by the Baptist Church. A teacher who said our militia broke and ran in countless battles would be confronted by the American Legion. A teacher who said contraception was a social and not a religious problem would be confronted by the Catholic Church. A teacher who said man was evolved from the lower animals would be (and was) tried in court. It happened not so many years ago in the sovereign, dim-brained state of Tennessee.

Yet, upon exact perspective of such matters our nation's future depends. We cannot even hope to plan effectively without knowing *all* the facts we can scrape together about our past. Science will serve only the avarice of molten asses if asses can outvote the wise. We will go on believing such utter rot as that we are Christian and rational and have organized law, if we go on trying to educate saps and thereby make saps of the intelligent. The result will be chaos. The result *is* chaos, in fact.

Most of our people have been taken with the idea of easy living. Because machines can produce so much, they argue, man must be on the threshold of a cinch. But goods, as I have said in one way, and will in another, add little real ease to life and the total worship of goods, in the end, takes away all peace and all security. A man who sets out to find the economic solution of today's problems is merely burning joss sticks to goods. In a world that is engaged in the reckless rush for mass-produced material objects there is neither room nor time for honesty, consideration, integrity of thought, introspection, or the operation of conscience. In such a world—democratic, fascist, soviet, whatever the form of government—there will be no security because security comes from man's trust of man—man's confidence in man—and the mills cannot manufacture it and the state cannot guarantee it. Only each man, working within himself to the best of his ability, can create temporal security. So long as the few basic hungers in man are contented, more goods cannot add anything even to that security.

But we are in a goods-mad world. Our statesmen tonight are trying to figure out how to make security out of this madness for things. It cannot be done. If we do not turn upon ourselves the terrible honesty our science has turned upon goods, we are done for. This war, this uprooting—the second—will be only a stumble on the path back to a new start in a new savagery far deeper than that of a thousand years ago.

We will probably win this one. Then what? Does anybody believe that trade treaties and economic agreements will point the way to the reorientation of man and the discipline of his instinct by his head and heart? Sure. Our school-taught public. But will they not, rather, point to some vast new competition of nations? Inevitably, they will.

When the sons of those who do not die now are grown old enough to die, the sour-breathed economic uplifters' peace will be decaying. These United States, secure again, goods-crazed again, suffering still the inevitable cycle of boom and depression, isolated again, may find the valiant Russians have taken the production bit in their teeth and are not only "plundering" world trade but storing up arms to make a conquest of the U.S.A. Or, perhaps, out of Tibet and Mongolia will come direful rumors of new weapons, new engines, new trade policies, new ways to invest and seize a neighboring land—and the sons of those sons will go out into the night in bigger aircraft, with guns that poison a cubic mile of sky with gas, and set about to restore "decency" where there never was much decency to start with.

Man's destiny lies half within himself, half without. To advance in either half at the expense of the other is literally insane. We are almost all, of course, as mad as hatters. Our statesmen, our scientists, ourselves. You. Indeed, if you go on reading this book, unless it makes you wiser, it will very likely cause you to cork off screaming to the nut factory. You belong there anyway and, deep inside yourself, you know it. A self-made fool, like most others who are professional lunatics—a spot of protoplasm—wet blather on a wet globe—at heart a murderer, a thief, a hypocrite, a desperate jackanapes—because you are ashamed to face the truth.

There is the Cinderella myth, which makes you spend your days in any sort of travail, however nonsensical, dull or destructive, in order to get together the goods which will enable you (you think) to be or to create a Cinderella, depending on your sex. There is the stork myth, which makes you believe all sorts of rubbish but keeps you from the horrible necessity of having to meditate on what is real. Such bilge and its promulgator, the school, which ought really to teach you a few scientific lies just to give you a start at primitive reasoning and which actually teaches you a pottage of data and no route to reason at all, are the stuff you consider your education.

There is just a chance, a slim, angry chance, that the disastrous state of things, these days, may enable us to notch ourselves forward a small inch on the road of our common evolution. Because, at last, we know we must do *something*. We might, in consequence, get a glimmering of what to do. We will not be able to pat out a nifty global recipe as easily as Dorothy Thompson solves an international problem on three sheets of typewriter paper. But we may start doing better.

To the extent that we have denied the power of our instincts—to the extent that we have really believed the extravagant piffle that we are Christian, rational, and legal—they have kicked us to pieces.

But to the extent that the wide world is a tortured, screaming insult to the very word "man," our instincts have been at work on the other side, trying to get the pieces back together. We have been frightened by the magnitude of our incompetence. The indecency of the danger that rides the night wind over every home has made us willing to yield a little of our tradition and prejudice if it will seem to promise something of security in the times ahead. But we are reluctant, still, to give much—even a few weekly gallons of gasoline—for the chance of ourselves and our families to survive. That is a measure of our stupidity, and of our slavishness to ourselves.

We are going to kill people—which is a relief. They are people, in the aggregate, more bestial and conceited than we—and that makes the relief a holy cause. We propose, in this moment of fear anyway, to share the world's goods a trifle more generously. That is a forward step. We are discovering, in a score of nations, that vivid life can be maintained without the accustomed luxuries and comforts. That lesson will have value if there is added to it the discovery that man's spirit can flame higher, and man himself feel far more noble, in the execution of his duty to other men than in the mere acquisition of junk at the expense of duty. But, looking back over history and looking forward at the peace proposals, no one can be certain we will learn, in this age, much of that last lesson—the only important one.

The pleasure-lusting halves of all the legends are finished, for the nonce. Across the planet stalk the evil archetypes in such plain view that all men have to admit their power. It would be good if we would try to remember them afterward, if we would take the skeletons out of our closets and put them where they belong—in places of honor at our future feasts: thus, at last, giving the devil his due and denying—nothing. They have been so carefully hidden by—the "educators"!

Questions

1. What is Wylie's major complaint against modern American education? What illustrations does he provide to support his argument?

2. Whom and what does he blame for this dangerous situation?

3. What values does he believe in and how does he support them?

4. Wylie is a master of the use of the disabling adjective and the unpleasant comparison. Go through "A Specimen American Institution" and pick out several adjectives and comparisons which seem innocuous enough but in fact discredit the persons, ideas, or institutions to which they are applied.

5. Analyze in the same way some of Wylie's other stylistic devices: the sudden shift in tone, the exaggerated example, the unpleasant or shocking reference, the use of quotation marks and italics.

6. Pick some "fact" which Wylie offers—for example, his "true history of the United States"—and discuss whether or not he *is* being factual.

7. One reviewer said of *Generation of Vipers* when it first appeared that it "was meant to shock." Is there any evidence that Wylie is deliberately overstating his case? If so, does he do so merely to be sensational, or can his exaggeration and overstatement be defended as a necessary part of his satire?

SAMUEL CLEMENS

To the Person Sitting in Darkness

Samuel Clemens, universally known as Mark Twain (1835-1910), was one of America's most famous comic writers and one of the few original satirists this country has produced. He is best known, of course, for his novels *The Adventures of Tom Sawyer* and *The Adventures of Huckleberry Finn.*

"To the Person Sitting in Darkness" appeared in the *North American Review* in 1901, shortly after the Boxer Rebellion had been put down in China. The savagery of European and American reprisals, masked under the hypocritical pretense of restoring civilization, order, and Christianity, offered Mark Twain an opportunity to question the meaning and value of the entire effort of the Western peoples to "civilize" their more primitive brethren in various parts of the world. Although the Boxer Rebellion and the relief of Peking interest us little today, the questions which Twain raises are of more crucial interest now than they were in 1900: there is more than one kind of missionary work.

Twain is quite a different satirist from Wylie, and a comparison of the two pieces will be enlightening. Where one uses the bludgeon on his victims, the other employs an extremely sharp knife to cut his antagonist slowly and neatly to pieces, smiling and pretending to be the most agreeable of men all the while. Much of the pleasure, and much of the meaning, of "To the Person Sitting in Darkness" comes from watching the clever way in which Twain works.

Christmas will dawn in the United States over a people full of hope and aspiration and good cheer. Such a condition means contentment and happiness. The carping grumbler who may here and there go forth will find few to listen to him. The majority will wonder what is the matter with him and pass on.—New York *Tribune,* on Christmas Eve.

From the *Sun,* of New York:

The purpose of this article is not to describe the terrible offenses against humanity committed in the name of Politics in some of the most notorious East Side districts. *They could not be described, even verbally.* But it is the intention to let the great mass of more or less careless citizens of this beautiful metropolis of the New World get some conception of the havoc and ruin wrought to man, woman, and child in the most densely populated and least-known section of the city. Name, date, and place can be supplied to those of little faith—or to any man who feels himself aggrieved. It is a plain statement of record and observation, written without license and without garnish.

Imagine, if you can, a section of the city territory completely dominated by one man, without whose permission neither legitimate nor illegitimate business can be conducted; *where illegitimate business is encouraged and legitimate business discouraged;* where the respectable residents have to fasten their doors and windows summer nights and sit in their rooms with asphyxiating air and 100-degree temperature, rather than try to catch the faint whiff of breeze in their natural breathing places, the stoops of their homes; *where naked women dance by night in the streets, and unsexed men prowl like vultures through the darkness on "business"* not only permitted but encouraged by the police; *where the education of infants begins with the knowledge of prostitution* and the training of little girls is training in the arts of Phryne; where *American* girls brought up with the refinements of *American* homes are imported from small towns upstate, Massachusetts, Connecticut, and New Jersey, and kept as virtually prisoners as if they were locked up behind jail bars until they have lost all semblance of womanhood; *where small boys are taught to solicit for the women of disorderly houses;* where there is an organized society of young men *whose sole business in life is to corrupt young girls and turn them over to bawdy houses;* where men walking with their wives along the street are openly insulted; *where children that have adult diseases are the chief patrons of the hospitals and dispensaries;* where it is the rule, rather than the exception, that *murder, rape, robbery, and theft go unpunished—* in short where the Premium of the most awful forms of Vice is the Profit of the politicians.

The following news from China appeared in the *Sun,* of New York, on Christmas Eve. The italics are mine:

The Rev. Mr. Ament, of the American Board of Foreign Missions, has returned from a trip which he made for the purpose of collecting indemnities for damages done by Boxers. *Everywhere he went he compelled the Chinese to pay.* He says that all his native Christians are now provided for. He had 700 of them under his charge, and 300 were killed. He has *collected 300 taels for each* of these murders, and has *compelled full payment for all the property belonging to Christians* that was destroyed. He also assessed *fines* amounting to THIRTEEN TIMES the amount of the indemnity. *This money will be used for the propagation of the Gospel.*

Mr. Ament declares that the compensation he has collected is *moderate* when compared with the amount secured by the Catholics, who demand, in addition to money, *head for head.* They collect 500 taels for each murder of a Catholic. In the Wenchiu country, 680 Catholics were killed, and for this the European Catholics here demand 750,000 strings of cash and 680 *heads.*

In the course of a conversation, Mr. Ament referred to the attitude of the missionaries toward the Chinese. He said:

"I deny emphatically that the missionaries are *vindictive,* that they *generally* looted, or that they have done anything *since* the siege that *the circumstances did not demand.* I criticize the Americans. *The soft hand of the Americans is not as good as the mailed fist of the Germans.* If you deal with the Chinese with a soft hand they will take advantage of it.

"The statement that the French government will return the loot taken by the French soldiers is the source of the greatest amusement here. The French soldiers were more systematic looters than the Germans, and it is a fact that to-day *Catholic Christians,* carrying French flags and armed with modern guns, *are looting villages* in the Province of Chili."

By happy luck, we get all these glad tidings on Christmas Eve—just in time to enable us to celebrate the day with proper gayety and enthusiasm. Our spirits soar, and we find we can even make jokes: Taels, I win, Heads you lose.

Our Reverend Ament is the right man in the right place. What we want of our missionaries out there is, not that they shall merely represent in their acts and persons the grace and gentleness and charity and loving-kindness of our religion, but that they shall also represent the American spirit. The oldest Americans are the Pawnees. Macallum's History says:

When a white Boxer kills a Pawnee and destroys his property, the other Pawnees do not trouble to seek *him* out, they kill any white person that comes along; also, they make some white village pay deceased's heirs the full cash value of deceased, together with full cash value of the property destroyed; they also make the village pay, in addition, *thirteen times* the value of that property into a fund for the dissemination of the Pawnee religion, which they regard as the best of all religions for the softening and humanizing of the heart of man. It is their idea that it is only fair and right that the innocent should be made to suffer for the guilty, and that it is better that ninety and nine innocent should suffer than that one guilty person should escape.

Our Reverend Ament is justifiably jealous of those enterprising Catholics, who not only get big money for each lost convert, but get "head for head" besides. But he should soothe himself with the reflections that the entirety of their exactions are for their own pockets, whereas he, less selfishly, devotes only 300 taels per head to that service, and gives the whole vast thirteen repetitions of the property-indemnity to the service of propagating the Gospel. His magnanimity has won him the approval of his nation, and will get him a monument. Let him be content with these rewards. We all hold him dear for manfully defending his fellow missionaries from ex-aggerated charges which were beginning to distress us, but which his testimony has so considerably modified that we can now con-template them without noticeable pain. For now we know that, even before the siege, the missionaries were not "generally" out looting, and that, "since the siege," they have acted quite handsomely, except when "circum-stances" crowded them. I am arranging for the monument. Subscriptions for it can be sent to the American Board; designs for it can be sent to me. Designs must allegorically set forth the Thirteen Reduplications of the Indemnity, and the Object for which they were exacted; as Ornaments, the designs must exhibit 680 Heads, so disposed as to give a pleasing and pretty effect; for the Catholics have done nicely, and are entitled to notice in the monu-ment. Mottoes may be suggested, if any shall be discovered that will satisfactorily cover the ground.

Mr. Ament's financial feat of squeezing a thirteen-fold indemnity out of the pauper peasants to square other people's offenses, thus condemning them and their women and inno-cent little children to inevitable starvation and lingering death, in order that the blood money so acquired might be *used for the propaga-tion of the Gospel*," does not flutter my seren-ity; although the act and the words, taken together, concrete a blasphemy so hideous and so colossal that, without doubt, its mate is not findable in the history of this or of any other age. Yet, if a layman had done that thing and justified it with those words, I should have shuddered, I know. Or, if I had done the thing and said the words myself—However, the thought is unthinkable, irreverent as some im-perfectly informed people think me. Some-times an ordained minister sets out to be blasphemous. When this happens, the layman is out of the running; he stands no chance.

We have Mr. Ament's impassioned assur-ance that the missionaries are not "vindic-tive." Let us hope and pray that they will never become so, but will remain in the almost morbidly fair and just and gentle temper which is affording so much satisfaction to their brother and champion to-day.

The following is from the New York *Trib-une* of Christmas Eve. It comes from that jour-nal's Tokyo correspondent. It has a strange and impudent sound, but the Japanese are but partially civilized as yet. When they be-come wholly civilized they will not talk so:

> The missionary question, of course, occupies a foremost place in the discussion. It is now felt as essential that the Western Powers take cog-nizance of the sentiment here, that religious in-vasions of Oriental countries by powerful West-ern organizations are tantamount to filibustering expeditions, and should not only be discounte-nanced, but that stern measures should be adopted for their suppression. The feeling here is that the missionary organizations constitute a constant menace to peaceful international rela-tions.

Shall we? That is, shall we go on conferring our Civilization upon the peoples that sit in darkness, or shall we give those poor things a rest? Shall we bang right ahead in our old-time, loud, pious way, and commit the new century to the game; or shall we sober up and sit down and think it over first? Would it not be prudent to get our Civilization tools to-gether, and see how much stock is left on hand in the way of Glass Beads and Theology, and Maxim Guns and Hymn Books, and Trade Gin and Torches of Progress and Enlighten-ment (patent adjustable ones, good to fire vil-lages with, upon occasion), and balance the books, and arrive at the profit and loss, so that we may intelligently decide whether to con-tinue the business or sell out the property and start a new Civilization Scheme on the pro-ceeds?

Extending the Blessings of Civilization to our Brother who Sits in Darkness has been a good trade and has paid well, on the whole; and there is money in it yet, if carefully worked—but not enough, in my judgment, to make any considerable risk advisable. The People that Sit in Darkness are getting to be too scarce—too scarce and too shy. And such darkness as is now left is really of but an indifferent quality, and not dark enough for the game. The most of those People that Sit in Darkness have been furnished with more light than was good for them or profitable for us. We have been injudicious.

The Blessings-of-Civilization Trust, wisely and cautiously administered, is a Daisy. There is more money in it, more territory, more sovereignty, and other kinds of emolument, than there is in any other game that is played. But Christendom has been playing it badly of late years, and must certainly suffer by it, in my opinion. She has been so eager to get every stake that appeared on the green cloth, that the People who Sit in Darkness have noticed it—they have noticed it, and have begun to show alarm. They have become suspicious of the Blessings of Civilization. More—they have begun to examine them. This is not well. The Blessings of Civilization are all right, and a good commercial property; there could not be a better, in a dim light. In the right kind of a light, and at a proper distance, with the goods a little out of focus, they furnish this desirable exhibit to the Gentlemen who Sit in Darkness:

Love,	Law and Order,
Justice,	Liberty,
Gentleness,	Equality,
Christianity,	Honorable Dealing,
Protection to the Weak,	Mercy,
Temperance,	Education,

—and so on.

There. Is it good? Sir, it is pie. It will bring into camp any idiot that sits in darkness anywhere. But not if we adulterate it. It is proper to be emphatic upon that point. This brand is strictly for Export—apparently. *Apparently.* Privately and confidentially, it is nothing of the kind. Privately and confidentially, it is merely an outside cover, gay and pretty and attractive, displaying the special patterns of our Civilization which we reserve for Home Consumption, while *inside* the bale is the Actual Thing that the Customer Sitting in Darkness buys with his blood and tears and land and liberty. That Actual Thing is, indeed, Civilization, but it is only for Export. Is there a difference between the two brands? In some of the details, yes.

We all know that the Business is being ruined. The reason is not far to seek. It is because our Mr. McKinley, and Mr. Chamberlain, and the Kaiser, and the Tsar and the French have been exporting the Actual Thing *with the outside cover left off*. This is bad for the Game. It shows that these new players of it are not sufficiently acquainted with it.

It is a distress to look on and note the mismoves, they are so strange and so awkward. Mr. Chamberlain manufactures a war out of materials so inadequate and so fanciful that they make the boxes grieve and the gallery laugh, and he tries hard to persuade himself that it isn't purely a private raid for cash, but has a sort of dim, vague respectability about it somewhere, if he could only find the spot; and that, by and by, he can scour the flag clean again after he has finished dragging it through the mud, and make it shine and flash in the vault of heaven once more as it had shone and flashed there a thousand years in the world's respect until he laid his unfaithful hand upon it. It is bad play—bad. For it exposes the Actual Thing to Them that Sit in Darkness, and they say: "What! Christian against Christian? And only for money? Is *this* a case of magnanimity, forbearance, love, gentleness, mercy, protection of the weak—this strange and overshowy onslaught of an elephant upon a nest of field mice, on the pretext that the mice had squeaked an insolence at him—conduct which "no self-respecting government could allow to pass unavenged"? as Mr. Chamberlain said. Was that a good pretext in a small case, when it had not been a good pretext in a large one? —for only recently Russia had affronted the elephant three times and survived alive and unsmitten. Is this Civilization and Progress? Is it something better than we already possess? These harryings and burnings and desert-makings in the Transvaal—is this an improvement on our darkness? Is it, perhaps, possible that there are two kinds of Civilization—one for home consumption and one for the heathen market?"

Then They that Sit in Darkness are troubled, and shake their heads; and they read this extract from a letter of a British private, recounting his exploits in one of Methuen's victories, some days before the affair of Magersfontein, and they are troubled again:

> We tore up the hill and into the intrenchments, and the Boers saw we had them; so they dropped their guns and went down on their knees and put up their hands clasped, and begged for mercy. And we gave it them—*with the long spoon.*

The long spoon is the bayonet. See *Lloyd's Weekly,* London, of those days. The same number—and the same column—contained some quite unconscious satire in the form of shocked and bitter upbraidings of the Boers for their brutalities and inhumanities!

Next, to our heavy damage, the Kaiser went to playing the game without first mastering it. He lost a couple of missionaries in a riot in Shantung, and in his account he made an overcharge for them. China had to pay a hundred thousand dollars apiece for them, in money; twelve miles of territory, containing several millions of inhabitants and worth twenty million dollars; and to build a monument, and also a Christian church; whereas the people of China could have been depended upon to remember the missionaries without the help of these expensive memorials. This was all bad play. Bad, because it would not, and could not, and will not now or ever, deceive the Person Sitting in Darkness. He knows that it was an overcharge. He knows that a missionary is like any other man: he is worth merely what you can supply his place for, and no more. He is useful, but so is a doctor, so is a sheriff, so is an editor; but a just Emperor does not charge war prices for such. A diligent, intelligent, but obscure missionary, and a diligent, intelligent country editor are worth much, and we know it; but they are not worth the earth. We esteem such an editor, and we are sorry to see him go; but, when he goes, we should consider twelve miles of territory, and a church, and a fortune, overcompensation for his loss. I mean, if he was a Chinese editor, and we had to settle for him. It is no proper figure for an editor or a missionary; one can get shop-worn kings for less. It was bad play on the Kaiser's part. It got this property, true; but it *produced the Chinese revolt,* the indignant uprising of China's traduced patriots, the Boxers. The results have been expensive to Germany, and to the other Disseminators of Progress and the Blessings of Civilization.

The Kaiser's claim was paid, yet it was bad play, for it could not fail to have an evil effect upon Persons Sitting in Darkness in China. They would muse upon the event, and be likely to say: "Civilization is gracious and beautiful, for such is its reputation; but can we afford it? There are rich Chinamen, perhaps they can afford it; but this tax is not laid upon them, it is laid upon the peasants of Shantung; it is they that must pay this mighty sum, and their wages are but four cents a day. Is this a better civilization than ours, and holier and higher and nobler? Is not this rapacity? Is not this extortion? Would Germany charge America two hundred thousand dollars for two missionaries, and shake the mailed fist in her face, and send warships, and send soldiers, and say: 'Seize twelve miles of territory, worth twenty millions of dollars, as additional pay for the missionaries; and make those peasants build a monument to the missionaries, and a costly Christian church to remember them by?' And later would Germany say to her soldiers: 'March through America and slay, *giving no quarter;* make the German face there, as has been our Hun-face here, a terror for a thousand years; march through the Great Republic and slay, slay, slay, carving a road for our offended religion through its heart and bowels?' Would Germany do like this to America, to England, to France, to Russia? Or only to China, the helpless—imitating the elephant's assault upon the field mice? Had we better invest in this Civilization—this Civilization which called Napoleon a buccaneer for carrying off Venice's bronze horses, but which steals our ancient astronomical instruments from our walls, and goes looting like common bandits—that is, all the alien soldiers except America's; and (Americans again excepted) storms frightened villages and cables the result to glad journals at home every day: 'Chinese losses, 450 killed; ours, *one officer and two men wounded.* Shall proceed against neighboring village to-morrow, where a *massacre* is reported.' Can we afford Civilization?"

And next Russia must go and play the game injudiciously. She affronts England once or twice—with the Person Sitting in Darkness observing and noting; by moral assistance of France and Germany, she robs Japan of her hard-earned spoil, all swimming in Chinese blood—Port Arthur—with the Person again observing and noting; then she seizes Manchuria, raids its villages, and chokes its great river with the swollen corpses of countless massacred peasants—that astonished Person still observing and noting. And perhaps he is saying to himself: "It is yet *another* Civilized Power, with its banner of the Prince of Peace in one hand and its loot basket and its butcher knife in the other. Is there no salvation for us but to adopt Civilization and lift ourselves down to its level?"

And by and by comes America, and our Master of the Game plays it badly—plays it as Mr. Chamberlain was playing it in South Africa. It was a mistake to do that; also, it was one which was quite unlooked for in a Master who was playing it so well in Cuba. In Cuba, he was playing the usual and regular *American* game, and it was winning, for there is no way to beat it. The Master, contemplating Cuba, said: "Here is an oppressed and friendless little nation which is willing to fight to be free; we go partners, and put up the strength of seventy million sympathizers and the resources of the United States: play!" Nothing but Europe combined could call that hand: and Europe cannot combine on anything. There, in Cuba, he was following our great traditions in a way which made us very proud of him, and proud of the deep dissatisfaction which his play was provoking in continental Europe. Moved by a high inspiration, he threw out those stirring words which proclaimed that forcible annexation would be "criminal aggression"; and in that utterance fired another "shot heard round the world." The memory of that fine saying will be outlived by the remembrance of no act of his but one—that he forgot it within the twelvemonth, and its honorable gospel along with it.

For, presently, came the Philippine temptation. It was strong; it was too strong, and he made that bad mistake: he played the European game, the Chamberlain game. It was a pity; it was a great pity, that error; that one grievous error, that irrevocable error. For it was the very place and time to play the American game again. And at no cost. Rich winnings to be gathered in, too; rich and permanent; indestructible; a fortune transmissible forever to the children of the flag. Not land, not money, not dominion—no, something worth many times more than that dross: our share, the spectacle of a nation of long harassed and persecuted slaves set free through our influence; our posterity's share, the golden memory of that fair deed. The game was in our hands. If it had been played according to the American rules, Dewey would have sailed away from Manila as soon as he had destroyed the Spanish fleet—after putting up a sign on shore guaranteeing foreign property and life against damage by the Filipinos, and warning the Powers that interference with the emancipated patriots would be regarded as an act unfriendly to the United States. The Powers cannot combine, in even a bad cause, and the sign would not have been molested.

Dewey could have gone about his affairs elsewhere, and left the competent Filipino army to starve out the little Spanish garrison and send it home, and the Filipino citizens to set up the form of government they might prefer, and deal with the friars and their doubtful acquisitions according to Filipino ideas of fairness and justice—ideas which have since been tested and found to be of as high an order as any that prevail in Europe or America.

But we played the Chamberlain game, and lost the chance to add another Cuba and another honorable deed to our good record.

The more we examine the mistake, the more clearly we perceive that it is going to be bad for the Business. The Person Sitting in Darkness is almost sure to say: "There is something curious about this—curious and unaccountable. There must be two Americas: one that sets the captive free, and one that takes a once-captive's new freedom away from him, and picks a quarrel with him with nothing to found it on; then kills him to get his land."

The truth is, the Person Sitting in Darkness *is* saying things like that; and for the sake of the Business we must persuade him to look at the Philippine matter in another and healthier way. We must arrange his opinions for him. I believe it can be done; for Mr. Chamberlain has arranged England's opinion of the South African matter, and done it most cleverly and successfully. He presented the facts—some of the facts—and showed those confiding people what the facts meant. He did it statistically, which is a good way. He used the formula: "Twice 2 are 14, and 2 from 9 leaves 35." Figures are effective; figures will convince the elect.

Now, my plan is a still bolder one than Mr. Chamberlain's, though apparently a copy of it. Let us be franker than Mr. Chamberlain; let us audaciously present the whole of the facts, shirking none, then explain them according to Mr. Chamberlain's formula. This daring truthfulness will astonish and dazzle the Person Sitting in Darkness, and he will take the Explanation down before his mental vision has had time to get back into focus. Let us say to him:

"Our case is simple. On the first of May, Dewey destroyed the Spanish fleet. This left the Archipelago in the hands of its proper and rightful owners, the Filipino nation. Their army numbered 30,000 men, and they were competent to whip out or starve out the little Spanish garrison; then the people could set up a government of their own devising. Our traditions required that Dewey should now set up his warning sign, and go away. But the Master of the Game happened to think of another plan—the European plan. He acted upon it. This was, to send out an army—ostensibly to help the native patriots put the finishing touch upon their long and plucky struggle for independence, but really to take their land away from them and keep it. That is, in the interest of Progress and Civilization. The plan developed, stage by stage, and quite satisfactorily. We entered into a military alliance with the trusting Filipinos, and they hemmed in Manila on the land side, and by their valuable help the place, with its garrison of 8,000 or 10,000 Spaniards, was captured—a thing which we could not have accomplished unaided at that time. We got their help by—by ingenuity. We knew they were fighting for their independence, and that they had been at it for two years. We knew they supposed that we also were fighting in their worthy cause—just as we

had helped the Cubans fight for Cuban independence—and we allowed them to go on thinking so. *Until Manila was ours and we could get along without them.* Then we showed our hand. Of course, they were surprised—that was natural; surprised and disappointed; disappointed and grieved. To them it looked un-American; uncharacteristic; foreign to our established traditions. And this was natural, too; for we were only playing the American Game in public—in private it was the European. It was neatly done, very neatly, and it bewildered them. They could not understand it; for we had been so friendly—so affectionate, even—with those simple-minded patriots! We, our own selves, had brought back out of exile their leader, their hero, their hope, their Washington—Aguinaldo; brought him in a warship, in high honor, under the sacred shelter and hospitality of the flag; brought him back and restored him to his people, and got their moving and eloquent gratitude for it. Yes, we had been so friendly to them, and had heartened them up in so many ways! We had lent them guns and ammunition; advised with them; exchanged pleasant courtesies with them; placed our sick and wounded in their kindly care; intrusted our Spanish prisoners to their humane and honest hands; fought shoulder to shoulder with them against "the common enemy" (our own phrase); praised their courage, praised their gallantry, praised their mercifulness, praised their fine and honorable conduct; borrowed their trenches, borrowed strong positions which they had previously captured from the Spaniards; petted them, lied to them—officially proclaiming that our land and naval forces came to give them their freedom and displace the bad Spanish Government—fooled them, used them until we needed them no longer; then derided the sucked orange and threw it away. We kept the positions which we had beguiled them of; by and by, we moved a force forward and overlapped patriot ground—a clever thought, for we needed trouble, and this would produce it. A Filipino soldier, crossing the ground, where no one had a right to forbid him, was shot by our sentry. The badgered patriots resented this with arms, without waiting to know whether Aguinaldo, who was absent, would approve or not.

Aguinaldo did not approve; but that availed nothing. What we wanted, in the interest of Progress and Civilization, was the Archipelago, unencumbered by patriots struggling for independence; and War was what we needed. We clinched our opportunity. It is Mr. Chamberlain's case over again—at least in its motive and intention; and we played the game as adroitly as he played it himself."

At this point in our frank statement of fact to the Person Sitting in Darkness, we should throw in a little trade taffy about the Blessings of Civilization—for a change, and for the refreshment of his spirit—then go on with our tale:

"We and the patriots have captured Manila, Spain's ownership of the Archipelago and her sovereignty over it were at an end—obliterated—annihilated—not a rag or shred of either remaining behind. It was then that we conceived the divinely humorous idea of *buying* both of these specters from Spain! [It is quite safe to confess this to the Person Sitting in Darkness, since neither he nor any other sane person will believe it.] In buying those ghosts for twenty millions, we also contracted to take care of the friars and their accumulations. I think we also agreed to propagate leprosy and smallpox, but as to this there is doubt. But it is not important; persons afflicted with the friars do not mind other diseases.

"With our Treaty ratified, Manila subdued, and our Ghosts secured, we had no further use for Aguinaldo and the owners of the Archipelago. We forced a war, and we have been hunting America's guest and ally through the woods and swamps ever since."

At this point in the tale, it will be well to boast a little of our war work and our heroisms in the field, so as to make our performance look as fine as England's in South Africa; but I believe it will not be best to emphasize this too much. We must be cautious. Of course, we must read the war telegrams to the Person, in order to keep up our frankness; but we can throw an air of humorousness over them, and that will modify their grim eloquence a little, and their rather indiscreet exhibitions of gory exultation. Before reading to him the following display heads of the dispatches of November 18, 1900, it will be well to practice on them in private first, so as to get the right tang of lightness and gayety into them:

ADMINISTRATION WEARY OF
PROTRACTED HOSTILITIES!

REAL WAR AHEAD FOR FILIPINO
REBELS![1]

WILL SHOW NO MERCY!
KITCHENER'S PLAN ADOPTED!

Kitchener knows how to handle disagreeable people who are fighting for their homes and their liberties, and we must let on that we are merely imitating Kitchener, and have no national interest in the matter, further than to get ourselves admired by the Great Family of Nations, in which august company our Master of the Game has bought a place for us in the back row.

Of course, we must not venture to ignore our General MacArthur's reports—oh, why do they keep on printing those embarrassing things?—we must drop them trippingly from the tongue and take the chances:

During the last ten months our losses have been 268 killed and 750 wounded; Filipino loss, *three thousand two hundred and twenty-seven killed,* and 694 wounded.

We must stand ready to grab the Person Sitting in Darkness, for he will swoon away at this confession, saying: "Good God! those 'niggers' spare their wounded, and the Americans massacre theirs!"

We must bring him to, and coax him and coddle him, and assure him that the ways of Providence are best, and that it would not become us to find fault with them; and then, to show him that we are only imitators, not originators, we must read the following passage from the letter of an American soldier lad in the Philippines to his mother, published in *Public Opinion,* of Decorah, Iowa, describing the finish of a victorious battle: *"We never left one alive. If one was wounded, we would run our bayonets through him."*

Having now laid all the historical facts before the Person Sitting in Darkness, we should bring him to again, and explain them to him. We should say to him:

1 "Rebels!" Mumble that funny word—don't let the Person catch it distinctly.

"They look doubtful, but in reality they are not. There have been lies; yes, but they were told in a good cause. We have been treacherous; but that was only in order that real good might come out of apparent evil. True, we have crushed a deceived and confiding people; we have turned against the weak and the friendless who trusted us; we have stamped out a just and intelligent and well-ordered republic; we have stabbed an ally in the back and slapped the face of a guest; we have bought a Shadow from an enemy that hadn't it to sell; we have robbed a trusting friend of his land and his liberty; we have invited our clean young men to shoulder a discredited musket and do bandits' work under a flag which bandits have been accustomed to fear, not to follow; we have debauched America's honor and blackened her face before the world; but each detail was for the best. We know this. The Head of every State and Sovereignty in Christendom and 90 per cent of every legislative body in Christendom, including our Congress and our fifty state legislatures, are members not only of the church, but also of the Blessings-of-Civilization Trust. This world-girdling accumulation of trained morals, high principles, and justice cannot do an unright thing, an unfair thing, an ungenerous thing, an unclean thing. It knows what it is about. Give yourself no uneasiness; it is all right."

Now then, that will convince the Person. You will see. It will restore the Business. Also, it will elect the Master of the Game to the vacant place in the Trinity of our national gods; and there on their high thrones the Three will sit, age after age, in the people's sight, each bearing the Emblem of his service: Washington, the Sword of the Liberator; Lincoln, the Slave's Broken Chains; the Master, the Chains Repaired.

It will give the Business a spendid new start. You will see.

Everything is prosperous, now; everything is just as we should wish it. We have got the Archipelago, and we shall never give it up. Also, we have every reason to hope that we shall have an opportunity before very long to slip out of our congressional contract with Cuba and give her something better in the place of it. It is a rich country, and many of us are already beginning to see that the contract was a sentimental mistake. But now—right now—is the best time to do some profitable rehabilitating work—work that will set us up and make us comfortable, and discourage gossip. We cannot conceal from ourselves that, privately, we are a little troubled about our uniform. It is one of our prides; it is acquainted with honor; it is familiar with great deeds and noble; we love it, we revere it; and so this errand it is on makes us uneasy. And our flag—another pride of ours, our chiefest! We have worshiped it so; and when we have seen it in far lands—glimpsing it unexpectedly in that strange sky, waving its welcome and benediction to us—we have caught our breaths, and uncovered our heads, and couldn't speak, for a moment, for the thought of what it was to us and the great ideals it stood for. Indeed, we *must* do something about these things; it is easily managed. We can have a special one—our states do it: we can have just our usual flag, with the white stripes painted black and the stars replaced by the skull and crossbones.

And we do not need that Civil Commission out there. Having no powers, it has to invent them, and that kind of work cannot be effectively done by just anybody; an expert is required. Mr. Croker can be spared. We do not want the United States represented there, but only the Game.

By help of these suggested amendments, Progress and Civilization in that country can have a boom, and it will take in the Persons who are Sitting in Darkness, and we can resume Business at the old stand.

Questions

1. The major satiric device Twain employs here is known as the "mock encomium," pretended praise which is actually blame. How do we know that what appears literally to be praise is in fact blame; for example, is

he consistent in his praise? You will probably have to analyze carefully one of Twain's paragraphs to answer this last question effectively.

2. What value is there for the satirist in the use of the mock encomium? Does it permit him to make his point more convincingly than the technique of direct attack?

3. What metaphor does Twain make use of throughout this satiric essay? Give some examples and discuss the part this metaphor plays in the over-all meaning.

4. Does the meaning of the phrase "person sitting in darkness" shift as it is repeated? Trace the progression of meaning through the work.

W. H. AUDEN

Letter to Lord Byron

Since W. H. Auden (b. 1907) includes in his "Letter to Lord Byron" a brief and very amusing autobiography, there is no need for recounting the details of his life here, except perhaps to remark that he has lived in the United States since 1939 and is by now recognized as one of the major poets of this century. The "Letter to Lord Byron" formed a large part of a travel book written with Louis MacNeice in 1937 after the two took a journey to Iceland. *Letters from Iceland* contains some remarkable poetry by both MacNeice and Auden, but it is for the most part an elaborate and extremely witty parody, complete with statistical charts on population, livestock, and foreign trade, on the travel literature which enjoyed such a vogue during the 1930's when Christopher Isherwood went to Berlin, Graham Greene to darkest Africa, and Evelyn Waugh to Guiana.

Auden has always shown a pronounced satirical talent, which has usually found expression in short, sardonic poems such as "The Unknown Citizen." The "Letter to Lord Byron" is his longest excursion of this kind and is reprinted here in full. The model for the poem was, of course, Lord Byron's *Don Juan*, selected sections of which are printed, for purposes of comparison, in the supplementary material. Footnotes are provided by the editor to give information on details which are not common knowledge and which cannot be looked up in a dictionary.

PART I

Excuse, my lord, the liberty I take
    In thus addressing you. I know that you
Will pay the price of authorship and make
    The allowances an author has to do.
    A poet's fan-mail will be nothing new.
And then a lord—Good Lord, you must be peppered,
Like Gary Cooper, Coughlin, or Dick Sheppard,°

With notes from perfect strangers starting, "Sir,
    I liked your lyrics, but *Childe Harold*'s° trash,"
"My daughter writes, should I encourage her?"   10
    Sometimes containing frank demands for cash,
    Sometimes sly hints at a platonic pash,
And sometimes, though I think this rather crude,
The correspondent's photo in the rude.

FROM *Letters from Iceland,* by W. H. Auden and Louis MacNeice. Copyright 1937 by Wystan Hugh Auden. Reprinted by permission of Random House, Inc. and Curtis Brown Ltd.

I.   7. Hugh Richard Lawrie Sheppard (1880-1937),

Dean of Canterbury. A popular English clergyman who was the first to broadcast sermons over the radio. 9. Byron's most famous serious poem, completed in

And as for manuscripts—by every post . . .
    I can't improve on Pope's shrill indig-
        nation,°
But hope that it will please his spiteful ghost
    To learn the use in culture's propagation
    Of modern methods of communication;
New roads, new rails, new contacts, as we
    know   20
From documentaries by the G.P.O.°

For since the British Isles went Protestant
    A church confession is too high for most.
But still confession is a human want,
    So Englishmen must make theirs now by
        post
    And authors hear them over breakfast
        toast.
For, failing them, there's nothing but the wall
Of public lavatories on which to scrawl.

So if ostensibly I write to you
    To chat about your poetry or mine,   30
There're many other reasons; though it's true
    That I have, at the age of twenty-nine
    Just read *Don Juan* and I found it fine.
I read it on the boat to Reykjavik
Except when eating or asleep or sick.

The fact is, I'm in Iceland all alone
    —MacKenzie's prints are not unlike the
        scene—
Ich hab'zu Haus, ein Gra, ein Gramophone.
    Les gosses anglais aiment beaucoup les
        machines.
    To χαλον. *glubit. che* . . . what this may
        mean   40
I do not know, but rather like the sound
Of foreign languages like Ezra Pound.°

And home is miles away, and miles away
    No matter who, and I am quite alone
And cannot understand what people say,
    But like a dog must guess it by the tone;
    At any language other than my own
I'm no great shakes, and here I've found no
    tutor
Nor sleeping lexicon to make me cuter.

The thought of writing came to me to-day   50
    (I like to give these facts of time and
        space);
The bus was in the desert on its way
    From Mothrudalur to some other place:
    The tears were streaming down my burn-
        ing face;
I'd caught a heavy cold in Akureyri,
And lunch was late and life looked very dreary.

Professor Housman° was I think the first
    To say in print how very stimulating
The little ills by which mankind is cursed,
    The colds, the aches, the pains are to
        creating;   60
    Indeed one hardly goes too far in stating
That many a flawless lyric may be due
Not to a lover's broken heart, but 'flu.

But still a proper explanation's lacking;
    Why write to you? I see I must begin
Right at the start when I was at my packing.
    The extra pair of socks, the airtight tin
    Of China tea, the anti-fly were in;
I asked myself what sort of books I'd read
In Iceland, if I ever felt the need.   70

I can't read Jefferies° on the Wiltshire Downs,
    Nor browse on limericks in a smoking-
        room;
Who would try Trollope in cathedral towns,
    Or Marie Stopes° inside his mother's
        womb?
    Perhaps you feel the same beyond the
        tomb.
Do the celestial highbrows only care
For works on Clydeside,° Fascists, or Mayfair?

In certain quarters I had heard a rumour
    (For all I know the rumour's only silly)
That Icelanders have little sense of hu-
        mour.   80
    I knew the country was extremely hilly,
    The climate unreliable and chilly;

1818.   **16.** Alexander Pope complains at the beginning of his satire, "Epistle to Dr. Arbuthnot," of the
deluge of manuscripts which are sent him for comment by the scribblers of the day.   **21.** The General Post Office.   **42.** The reference is to Pound's
penchant for mixing many languages together, as in
his *Cantos.* The passages from other languages which
Auden uses here are a purposeful mishmash.   **57.**
A. E. Housman, author of *A Shropshire Lad.*   **71.**
Richard Jefferies (1848-87), a naturalist and novelist
who wrote about his native Wiltshire.   **74.** An English biologist whose name became synonymous with
birth control because of her books on the subject and
her attempts to set up clinics.   **77.** A highly in-
dustrialized area on the banks of the Clyde River at

So looking round for something light and easy
I pounced on you as warm and *civilisé*.

There is one other author in my pack:
    For some time I debated which to write to.
Which would least likely send my letter back?
    But I decided that I'd give a fright to
    Jane Austen if I wrote when I'd no right to,
And share in her contempt the dreadful fates   90
Of Crawford, Musgrave, and of Mr. Yates.°

Then she's a novelist. I don't know whether
    You will agree, but novel writing is
A higher art than poetry altogether
    In my opinion, and success implies
    Both finer character and faculties?
Perhaps that's why real novels are as rare
As winter thunder or a polar bear.

The average poet by comparison
    Is unobservant, immature, and lazy.   100
You must admit, when all is said and done,
    His sense of other people's very hazy,
    His moral judgments are too often crazy,
A slick and easy generalisation
Appeals too well to his imagination.

I must remember, though, that you were dead
    Before the four great Russians° lived, who brought
The art of novel writing to a head;
    The help of Boots° had not been sought.
    But now the art for which Jane Austen fought,   110
Under the right persuasion bravely warms
And is the most prodigious of the forms.

She was not an unshockable blue-stocking;
    If shades remain the characters they were,
No doubt she still considers you as shocking.
    But tell Jane Austen, that is, if you dare,
    How much her novels are beloved down here.
She wrote them for posterity, she said;
'Twas rash, but by posterity she's read.

You could not shock her more than she shocks me;   120

Glasgow.   **91.** Characters in Jane Austen's novels who display a lack of taste and feeling.   **107.** Gogol, Turgenev, Dostoevski, and Tolstoy.   **109.** A large

Beside her Joyce° seems innocent as grass.
It makes me most uncomfortable to see
    An English spinster of the middle-class
    Describe the amorous effects of "brass,"
Reveal so frankly and with such sobriety
The economic basis of society.

So it is you who is to get this letter.
    The experiment may not be a success.
There're many others who could do it better,
    But I shall not enjoy myself the less.   130
    Shaw of the Air Force° said that happiness
Comes in absorption: he was right, I know it;
Even in scribbling to a long-dead poet.

Every exciting letter has enclosures,
    And so shall this—a bunch of photographs,
Some out of focus, some with wrong exposures,
    Press cuttings, gossip, maps, statistics, graphs;
    I don't intend to do the thing by halves.
I'm going to be very up to date indeed.
It is a collage that you're going to read.   140

I want a form that's large enough to swim in,
    And talk on any subject that I choose,
From natural scenery to men and women,
    Myself, the arts, the European news:
    And since she's on a holiday, my Muse
Is out to please, find everything delightful
And only now and then be mildly spiteful.

Ottava Rima would, I know, be proper,
    The proper instrument on which to pay
My compliments, but I should come a cropper;°   150
    Rhyme-royal's difficult enough to play.
    But if no classics as in Chaucer's day,
At least my modern pieces shall be cheery
Like English bishops on the Quantum Theory.°

Light verse, poor girl, is under a sad weather;
    Except by Milne° and persons of that kind

chain of English chemists—drugstores—having novel-lending libraries in their stores.   **121.** James Joyce. **131.** T. E. Shaw, Lawrence of Arabia, who joined the Royal Air Force as an airman after World War I. **150.** "Come a cropper" means "fail miserably." **154.** It was the fashion during these years for optimistic churchmen to argue that various scientific theories, like the quantum theory, really fitted very nicely into a religious scheme of the world.   **156.**

She's treated as *démodé* altogether.
　　It's strange and very unjust to my mind
　　Her brief appearances should be confined,
Apart from Belloc's° *Cautionary Tales,*　160
To the more bourgeois periodicals.

"The fascination of what's difficult,"
　　The wish to do what one's not done be-
　　　fore,
Is, I hope, proper to *Quicunque Vult,*
　　The proper card to show at Heaven's
　　　door.
　　"*Gerettet*" not "*Gerichtet*"° be the Law,
Et cetera, et cetera. O curse,
That is the flattest line in English verse.

Parnassus after all is not a mountain,
　　Reserved for A.1. climbers such as you;
It's got a park, it's got a public fountain.　171
　　　The most I ask is leave to share a pew
　　　With Bradford° or with Cottam,° that
　　　　will do:
To pasture my few silly sheep with Dyer°
And picnic on the lower slopes with Prior.°

A publisher's an author's greatest friend,
　　A generous uncle, or he ought to be.
(I'm sure we hope it pays him in the end.)
　　　I love my publishers and they love me,
　　　At least they paid a very handsome
　　　　fee　180
To send me here. I've never heard a grouse
Either from Russell Square or Random House.

But now I've got uncomfortable suspicions,
　　I'm going to put their patience out of
　　　joint.
Though it's in keeping with the best traditions
　　For Travel Books to wander from the
　　　point
　　(There is no other rhyme except anoint),

They well may charge me with—I've no de-
　　fences—
Obtaining money under false pretences.

I know I've not the least chance of sur-
　　vival　190
　　Beside the major travellers of the day.
I am no Lawrence° who, on his arrival,
　　Sat down and typed out all he had to say;
　　I am not even Ernest Hemingway.
I shall not run to a two-bob edition,
So just won't enter for the competition.

And even here the steps I flounder in
　　Were worn by most distinguished boots of
　　　old.
Dasent and Morris and Lord Dufferin,
　　Hooker° and men of that heroic
　　　mould　200
　　Welcome me icily into the fold;
I'm not like Peter Fleming° an Etonian,
But, if I'm Judas, I'm an old Oxonian.

The Haig Thomases° are at Myvatn now,
　　At Hvitavatn and at Vatnajökull
Cambridge research goes on, I don't know
　　how:
　　The shades of Asquith° and of Auden
　　　Skökull
　　Turn in their coffins a three-quarter circle
To see their son, upon whose help they
　　reckoned,
Being as frivolous as Charles the Second.　210

So this, my opening chapter, has to stop
　　With humbly begging everybody's pardon.

A. A. Milne. 　**160.** Hilaire Belloc, an English writer of light verse. 　**166.** "Saved," not "judged." 　**173.** There are two literary Bradfords, John (1510-55) and William (1590-1657). Which one Auden has in mind is not ascertainable, but his point is not in question; he is comparing himself to minor poets of the past. **173.** Does Auden here mean Cotton rather than Cottam? Charles Cotton was a graceful but unimportant seventeenth-century poet. 　**174.** Sir Edward Dyer, a minor pastoral poet of the Renaissance. 　**175.** Matthew Prior, an eighteenth-century poet of the second or third rank. 　**192.** D. H. Lawrence, who also wrote many travel books. 　**200.** All four of these men had associations with Iceland. Sir George Dasent (1817-96) was a scholar and translator of Icelandic sagas. William Morris (1834-96), a famous poet and designer, wrote an imitation of an Icelandic epic, *Sigurd the Volsung* (1876). Lord Dufferin, Frederick Blackwood (1826-1902), a British diplomat, and Sir William Hooker (1785-1865), a botanist and world traveler, wrote descriptions of Iceland. 　**202.** An English novelist and traveler (b. 1907) who, obviously, went to Eton, while Auden did not. They attended Oxford at the same time and may have known each other there. **204.** H. H. Thomas (1876-1935) was a famous geologist who traveled in Iceland with a scientific expedition in 1900. Auden is using the name as a general term for serious scientific work in contrast to his own "frivolous" methods of observation. 　**207.** Henry Herbert Asquith (1852-1928), a prominent British politician. Asquith, born poor, won a scholarship to Oxford by

From Faber° first in case the book's a flop,
   Then from the critics lest they should be
      hard on
   The author when he leads them up the
      garden,
Last from the general public he must beg
Permission now and then to pull their leg.

PART II

I'm writing this in pencil on my knee,
   Using my other hand to stop me yawning,
Upon a primitive, unsheltered quay
   In the small hours of a Wednesday
      morning.
   I cannot add the summer day is dawning;
In Seythisfjördur every schoolboy knows
That daylight in the summer never goes.

To get to sleep in latitudes called upper
   Is difficult at first for Englishmen.
It's like being sent to bed before your sup-
      per   10
   For playing darts with father's fountain-
      pen,
   Or like returning after orgies, when
Your breath's like luggage and you realise
You've been more confidential than was wise.

I've done my duty, taken many notes
   Upon the almost total lack of greenery,
The roads, the illegitimates, the goats:
   To use a rhyme of yours, there's hand-
      some scenery
   But little agricultural machinery;
And with the help of Sunlight Soap° the Gey-
   sir   20
Affords to visitors *le plus grand plaisir*.

The North, though, never was your cup of tea;
   "Moral" you thought it so you kept away.°
And what I'm sure you're wanting now from
      me
   Is news about the England of the day,

What sort of things *La Jeunesse* do and
   say.
Is Brighton still as proud of her pavilion,
And is it safe for girls to travel pillion?

I'll clear my throat and take a Rover's breath
   And skip a century of hope and sin— 30
For far too much has happened since your
   death.
   Crying went out and the cold bath came
      in,
   With drains, bananas, bicycles, and tin,
And Europe saw from Ireland to Albania
The Gothic revival and the Railway Mania.

We're entering now the Eotechnic Phase°
   Thanks to the Grid and all those new
      alloys;
That is, at least, what Lewis Mumford says.
   A world of Aertex underwear for boys,
   Huge plate-glass windows, walls absorb-
      ing noise,   40
Where the smoke nuisance is utterly abated
And all the furniture is chromium-plated.

Well, you might think so if you went to
      Surrey
   And stayed for week-ends with the well
      to do,
Your car too fast, too personal your worry
   To look too closely at the wheeling view.
   But in the north it simply isn't true.
To those who live in Warrington or Wigan,°
It's not a white lie, it's a whacking big 'un.

There on the old historic battlefield,   50
   The cold ferocity of human wills,
The scars of struggle are as yet unhealed;
   Slattern the tenements on sombre hills,
   And gaunt in valleys the square-win-
      dowed mills
That, since the Georgian house, in my conjec-
   ture
Remain our finest native architecture.

On economic, health, or moral grounds
   It hasn't got the least excuse to show;
No more than chamber pots or otter hounds:
   But let me say before it has to go,   60
   It's the most lovely country that I know;

brilliance and effort and went on to become one of
the greatest men in England. Auden is wryly com-
menting again on the fact that he is not the rags-to-
riches type and that his approach to experience differs
a great deal from that of his ancestor (Auden Skökull).
213. Faber and Faber, Auden's English publisher.
   II.   20. Sunlight Soap was, according to Auden,
the brand of soap the Icelanders fed their "Great
Gesir" (geyser) to make it erupt with froth and
bubbles.   **23.** Byron in *Don Juan* expresses distaste
for the cold and "moral" northern climates.   **36.**
See the Lewis Mumford selection printed in the supplementary material of this volume.   **48.** Industrial

Clearer than Scafell Pike, my heart has
    stamped on
The view from Birmingham to Wolverhamp-
    ton.

Long, long ago, when I was only four,
    Going towards my grandmother, the line
Passed through a coal-field. From the corridor
    I watched it pass with envy, thought
       "How fine!
    Oh how I wish that situation mine."
Tramlines and slagheaps, pieces of machinery,
That was, and still is, my ideal scenery.   70

Hail to the New World! Hail to those who'll
    love
    Its antiseptic objects, feel at home.
Lovers will gaze at an electric stove,
    Another *poésie de départ*° come
    Centered round bus-stops or the aero-
      drome.
But give me still, to stir imagination
The chiaroscuro of the railway station.

Preserve me from the Shape of Things to Be;
    The high-grade posters at the public
      meeting,
The influence of Art on Industry,   80
    The cinemas with perfect taste in seating;
    Preserve me, above all, from central
      heating.
It may be D. H. Lawrence hocus-pocus,
But I prefer a room that's got a focus.°

But you want facts, not sighs. I'll do my best
    To give a few; you can't expect them all.
To start with, on the whole we're better
      dressed;
    For chic the difference to-day is small
    Of barmaid from my lady at the Hall.
It's sad to spoil this democratic vision   90
With millions suffering from malnutrition.

Again, our age is highly educated;
    There is no lie our children cannot read,
And as MacDonald° might so well have stated
    We're growing up and up and up indeed.

Advertisements can teach us all we need;
And death is better, as the millions know,
Than dandruff, night-starvation, or **B.O.**

We've always had a penchant for field sports,
    But what do you think has grown up in
      our towns?   100
A passion for the open air and shorts;
    The sun is one of our emotive nouns.
    Go down by chara'° to the Sussex Downs,
Watch the manoeuvres of the week-end hikers
Massed on parade with Kodaks or with Leicas.

These movements signify our age-long rule
    Of insularity has lost its powers;
The cult of salads and the swimming pool
    Comes from a climate sunnier than ours,
    And lands which never heard of licensed
      hours.°   110
The south of England before very long
Will look no different from the Continong.

You lived and moved among the best society
    And so could introduce your hero to it
Without the slightest tremor of anxiety;
    Because he was your hero and you knew it,
    He'd know instinctively what's done, and
      do it.
He'd find our day more difficult than yours
For Industry has mixed the social drawers.

We've grown, you see, a lot more demo-
    cratic,   120
    And Fortune's ladder is for all to climb;
Carnegie on this point was most emphatic.
    A humble grandfather is not a crime,
    At least, if father made enough in time!
To-day, thank God, we've got no snobbish
    feeling
Against the more efficient modes of stealing.

The porter at the Carlton is my brother,
    He'll wish me a good evening if I pay,
For tips and men are equal to each other.
    I'm sure that *Vogue* would be the first to
      say   130
    Que le Beau Monde is socialist to-day;

towns in the English Midlands.   **74.** A type of
poetry written on the occasion of leaving a certain
place.   **84.** Auden is punning on the Latin meaning
of *focus*, i.e., hearth.   **94.** Ramsay MacDonald (1886-
1937), first Labor Prime Minister of England in 1924

and still active in politics at the time this was written.
103. Charabanc, a public conveyance, particularly an
open bus.   **110.** In England since World War I the
public houses have been allowed to open only at cer-

And many a bandit, not so gently born
Kills vermin every winter with the Quorn.°

Adventurers, though, must take things as they
    find them
      And look for pickings where the pickings
      are.
The drives of love and hunger are behind
    them,
      They can't afford to be particular:
      And those who like good cooking and a
      car,
A certain kind of costume or of face,
Must seek them in a certain kind of place. 140

Don Juan was a mixer and no doubt
    Would find this century as good as any
For getting hostesses to ask him out,
    And mistresses that need not cost a penny.
    Indeed our ways to waste time are so
    many,
Thanks to technology, a list of these
Would make a longer book than *Ulysses*.

Yes, in the smart set he would know his way
    By second nature with no tips from me.
Tennis and Golf have come in since your
    day; 150
    But those who are as good at games as he
    Acquire the back-hand quite instinctively,
Take to the steel-shaft and hole out in one,
Master the books of Ely Culbertson.

I see his face in every magazine.
    "Don Juan at lunch with one of Coch-
    ran's ladies.'"
"Don Juan with his red setter May Mac-
Queen."
    "Don Juan, who's just been wintering in
    Cadiz,
    Caught at the wheel of his maroon Mer-
    cedes."
"Don Juan at Croydon Aerodrome." "Don
Juan 160
Snapped in the paddock with the Agha Khan."

But if in highbrow circles he would sally
    It's just as well to warn him there's no
    stain on

Picasso, all-in-wrestling, or the Ballet.
    Sibelius is the man. To get a pain on°
    Listening to Elgar is a *sine qua non*.
A second-hand acquaintance of Pareto's°
Ranks higher than an intimate of Plato's.

The vogue for Black Mass and the cult of
    devils
    Has sunk. The Good, the Beautiful, the
    True 170
Still fluctuate about the lower levels.
    Joyces are firm and there there's nothing
    new.
    Eliots° have hardened just a point or two.
Hopkins° are brisk, thanks to some recent
    boosts.
There's been some further weakening in
    Prousts.°

I'm saying this to tell you who's the rage,
    And not to loose a sneer from my interior.
Because there's snobbery in every age,
    Because some names are loved by the su-
    perior,
    It does not follow they're the least in-
    ferior: 180
For all I know the Beatific Vision's
On view at all Surrealist Exhibitions.

Now for the spirit of the people. Here
    I know I'm treading on more dangerous
    ground:
I know they're many changes in the air,
    But know my data too slight to be sound.
    I know, too, I'm inviting the renowned
Retort of all who love the Status Quo:
"You can't change human nature, don't you
    know!"

We've still, it's true, the same shape and ap-
    pearance, 190
    We haven't changed the way that kiss-
    ing's done;
The average man still hates all interference,
    Is just as proud still of his new-born son:
    Still, like a hen, he likes his private run,

girls."   **165.** "Get a pain on" means "be annoyed."
167. Vilfredo Pareto (1848-1923), an Italian sociologist
who advocated an absolute state controlled by an intellectual elite. Mussolini called Pareto the theoretician
of fascism.   **173.** T. S. Eliot.   **174.** Gerard Manley
Hopkins (1844-89), whose poetry was not much read or
appreciated until this century.   **175.** Marcel Proust.

tain hours.   **133.** A fashionable hunt.   **156.** Charles
Blake Cochran was a theatrical producer. "Cochran's
ladies" are something like the equivalent of "Ziegfeld

Scratches for self-esteem, and slyly pecks
A good deal in the neighbourhood of sex.

But he's another man in many ways:
    Ask the cartoonist first, for he knows best.
Where is the John Bull of the good old days,
    The swaggering bully with the clumsy
        jest?   200
    His meaty neck has long been laid to rest,
His acres of self-confidence for sale;
He passed away at Ypres and Passchendaele.°

Turn to the work of Disney or of Strube;°
    There stands our hero in his threadbare
        seams;
The bowler hat who straphangs in the tube,°
    And kicks the tyrant only in his dreams,
    Trading on pathos, dreading all extremes;
The little Mickey with the hidden grudge;
Which is the better, I leave you to judge.   210

Begot on Hire-Purchase° by Insurance,
    Forms at his christening worshipped and
        adored;
A season ticket schooled him in endurance,
    A tax collector and a waterboard
    Admonished him. In boyhood he was
        awed
By a matric,° and complex apparatuses
Keep his heart conscious of Divine Afflatuses.

"I am like you," he says, "and you, and you,
    I love my life, I love the home-fires,
        have
To keep them burning. Heroes never do.   220
    Heroes are sent by ogres to the grave.
    I may not be courageous, but I save.
I am the one who somehow turns the corner,
I may perhaps be fortunate Jack Horner.

I am the ogre's private secretary;
    I've felt his stature and his powers, learned
To give his ogreship the raspberry
    Only when his gigantic back is turned.
    One day, who knows, I'll do as I have
        yearned.

The short man, all his fingers on the door,   230
With repartee shall send him to the floor."

One day, which day? O any other day,
    But not to-day. The ogre knows his man.
To kill the ogre that would take away
    The fear in which his happy dreams
        began,
    And with his life he'll guard dreams while
        he can.
Those who would really kill his dream's con-
        tentment
He hates with real implacable resentment.

He dreads the ogre, but he dreads yet more
    Those who conceivably might set him
        free,   240
Those the cartoonist has no time to draw.
    Without his bondage he'd be all at sea;
    The ogre need but shout "Security,"
To make this man, so loveable, so mild,
As madly cruel as a frightened child.

Byron, thou should'st be living at this hour!
    What would you do, I wonder, if you
        were?
Britannia's lost prestige and cash and power,
    Her middle classes show some wear and
        tear,
    We've learned to bomb each other from
        the air;   250
I can't imagine what the Duke of Wellington
Would say about the music of Duke Ellington.

Suggestions have been made that the Teutonic
    Führer-Prinzip° would have appealed to
        you
As being the true heir to the Byronic—
    In keeping with your social status too
    (It has its English converts, fit and few),
That you would, hearing honest Oswald's° call,
Be *gleichgeschaltet*° in the Albert Hall.

"Lord Byron at the head of his storm-
    troopers!"   260
    Nothing, says science, is impossible:

---

203. Two long and bloody battles in 1916 and 1917 in which the English suffered an enormous number of casualties. **204.** A cartoonist well known to Londoners for his series of ads for the London Transport. One of his characters, "Billy Brown of London Town," is alluded to in ll. 205-06. **206.** The underground, or subway. **211.** Time-payment. **216.**

Matriculation. **254.** Literally "the leader principle," the Nazi theory that the state operates efficiently only if one man controls it and all others obey him absolutely. **258.** Oswald Mosley, leader of the fascist movement in England before the war. **259.** Forcibly patterned, or regimented—a term ordinarily used to describe what the Nazis did to the German

The Pope may quit to join the Oxford
    Groupers,°
    Nuffield° may leave one farthing in his
    Will,
    There may be someone who trusts Bald-
    win° still,
Someone may think that Empire wines are
    nice,
There may be people who hear Tauber° twice.

You liked to be the centre of attention,
    The gay Prince Charming of the fairy
    story,
Who tamed the Dragon by his intervention.
    In modern warfare though it's just as
    gory,   270
    There isn't any individual glory;
The Prince must be anonymous, observant,
A kind of lab-boy, or a civil servant.

You never were an Isolationist;
    Injustice you had always hatred for,
And we can hardly blame you, if you missed
    Injustice just outside your lordship's door:
    Nearer than Greece were cotton° and the
    poor.
To-day you might have seen them, might in-
    deed
Have walked in the United Front with
    Gide,°   280

Against the ogre, dragon, what you will;
    His many shapes and names all turn us
    pale,
For he's immortal, and to-day he still
    Swinges the horror of his scaly tail.
    Sometimes he seems to sleep, but will not
    fail

In every age to rear up to defend
Each dying force of history to the end.

Milton beheld him on the English throne.
    And Bunyan sitting in the Papal chair;
The hermits fought him in their caves
    alone,   290
    At the first Empire he was also there,
    Dangling his *Pax Romana* in the air:
He comes in dreams at puberty to man,
To scare him back to childhood if he can.

Banker or Landlord, booking-clerk or Pope,
    Whenever he's lost faith in choice and
    thought,
When a man sees the future without hope,
    Whenever he endorses Hobbes'° report
    "The life of man is nasty, brutish, short,"
The dragon rises from his garden border   300
And promises to set up law and order.

He that in Athens murdered Socrates,
    And Plato then seduced, prepares to make
A desolation and to call it peace
    To-day for dying magnates, for the sake
    Of generals who can scarcely keep awake,
And for that doughy mass in great and small
That doesn't want to stir itself at all.

Forgive me for inflicting all this on you,
    For asking you to hold the baby for
    us;   310
It's easy to forget that where you've gone, you
    May only want to chat with Set and
    Horus,°
    Bored to extinction with our earthly
    chorus:
Perhaps it sounds to you like a trunk-call,°
Urgent, it seems, but quite inaudible.

Yet though the choice of what is to be done
    Remains with the alive, the rigid nation
Is supple still within the breathing one;
    Its sentinels yet keep their sleepless sta-
    tion,
    And every man in every generation,   320

political system.   **262.** The Oxford Group was the name first used by Frank Buchman's Moral Rearmament Movement, which had as its basic principle absolute fidelity to the morality of the New Testament. **263.** Lord Nuffield, an extremely wealthy English industrialist.   **264.** Stanley Baldwin, Prime Minister in the middle 1930's.   **266.** Richard Tauber (1892-1948), an Austrian tenor who by 1937 had given up serious opera and was singing only in light opera. **278.** A reference to the cotton mills of England, which during the nineteenth century brought great wealth to a few but degraded and impoverished many who worked in them.   **280.** André Gide, a French man of letters who during this period was active in the extreme left. The United Front was a Communist movement of the 1930's based on the theory that the aim of Communism was no longer proletarian revolution but union with all democratic foes to oppose fascism. **298.** Thomas Hobbes (1588-1679), a philosopher who took a pessimistic view of natural man's ability to improve himself without the aid of an authoritarian government.   **312.** Egyptian gods of night and day. **314.** Long-distance call.

Tossing in his dilemma on his bed,
Cries to the shadows of the noble dead.

We're out at sea now, and I wish we weren't;
    The sea is rough, I don't care if it's blue;
I'd like to have a quick one, but I daren't.
    And I must interrupt this screed to you,
    For I've some other little jobs to do;
I must write home or mother will be vexed,
So this must be continued in our next.

PART III

My last remarks were sent you from a boat.
    I'm back on shore now in a warm bed-
        sitter,
And several friends have joined me since I
    wrote;
    So though the weather out of doors is
        bitter,
    I feel a great deal cheerier and fitter.
A party from a public school, a poet,
Have set a rapid pace, and make me go it.

We're starting soon on a big expedition
    Into the desert, which I'm sure is corking:
Many would like to be in my position.   10
    I only hope there won't be too much
        walking.
    Now let me see, where was I? We were
        talking
Of Social Questions when I had to stop;
I think it's time now for a little shop.

In setting up my brass-plate as a critic,
    I make no claim to certain diagnosis,
I'm more intuitive than analytic,
    I offer thought in homoeopathic doses
    (But someone may get better in the proc-
        ess).
I don't pretend to reasoning like Pritch-
    ard's°   20
Or the logomachy of I. A. Richards.°

I like your muse because she's gay and witty,
    Because she's neither prostitute nor
        frump,
The daughter of a European city,
    And country houses long before the
        slump;

    I like her voice that does not make me
        jump:
And you I find sympatisch, a good townee,
Neither a preacher, ninny, bore, nor Brownie.

A poet, swimmer, peer, and man of action,
    —It beats Roy Campbell's° record by a
        mile—   30
You offer every possible attraction.
    By looking into your poetic style,
    And love-life on the chance that both were
        vile,
Several have earned a decent livelihood,
Whose lives were uncreative but were good.

You've had your packet from the critics,
    though:
    They grant you warmth of heart, but at
        your head
Their moral and aesthetic brickbats throw.
    A "vulgar genius" so George Eliot said,
    Which doesn't matter as George Eliot's
        dead,   40
But T. S. Eliot, I am sad to find,
Damns you with: "an uninteresting mind."

A statement which I must say I'm ashamed at;
    A poet must be judged by his intention,
And serious thought you never said you
    aimed at.
    I think a serious critic ought to mention
    That one verse style was really your in-
        vention,
A style whose meaning does not need a span-
    ner,
You are the master of the airy manner.

By all means let us touch our humble caps
    to   50
    La poésie pure, the epic narrative;
But comedy shall get its round of claps, too.
    According to his powers, each may give;
    Only on varied diet can we live.
The pious fable and the dirty story
Share in the total literary glory.

There's every mode of singing robe in stock,
    From Shakespeare's gorgeous fur coat,
        Spenser's muff,

III. 20. Charles Pritchard (1808-93), a famous
astronomer. 21. A distinguished literary critic concerned with precision in the use and interpretation of
words. 30. Roy Campbell (1902-57), a South African poet who championed the extreme right in politics and advocated the physically vigorous, dangerous

Or Dryden's lounge suit to my cotton frock,
    And Wordsworth's Harris tweed with
      leathern cuff.   60
    Firbank,° I think, wore just a just-enough;
I fancy Whitman in a reach-me-down,
But you, like Sherlock,° in a dressing-gown.

I'm also glad to find I've your authority
    For finding Wordsworth a most bleak old
      bore,°
Though I'm afraid we're in a sad minority
    For every year his followers get more,
      Their number must have doubled since
      the war.
They come in train-loads to the Lakes, and
    swarms
Of pupil-teachers study him in *Storm's.*°   70

"I hate a pupil-teacher" Milton said,
    Who also hated bureaucratic fools;
Milton may thank his stars that he is dead,
    Although he's learnt by heart in public
      schools,
    Along with Wordsworth and the list of
      rules;
For many a don while looking down his nose
Calls Pope and Dryden classics of our prose.

And new plants flower from that old potato.
    They thrive best in a poor industrial soil,
Are hardier crossed with Rousseaus or a
    Plato;   80
    Their cultivation is an easy toil.
    William, to change the metaphor, struck
      oil;
His well seems inexhaustible, a gusher
That saves old England from the fate of Russia.

The mountain-snob is a Wordsworthian fruit;
    He tears his clothes and doesn't shave his
      chin,
He wears a very pretty little boot,
    He chooses the least comfortable inn;
    A mountain railway is a deadly sin;
His strength, of course, is as the strength of ten
    men,   90
He calls all those who live in cities wen-men.

I'm not a spoil-sport, I would never wish
    To interfere with anybody's pleasures;
By all means climb, or hunt, or even fish,
    All human hearts have ugly little treas-
      ures;
    But think it time to take repressive meas-
      ures
When someone says, adopting the "I know"
    line,
The Good Life is confined above the snow-
    line.

Besides, I'm very fond of mountains, too;
    I like to travel through them in a car;   100
I like a house that's got a sweeping view;
    I like to walk, but not to walk too far.
    I also like green plains where cattle are,
And trees and rivers, and shall always quarrel
With those who think that rivers are immoral.

Not that my private quarrel gives quietus to
    The interesting question that it raises;
Impartial thought will give a proper status to
    This interest in waterfalls and daisies,
    Excessive   love   for   the   non-human
      faces,   110
That lives in hearts from Golders Green to
    Teddington;
It's all bound up with Einstein, Jeans, and
    Eddington.°

It is a commonplace that's hardly worth
    A poet's while to make profound or terse,
That now the sun does not go round the earth,
    That man's no centre of the universe;
    And working in an office makes it worse.
The humblest is acquiring with facility
A Universal-Complex sensibility.

For now we've learnt we mustn't be so bump-
    tious   120
    We find the stars are one big family,
And send out invitations for a scrumptious
    Simple, old-fashioned, jolly romp with tea
    To any natural objects we can see.
We can't, of course, invite a Jew or Red
But birds and nebulae will do instead.

The Higher Mind's outgrowing the Barbarian,
    It's hardly thought hygienic now to kiss;
The world is surely turning vegetarian;

---

life.   **61.** Ronald Firbank (1886-1926), a good but not great novelist popular at this time with the intelligentsia.   **63.** Sherlock Holmes.   **65.** Byron in *Don Juan* has some harsh things to say about the poetry of Wordsworth, styling him "Wordswords" on one occasion.   **70.** A text for teachers of literature.

112. Sir James Jeans and Arthur Eddington, two dis-

And as it grows too sensitive for this,　130
It won't be long before we find there is
A Society of Everybody's Aunts
For the Prevention of Cruelty to Plants.

I dread this like the dentist, rather more so:
　　To me Art's subject is the human clay,
And landscape but a background to a torso;
　　All Cézanne's apples I would give away
　　For one small Goya or a Daumier.
I'll never grant a more than minor beauty
To　pudge　or　pilewort,　petty-chap　or
　　pooty.°　　　　　　　　　　　　140

Art, if it doesn't start there, at least ends,
　　Whether aesthetics like the thought or
　　not,
In an attempt to entertain our friends;
　　And our first problem is to realise what
　　Peculiar friends the modern artist's got;
It's possible a little dose of history
May help us in unravelling this mystery.

At the Beginning I shall *not* begin,
　　Not with the scratches in the ancient
　　caves;
Heard° only knows the latest bulletin　　150
　　About the finds in the Egyptian graves;
　　I'll skip the war-dance of the Indian
　　braves;
Since, for the purposes I have in view,
The English eighteenth century will do.

We find two arts in the Augustan age:
　　One quick and graceful, and by no means
　　holy,
Relying on his lordship's patronage;
　　The other pious, sober, moving slowly,
　　Appealing mainly to the poor and lowly:
So Isaac Watts and Pope, each forced his
　　entry　　　　　　　　　　　　160
To lower middle class and landed gentry.

Two arts as different as Jews and Turks,
　　Each serving aspects of the Reformation,

tinguished astronomers and physicists.　**140.** A pudge
is a puddle, pilewort is an early spring flower similar
to the buttercup, petty-chap is a small article for sale
in a store, and pooty refers to young fowl or fish.
These are all ludicrous terms for the standard objects
used in still lifes.　**150.** Charles Heard, the author
of a number of popular books on science and history.

Luther's division into faith and works:
　　The God of the unique imagination,
　　A friend of those who have to know their
　　station;
And the Great Architect, the Engineer
Who keeps the mighty in their higher sphere.

The important point to notice, though, is this:
　　Each poet knew for whom he had to
　　write,　　　　　　　　　　　　170
Because their life was still the same as his.
　　As long as art remains a parasite,
　　On any class of persons it's alright;
The only thing it must be is attendant,
The only thing it mustn't, independent.

But artists, though, are human; and for man
　　To be a scivvy° is not nice at all:
So everyone will do the best he can
　　To get a patch of ground which he can
　　call
　　His own. He doesn't really care how
　　small,　　　　　　　　　　　　180
So long as he can style himself the master:
Unluckily for art, it's a disaster.

To be a highbrow is the natural state:
　　To have a special interest of one's own,
Rock gardens, marrows, pigeons, silver plate,
　　Collecting butterflies or bits of stone;
　　And then to have a circle where one's
　　known
Of hobbyists and rivals to discuss
With expert knowledge what appeals to us.

But to the artist this is quite forbidden:　190
　　On this point he must differ from the
　　crowd,
And, like a secret agent, must keep hidden
　　His passion for his shop. However proud,
　　And rightly, of his trade, he's not allowed
To etch his face with his professional creases,
Or die from occupational diseases.

Until the great Industrial Revolution
　　The artist had to earn his livelihood:
However much he hated the intrusion
　　Of patron's taste or public's fickle
　　mood,　　　　　　　　　　　　200
　　He had to please or go without his food;

177. Slang term for slavey, or servant who does the

He had to keep his technique to himself
Or find no joint upon his larder shelf.

But Savoury and Newcomen and Watt°
    And all those names that I was told to
      get up
In history preparation and forgot,
    A new class of creative artist set up,
    On whom the pressure of demand was let
      up:
He sang and painted and drew dividends,
But lost responsibilities and friends.   210

Those most affected were the very best:
    Those with originality of vision,
Those whose technique was better than the
    rest,
    Jumped at the chance of a secure position
With freedom from the bad old hack
    tradition,
Leave to be sole judges of the artist's brandy,
Be Shelley, or Childe Harold, or the Dandy.°

So started what I'll call the Poet's Party:
    (Most of the guests were painters, never
      mind)—
The first few hours the atmosphere was
    hearty,   220
    With fireworks, fun, and games of every
    kind;
    All were enjoying it, no one was blind;
Brilliant the speeches improvised, the dances,
And brilliant, too, the technical advances.

How nice at first to watch the passers-by
    Out of the upper window, and to say
"How glad I am that though I have to die
    Like all those cattle, I'm less base than
    they!"
    How we all roared when Baudelaire went
    fey.
"See this cigar," he said, "it's Baude-
    laire's.   230
What happens to perception? Ah, who cares?"

To-day, alas, that happy crowded floor
    Looks very different: many are in tears:

Some have retired to bed and locked the door;
    And some swing madly from the chande-
    liers;
    Some have passed out entirely in the
    rears;
Some have been sick in corners; the sobering
    few
Are trying hard to think of something new.

I've made it seem the artist's silly fault,
    In which case why these sentimental
    sobs?   240
In fact, of course, the whole tureen was salt.
    The soup was full of little bits of snobs.
    The common clay and the uncommon
    nobs
Were far too busy making piles or starving
To look at pictures, poetry, or carving.

I've simplified the facts to be emphatic,
    Playing Macaulay's° favourite little trick
Of lighting that's contrasted and dramatic;
    Because it's true Art feels a trifle sick,
    You mustn't think the old girl's lost her
    kick.   250
And those, besides, who feel most like a sewer
Belong to Painting not to Literature.

You know the terror that for poets lurks
    Beyond the ferry when to Minos°
    brought.
Poets must utter their Collected Works,
    Including Juvenilia. So I thought
    That you might warn him. Yes, I think
    you ought,
In case, when my turn comes, he shall cry
    "Atta boys,
Off with his bags,° he's crazy as a hatter, boys!"

The clock is striking and it's time for
    lunch;   260
    We start at four. The weather's none too
    bright.
Some of the party look as pleased as Punch.
    We shall be travelling, as they call it,
    light;
    We shall be sleeping in a tent to-night.

---

roughest work.   **204.** Thomas Savery, Thomas Newcomen, and James Watt were engineers involved in the
development of the steam engine and the pump, the
machines which made possible the industrial revolution, and, by extension, the payment of dividends on
invested capital.   **217.** The sense of these two concluding lines of the stanza is difficult, but Auden is
probably referring to the fact that during the nineteenth century minor poets tried to imitate Shelley or
the Byronic hero, or to play the role of the dandy.
247. Thomas Babington Macaulay.   **254.** A judge in
the underworld.   **259.** Slacks. "Debagging" was once

You know what Baden-Powell's° taught us,
    don't you,
Ora pro nobis, please, this evening, won't you?

PART IV

A ship again; this time the *Dettifoss.*
    Grierson° can buy it; all the sea I mean,
All this Atlantic that we've now to cross
    Heading for England's pleasant pastures
      green.
    Pro tem I've done with the Icelandic
      scene;
I watch the hills receding in the distance,
I hear the thudding of an engine's pistons.

I hope I'm better, wiser for the trip:
    I've had the benefit of northern breezes,
The open road and good companionship,   10
    I've seen some very pretty little pieces;
    And though the luck was almost all Mac-
      Neice's,
I've spent some jolly evenings playing
    rummy—
No one can talk at Bridge, unless it's Dummy.

I've learnt to ride, at least to ride a pony,
    Taken a lot of healthy exercise,
On barren mountains and in valleys stony,
    I've tasted a hot spring (a taste was wise),
    And foods a man remembers till he dies.
All things considered, I consider Iceland,   20
Apart from Reykjavik, a very nice land.

The part can stand as symbol for the whole:
    So ruminating in these last few weeks,
I see the map of all my youth unroll,
    The mental mountains and the psychic
      creeks,
    The towns of which the master never
      speaks,
The various parishes and what they voted for,
The colonies, their size, and what they're
    noted for.

A child may ask when our strange epoch
    passes,
    During a history lesson, "Please, sir,
      what's   30

An intellectual of the middle classes?
    Is he a maker of ceramic pots
    Or does he choose his king by drawing
      lots?"
What follows now may set him on the rail,
A plain, perhaps a cautionary, tale.

My passport says I'm five feet and eleven,
    With hazel eyes and fair (it's tow-like)
      hair,
That I was born in York in 1907,
    With no distinctive markings anywhere.
    Which isn't quite correct. Conspicuous
      there   40
On my right cheek appears a large brown
    mole,
I think I don't dislike it on the whole.

My name occurs in several of the sagas,
    Is common over Iceland still. Down under
Where *Das Volk* order sausages and lagers
    I ought to be the prize, the living wonder,
    The really pure from any *Rassen-*
      schander,°
In fact I am the great big white barbarian,
The Nordic type, the too too truly Aryan.

In games which mark for beauty out of
    twenty,   50
    I'm doing well if my friends give me
      eight
(When played historically you still score
    plenty);
    My head looks like an egg upon a plate;
    My nose is not too bad, but isn't straight;
I have no proper eyebrows, and my eyes
Are far too close together to look nice.

Beauty, we're told, is but a painted show,
    But still the public really likes that best;
Beauty of soul should be enough, I know,
    The golden ingot in the plain deal
      chest.   60
    But mine's a rattle in a flannel vest;
I can't think what my It had on It's mind,
To give me flat feet and a big behind.

Apart from lyrics and poetic dramma,

---

a favorite Oxford sport. **265.** Founder of the Boy
Scouts.
  IV.   **2.** The reference is probably to John Grier-
son, a British film producer best known for his docu-

mentary films of distant places. **47.** Auden is al-
luding in this passage to the Nazi race theories. *Das
Volk* was the term for the German people; *Rassen-
schander* means, literally, "race-defiler," i.e., "of mixed

Which Ervine seems more angered by
    than sad at,
While Sparrow° fails to understand their
    grammar,
    I have some harmless hobbies; I'm not
        bad at
    Reading the slower movements, and may
        add that
Out of my hours of strumming most of them
Pass playing hymn tunes out of A. and M.°   70

Read character from taste. Who seem to me
    The great? I know that one as well as you.
"Why, Daunty, Gouty, Shopkeeper, the three
    Supreme Old Masters." You must ask me
        who
    Have written just as I'd have liked to do.
I stop to listen and the names I hear
Are those of Firbank, Potter, Carroll, Lear.°

Then phantasies? My anima, poor thing,
    Must take the dreams my Alter Ego sends
        her,
And he's a marvellous diver, not a king.   80
    But when I'm sickening for influenza,
    I play concertos with my own cadenza;
And as the fever rises find it properer
To sing the love duet from a grand opera.

My vices? I've no wish to go to prison.
    I am no Grouper, I will never share
With any prig who thinks he'd like to listen.
    At answering letters I am well aware
    I'm very slack; I ought to take more care
Over my clothes; my promise always fails   90
To smoke much less, and not to bite my nails.

I hate pompositas and all authority;
    Its air of injured rightness also sends
Me shuddering from the cultured smug
    minority.
    "Perpetual revolution," left-wing friends
    Tell me, "in counter-revolution ends.
Your fate will be to linger on outcast
A selfish pink old Liberal to the last."

"No, I am that I am, and those that level

blood."   **66.** Ervine and Sparrow were critics who
disliked the plays Auden wrote with Christopher Isherwood, *The Dog Beneath the Skin, The Ascent of F. 6,*
etc.   **70.** *Hymns Ancient and Modern.*   **77.** Ronald Firbank, Beatrix Potter, Lewis Carroll, and Ed-
mund Lear, all writers of amusing light verse and

At my abuses reckon up their own.   100
I may be straight though they, themselves, are
    bevel."
    So Shakespeare said, but Shakespeare
        must have known.
    I daren't say that except when I'm alone,
Must hear in silence till I turn my toes up,
"It's such a pity Wystan never grows up."

So I sit down this fine September morning
    To tell my story. I've another reason.
I've lately had a confidential warning
    That Isherwood is publishing next season
    A book about us all. I call that
        treason.   110
I must be quick if I'm to get my oar in
Before his revelations bring the law in.

My father's forbears were all Midland yeomen
    Till royalties from coal mines did them
        good;
I think they must have been phlegmatic slow-
    men.
    My mother's ancestors had Norman blood,
    From Somerset I've always understood;
My grandfathers on either side agree
In being clergymen and C. of E.

Father   and   Mother   each   was   one   of
    seven,   120
    Though one died young and one was not
        all there;
Their fathers both went suddenly to Heaven
    While they were still quite small and left
        them here
    To work on earth with little cash to spare;
A nurse, a rising medico, at Bart's°
Both felt the pangs of Cupid's naughty darts.

My home then was professional and "high."
    No gentler father ever lived, I'll lay
All Lombard Street against a shepherd's pie.
    We imitate our loves: well, neighbours
        say   130
    I grow more like my mother every day.
I don't like business men. I know a Prot
Will never really kneel, but only squat.

In pleasures of the mind they both delighted;
    The library in the study was enough
To make a better boy than me short-sighted;

stories.   **125.** St. Bartholomew's Hospital in London.

Our old cook Ada surely knew her stuff;
  My elder brothers did not treat me
    rough;
We lived at Solihull, a village then;
Those at the gasworks were my favourite
    men.   140

My earliest recollection to stay put
  Is of a white stone doorstep and a spot
Of pus where father lanced the terrier's foot;
  Next, stuffing shag into the coffee pot
  Which nearly killed my mother, but did
    not;
Both psycho-analyst and Christian minister,
Will think these incidents extremely sinister.

With northern myths my little brain was
    laden,
  With deeds of Thor and Loki and such
    scenes;
My favourite tale was Andersen's *Ice
  Maiden;*   150
  But better far than any kings or queens
  I liked to see and know about machines;
And from my sixth until my sixteenth year
I thought myself a mining engineer.

The mine I always pictured was for lead,
  Though copper mines might, *faute de
  mieux,* be sound.
To-day I like a weight upon my bed;
  I always travel by the Underground;
  For concentration I have always found
A small room best, the curtains drawn, the
    light on;   160
Then I can work from nine till tea-time,
  right on.

I must admit that I was most precocious
  (Precocious children rarely grow up
    good).
My aunts and uncles thought me quite atro-
    cious
  For using words more adult than I
    should;
  My first remark at school did all it could
To shake a matron's monumental poise;
"I like to see the various types of boys."

The Great War had begun: but masters'
  scrutiny

And fists of big boys were the war to
  us;   170
It was as harmless as the Indian Mutiny,
  A beating from the Head was dangerous.
  But once when half the form put down
    Bellus,°
We were accused of that most deadly sin,
Wanting the Kaiser and the Huns to win.

The way in which we really were affected
  Was having such a varied lot to teach us.
The best were fighting, as the King expected,
  The remnant either elderly grey creatures,
  Or characters with most peculiar fea-
    tures.   180
Many were raggable, a few were waxy,
One had to leave abruptly in a taxi.

Surnames I must not write—O Reginald,
  You at least taught us that which fadeth
    not,
Our earliest visions of the great wide world;
  The beer and biscuits that your favourites
    got,
  Your tales revealing you a first-class shot,
Your riding breeks, your drama called *The
  Waves,*
A few of us will carry to our graves.

"Half a lunatic, half a knave." No doubt   190
  A holy terror to the staff at tea;
A good headmaster must have soon found out
  Your moral character was all at sea;
  I question if you'd got a pass degree:
But little children bless your kind that knocks
Away the edifying stumbling blocks.

How can I thank you? For it only shows
  (Let me ride just this once my hobby-
    horse),
There're things a good headmaster never
    knows.
  There must be sober schoolmasters, of
    course,   200
  But what a prep school really puts across
Is knowledge of the world we'll soon be
    lost in:
To-day it's more like Dickens than Jane
  Austen.

173. The correct form is *bellum.*

I hate the modern trick, to tell the truth,
    Of straightening out the kinks in the
      young mind,
Our passion for the tender plant of youth,
    Our hatred for all weeds of any kind.
    Slogans are bad: the best that I can find
Is this: "Let each child have that's in our care
As much neurosis as the child can bear."   210

In this respect, at least, my bad old Adam is
    Pigheadedly against the general trend;
And has no use for all these new academies
    Where readers of the better weeklies send
    The child they probably did not intend,
To paint a lampshade, marry, or keep pigeons,
Or make a study of the world religions.

Goddess of bossy underlings, Normality!
    What murders are committed in thy
      name!
Totalitarian is thy state Reality,   220
    Reeking of antiseptics and the shame
    Of faces that all look and feel the same.
Thy Muse is one unknown to classic histories,
The topping figure of the hockey mistress.

From thy dread Empire not a soul's exempted:
    More than the nursemaids pushing prams
      in parks,
By thee the intellectuals are tempted,
    O, to commit the treason of the clerks,
    Bewitched by thee to literary sharks.
But I must leave thee to thy office stool,   230
I must get on now to my public school.

Men had stopped throwing stones at one an-
      other,
    Butter and Father had come back again;
Gone were the holidays we spent with
      Mother
      In furnished rooms on mountain, moor,
      and fen;
      And gone those summer Sunday evenings,
      when
Along the seafronts fled a curious noise,
"Eternal Father," sung by three young boys.

Nation spoke Peace, or said she did, with
      nation;
    The sexes tried their best to look the
      same;   240
Morals lost value during the inflation,

    The great Victorians kindly took the
      blame:
    Visions of Dada to the Post-War came,
Sitting in cafés, nostrils stuffed with bread,
Above the recent and the straight-laced dead.

I've said my say on public schools elsewhere:
    Romantic friendship, prefects, bullying,
I shall not deal with, *c'est une autre affaire.*
    Those who expect them, will get no such
      thing,
    It is the strictly relevant I sing.   250
Why should they grumble? They've the Greek
      Anthology,
And all the spicier bits of Anthropology.

We all grow up the same way, more or less;
    Life is not known to give away her pres-
      ents;
She only swops. The unself-consciousness
    That children share with animals and
      peasants
    Sinks in the *"sturm und drang"* of Ado-
      lescence.
Like other boys I lost my taste for sweets,
Discovered sunsets, passion, God, and Keats.

I shall recall a single incident   260
    No more. I spoke of mining engineering
As the career on which my mind was bent,
    But for some time my fancies had been
      veering;
    Mirages of the future kept appearing;
Crazes had come and gone in short, sharp
      gales,
For motor-bikes, photography, and whales.

But indecision broke off with a clean-cut end
    One afternoon in March at half-past three
When walking in a ploughed field with a
      friend;
    Kicking a little stone, he turned to
      me   270
    And said, "Tell me, do you write poetry?"
I never had, and said so, but I knew
That very moment what I wished to do.

Without a bridge passage this leads me
      straight
    Into the theme marked "Oxford" on my
      score
From pages twenty-five to twenty-eight.

Aesthetic trills I'd never heard before
 Rose from the strings, shrill poses from
  the cor;
The woodwind chattered like a pre-war
  Russian,
"Art" boomed the brass, and "Life" thumped
  the percussion.   280

A raw provincial, my good taste was tardy,
 And Edward Thomas° I as yet preferred;
I was still listening to Thomas Hardy
 Putting divinity about a bird;
 But Eliot spoke the still unspoken word;
For gasworks and dried tubers I forsook°
The clock at Granchester, the English rook.

All youth's intolerant certainty was mine as
 I faced life in a double-breasted suit;
I bought and praised but did not read
  Aquinas,   290
 At the *Criterion*'s° verdict I was mute,
 Though Arnold's° I was ready to refute;
And through the quads dogmatic words rang
  clear,
"Good poetry is classic and austere."

So much for Art. Of course Life had its pas-
  sions too;
 The student's flesh like his imagination
Makes facts fit theories and has fashions too.
 We were the tail, a sort of poor relation
 To that debauched, eccentric generation
That grew up with their fathers at the
  War,   300
And made new glosses on the noun Amor.

Three years passed quickly while the Isis°
  went
 Down to the sea for better or for worse;
Then to Berlin, not Carthage,° I was sent
 With money from my parents in my purse,
 And ceased to see the world in terms of
  verse.
I met a chap called Layard and he fed
New doctrines into my receptive head.

Part came from Lane,° and part from D. H.
  Lawrence;
 Gide, though I didn't know it then, gave
  part.   310
They taught me to express my deep abhor-
  rence
 If I caught anyone preferring Art
 To Life and Love and being Pure-in-
  Heart.
I lived with crooks but seldom was molested;
The Pure-in-Heart can never be arrested.

He's gay; no bludgeonings of chance can spoil
  it,
 The Pure-in-Heart loves all men on a par,
And has no trouble with his private toilet;
 The Pure-in-Heart is never ill; catarrh
 Would be the yellow streak, the brush of
  tar;   320
Determined to be loving and forgiving,
I came back home to try and earn my living.

The only thing you never turned your hand to
 Was teaching English in a boarding
  school.
To-day it's a profession that seems grand to
 Those whose alternative's an office stool;
 For budding authors it's become the rule.
To many an unknown genius postmen bring
Typed notices from Rabbitarse and String.°

The Head's M.A., a bishop is a patron,   330
 The assistant staff is highly qualified;
Health is the care of an experienced matron,
 The arts are taught by ladies from out-
  side;
 The food is wholesome and the grounds
  are wide;
Their aim is training character and poise,
With special coaching for the backward boys.

I found the pay good and had time to spend it,
 Though others may not have the good
  luck I did:
For You I'd hesitate to recommend it;
 Several have told me that they can't abide
  it.   340

282. Edward Thomas (1878-1917), a minor poet who
wrote about nature and his travels. 286. The details are from T. S. Eliot's *The Waste Land.* 291. A
critical journal edited by T. S. Eliot. 292. Matthew
Arnold (1822-88), a distinguished spokesman for the
Victorian literary tastes which Auden's generation re-
pudiated. 302. The Thames River is called the Isis
at Oxford. 304. St. Augustine was sent to Carthage
to complete his education. 309. Homer Lane, a psychologist whose theory that love was basic to human
character influenced some of Auden's early poetry.
329. Parody of a well-known scholastic agency, Gab-
bitas and Thring.

Still, if one tends to get a bit one-sided,
It's pleasant as it's easy to secure
The hero worship of the immature.

More, it's a job and jobs to-day are rare:
    All the ideals in the world won't feed us
Although they give our crimes a certain air.
      So barons of the press who know their
        readers
      Employ to write their more appalling
        leaders,
Instead of Satan's horned and hideous minions
Clever young men of liberal opinions.   350

Which brings me up to nineteen-thirty-five;
    Six months of film work is another story
I can't tell now. But, here I am, alive
      Knowing the true source of that sense of
        glory
      That still surrounds the England of the
        Tory,
Come only to the rather tame conclusion
That no man by himself has life's solution.

I know—the fact is really not unnerving—
    That what is done is done, that no past
      dies,
That what we see depends on who's observ-
    ing,   360
      And what we think on our activities.
      That envy warps the virgin as she dries
But *"Post coitum, homo tristis"* means
The lover must go carefully with the greens.

The boat has brought me to the landing-stage,
    Up the long estuary of mud and sedges;
The line I travel has the English gauge;
      The engine's shadow vaults the little
        hedges;
      And summer's done. I sign the usual
        pledges
To be a better poet, better man;   370
I'll really do it this time if I can.

I'm home again, and goodness knows to what,
    To read the papers and to earn my bread;
I'm home to Europe where I may be shot;
      "I'm home again," as William Morris
        said,
      "And nobody I really care for's dead."
I've got a round of visits now to pay,
So I must finish this another day.

PART V

Autumn is here. The beech leaves strew the
    lawn;
      The power stations take up heavier loads;
The massive lorries shake from dusk till dawn
      The houses on the residential roads;
      The shops are full of coming winter
        modes.
Dances have started at the Baths next door
Stray scraps of MS strew my bedroom floor.

I read that there's a boomlet on in Birming-
    ham,
      But what I hear is not so reassuring;
Rumours of War, the B.B.C. confirming
    'em,   10
      The prospects for the future aren't
        alluring;
      No one believes Prosperity enduring,
Not even Wykehamists,° whose golden mean
Maintains the All Souls' Parish Magazine.

The crack between employees and employers
    Is obvious already as the nose on
John Gielgud's face; the keels of new des-
    troyers
      Get laid down somehow though all
        credit's frozen;
      The Pope's turned protestant at last and
        chosen,
Thinking it safer in the temporal circs,   20
The Italian faith against the Russian works.

England, my England—you have been my
    tutrix—
      The *Mater,* on occasions, of the free,
Or, if you'd rather, *Dura Virum Nutrix,*°
      Whatever happens I am born of Thee;
      And Englishmen, all foreigners agree,
Taking them by and large, and as a nation,
All suffer from an Oedipus fixation.

With all thy faults, of course we love thee still;
    We'd better for we have to live with
      you,   30
From Rhondda Valley or from Bredon Hill,
      From Rotherhithe, or Regent Street, or
        Kew
      We look you up and down and whistle
        "Phew!

V.   **13.** Members of Winchester College.   **24.** "Stern

Mother looks odd to-day dressed up in peers,
Slums, aspidistras, shooting-sticks, and queers."

Cheer up! There're several singing birds that
    sing.
        There's six feet six of Spender° for a
        start;
Eliot has really stretched his eagle's wing,
        And Yeats has helped himself to Parnell's°
        heart;
        This book has samples of MacNeice's
        art;   40
There's Wyndham Lewis fuming out of sight,
That lonely old volcano of the Right.

I'm marking time because I cannot guess
    The proper place to which to send this
    letter,
c/o Saint Peter or The Infernal Press?
    I'll try the Press. World-culture is its
    debtor;
    It has a list that Faber's couldn't better.
For Heaven gets all the lookers for her pains,
But Hell, I think, gets nearly all the brains.

The congregation up there in the former   50
    Are those whose early upbringing was
    right,
Who never suffered from a childish trauma;
    As babies they were Truby King's° de-
    light;
    They're happy, lovely, but not overbright.
For no one thinks unless a complex makes
    him,
Or till financial ruin overtakes him.

Complex or Poverty; in short The Trap.
    Some set to work to understand the
    spring;
Others sham dead, pretend to take a nap;
    "It is a motor-boat," the madmen
    sing;   60
    The artist's action is the queerest thing:
He seems to like it, couldn't do without it,
And only wants to tell us all about it.

While Rome is burning or he's out of sorts
    "Causons, causons, mon bon," he's apt to
    say,
    "What does it matter while I have these
    thoughts?"
    Or so I've heard, but Freud's not quite
    O.K.
    No artist works a twenty-four hour day.
In bed, asleep or dead, it's hard to tell
The highbrow from *l'homme moyen sen-*
suel.   70

"Es neiget die weisen zu schönem sich."°
    Your lordship's brow that never wore a
    hat
Should thank your lordship's foot that did
    the trick.°
    Your mother in a temper cried, "Lame
    Brat!"
    Posterity should thank her much for that.
Had she been sweet she surely would have
    taken
Juan away and saved your moral bacon.

The match of Hell and Heaven was a nice
    Idea of Blake's,° but won't take place,
    alas.
You can choose either, but you can't choose
    twice;   80
    You can't, at least in this world, change
    your class;
    Neither is alpha plus though both will
    pass;
And don't imagine you can write like Dante,
Dive like your nephew, crochet like your
    auntie.

The Great Utopia, free of all complexes,
    The Withered State is, at the moment,
    such
A dream as that of being both the sexes.
    I like Wolf's° *Goethe-lieder* very much,
    But doubt if Ganymede's appeal will
    touch—

Nurse of Men." **37.** *Stephen Spender.* **39.** Charles Stewart Parnell (1846-1891), a leader of the Irish nationalist movement until he was discredited shortly before his death. W. B. Yeats was himself an ardent patriot. **53.** Sir Frederic Truby King (1858-1938), a New Zealander, founder of the science known as "Mothercraft." His main interest was in teaching women how to raise healthy children. **71.** "The wise incline to the beautiful." **73.** Byron was born lame, and his mother is reported to have called him a "lame brat." **79.** In William Blake's "Marriage of Heaven and Hell" (c. 1790) the two places or states of being are ultimately brought together. **88.** Hugo Wolf (1860-1903), a German composer most famous for

That marvellous cry with its ascending
    phrases—   90
Capitalism in its later phases.

Are Poets saved? Well, let's suppose they are,
    And take a peep. I don't see any books.
Shakespeare is lounging grandly at the bar,
    Milton is dozing, judging by his looks,
    Shelley is playing poker with two crooks,
Blake's adding pince-nez to an ad. for players,°
Chaucer is buried in the latest Sayers.°

Lord Alfred rags with Arthur° on the floor,
    Housman,° all scholarship forgot at
        last,   100
Sips up the stolen waters through a straw,

his *lieder.*   **97.** A brand of English cigarettes.   **98.**
Dorothy Sayers, a mystery writer.   **99.** Alfred, Lord
Tennyson. "Arthur" is probably Arthur Hallam, whose
death left Tennyson nearly inconsolable and occa-
sioned the poem *In Memoriam.*   **100.** A. E. Hous-

Browning's complaining that Keats bowls
    too fast,
    And you have been composing as they
        passed
A clerihew on Wordsworth and his tie,
A rather dirty limerick on Pye.°

I hope this reaches you in your abode,
    This letter that's already far too long,
Just like the Prelude° or the Great North
    Road;
    But here I end my conversational song.
    I hope you don't think mail from stran-
        gers wrong.   110
As to its length, I tell myself you'll need it,
You've all eternity in which to read it.

man was a great classical scholar as well as a poet.
105. Henry James Pye (1745-1813), a poet laureate
mocked by Byron in *Don Juan.*   **108.** "The Prelude," a very long and famous poem by Wordsworth.

Questions

1. Why does Auden select Byron as a correspondent? Why does he avoid writing to Jane Austen?

2. Do a character sketch of the poet based on biographical details, tastes, attitudes, opinions, and other such information provided by the poem. Is the character built up by Auden an effective one for his satiric purpose? Does it interfere with, or does it further, his criticism of his world?

3. Auden says that he will "only now and then be mildly spiteful." Is this so?

4. Describe the various techniques Auden uses to ridicule the modern belief in progress.

5. The poem is a tissue of references to particular persons, places, things, and events, many of which are not familiar to an American reader, or even to an Englishman who was born in the 1930's or after. Do you think that this particularity weakens the poem? Does it detract from its universal implications?

6. Discuss Auden's view of "normality."

7. The Latin word *satura,* from which our word "satire" is derived, means, roughly, "composed of many different things." Auden's poem certainly is a varied composition which apparently contains anything that came into his head. Can you see any way in which this loose form is appropriate to satire? Is there any ultimate unifying principle which keeps the poem from being a mere collection of fragments?

8. How would you describe the rhythms of the poem? the rhymes? the stanza form? How does the characteristic tone, which is built up from these elements, contribute to the meaning of the work?

EVELYN WAUGH

Love Among the Ruins:
A Romance of the Near Future

In Evelyn Waugh's novel *Helena* (1950), Constantius, father of the future Roman emperor Constantine, rides with his new bride Helena, later St. Helena, the discoverer of the true cross, along the rough Roman wall which separates Gaul from Germany and forms the outermost defense of the City of Rome. He tries to explain to Helena what the wall means:

> Think of it, mile upon mile, from snow to desert, a single great girdle round the civilized world; inside, peace, decency, the law, the altars of the gods, industry, the arts, order; outside, wild beasts and savages, forest and swamp, bloody mumbo-jumbo, men like wolf-packs; and along the wall the armed might of the Empire, sleepless, holding the line. Doesn't it make you see what The City means?

On one side barbarism, on the other civilization; on one side a desolate waste, on the other tilled fields; on one side the jungle, on the other the City. This is Waugh's image of the world, and though for most of us in the twentieth century the jungle and the barbarian hordes seem far away in time and space, for Waugh the jungle is always creeping into the City and the barbarians are always breaching the wall. In a series of remarkable satiric novels beginning with *Decline and Fall* in 1928 Waugh has traced the course of the invasion and shown that English society in particular, and Western civilization in general, at the very moment when they seem most progressive, most cultured, most affluent, are in the process of decay. In the fashionable sections of London, in Hollywood, in the great universities and schools, in the homes of the great, and in the houses of Parliament, Waugh chronicles the arrival of the new barbarism, the reversion of City to Wasteland. In these satires barbarism masquerades as progress, enlightened ways of thinking, more enjoyable and efficient ways of living.

"Love Among the Ruins" (1953) is an ironic projection of the brave new world promised by English socialism after World War II. But a close examination of the story will show that Waugh is not merely attacking the English Labor Party, or socialism in general; he presents these as only one form which the new barbarism takes.

"Love Among the Ruins" is an instance of what is known as the "mock

43

Utopia." In this type of satire the values, ideas, and hopes of a particular social philosophy are projected and given maximum realization in a fictitious Utopian society. And in instances of this kind of satire such as Aldous Huxley's *Brave New World* or George Orwell's *1984*, the "ideal" society always turns out to be a glittering sham which robs men of their humanity, or a ghastly failure in which life is reduced to mere existence.

The first three works in this volume have been first-person satire in which the satirists have rambled about attacking in a variety of ways a variety of subjects. In "Love Among the Ruins," and in the short stories, play, and novel which follow, the author has removed himself from his work, trusting to the story to make its satiric point without explicit comment from him. You will want to pay close attention to the methods the satirist uses in this kind of work as a substitute for direct moral statement. Further, in this type of satire the author is committed to "telling a story," and this means that he is not free, as is the first-person satirist, to turn without transition to a discussion of any subject or idea he chooses; he must instead find some way of working his various topics smoothly into his plot. This type of satire in which the attack is conveyed within a fable or story is generally more oblique, more indirect, than first-person satire. Analysis of the advantages and disadvantages of the two methods will lead toward an understanding of the relation of literary forms to the ideas they express.

I

Despite their promises at the last Election, the politicians had not yet changed the climate. The State Meteorological Institute had so far produced only an unseasonable fall of snow and two little thunderbolts no larger than apricots. The weather varied from day to day and from county to county as it had done of old, most anomalously.

This was a rich, old-fashioned Tennysonian night.

Strains of a string quartet floated out from the drawing-room windows and were lost amid the splash and murmur of the gardens. In the basin the folded lilies had left a brooding sweetness over the water. No gold fin winked in the porphyry font and any peacock which seemed to be milkily drooping in the moonshadows was indeed a ghost, for the whole flock of them had been found mysteriously and rudely slaughtered a day or two ago in the first disturbing flush of this sudden summer.

FROM *Tactical Exercise* by Evelyn Waugh, by permission of Little, Brown & Co. Copyright 1953 by Evelyn Waugh.

Miles, sauntering among the sleeping flowers, was suffused with melancholy. He did not much care for music and this was his last evening at Mountjoy. Never again, perhaps, would he be free to roam these walks.

Mountjoy had been planned and planted in the years of which he knew nothing; generations of skilled and patient husbandmen had weeded and dunged and pruned; generations of dilettanti had watered it with cascades and jets; generations of collectors had lugged statuary here; all, it seemed, for his enjoyment this very night under this huge moon. Miles knew nothing of such periods and processes, but he felt an incomprehensible tidal pull towards the circumjacent splendors.

Eleven struck from the stables. The music ceased. Miles turned back and, as he reached the terrace, the shutters began to close and the great chandeliers were one by one extinguished. By the light of the sconces which still shone on their panels of faded satin and clouded gold, he joined the company dispersing to bed through the islands of old furniture.

His room was not one of the grand succession which lay along the garden front.

Those were reserved for murderers. Nor was it on the floor above, tenanted mostly by sexual offenders. His was a humbler wing. Indeed he overlooked the luggage porch and the coal bunker. Only professional men visiting Mountjoy on professional business and very poor relations had been put here in the old days. But Miles was attached to this room, which was the first he had ever called his own in all his twenty years of Progress.

His next-door neighbor, a Mr. Sweat, paused at his door to say good-night. It was only now after twenty months' proximity, when Miles's time was up, that this veteran had begun to unbend. He and a man named Soapy, survivals of another age, had kept themselves to themselves, talking wistfully of cribs they had cracked, of sparklers, of snug bar-parlors where they had met their favorite fences, of strenuous penal days at the Scrubs and on the Moor. They had small use for the younger generation; crime, calvinism and classical music were their interests. But at last Mr. Sweat had taken to nodding, to grunting, and finally, too late for friendship, to speaking to Miles.

"What price the old strings tonight, chum?" he asked.

"I wasn't there, Mr. Sweat."

"You missed a treat. Of course nothing's ever good enough for old Soapy. Made me fair sick to hear Soapy going on all the time. The viola was scratchy, Soapy says. They played the Mozart just like it was Haydn. No feeling in the Debussy pizzicato, says Soapy."

"Soapy knows too much."

"Soapy knows a lot more than some I could mention, schooling or no schooling. Next time they're going to do the Grosse Fugue as the last movement of the B flat. That's something to look forward to, that is, though Soapy says no late Beethoven comes off. We'll see. Leastways, me and Soapy will; *you* won't. You're off tomorrow. Pleased?"

"Not particularly."

"No, no more wouldn't I be. It's a funny thing but I've settled down here wonderful. Never thought I should. It all seemed a bit too posh at first. Not like the old Scrubs. But it's a real pretty place once you're used to it. Wouldn't mind settling here for a lifer if

they'd let me. The trouble is there's no security in crime these days. Time was, you knew just what a job was worth, six months, three years; whatever it was, you knew where you were. Now what with prison commissioners and Preventative Custody and Corrective Treatment they can keep you in or push you out just as it suits them. It's not right.

"I'll tell you what it is, chum," continued Mr. Sweat. "There's no understanding of crime these days like what there was. I remember when I was a nipper, the first time I came up before the beak, he spoke up straight: 'My lad,' he says, 'you are embarking upon a course of life that can only lead to disaster and degradation in this world and everlasting damnation in the next.' Now that's talking. It's plain sense and it shows a personal interest. But last time I was up, when they sent me here, they called me an 'antisocial phenomenon;' said I was 'maladjusted.' That's no way to speak of a man what was doing time before they was in long trousers, now is it?"

"They said something of the same kind to me."

"Yes and now they're giving you the push, just like you hadn't no Rights. I tell you it's made a lot of the boys uncomfortable your going out all of a sudden like this. Who'll it be next time, that's what we're wondering?

"I tell you where you went wrong, chum. You didn't give enough trouble. You made it too easy for them to say you was cured. Soapy and me got wise to that. You remember them birds as got done in? That was Soapy and me. They took a lot of killing too; powerful great bastards. But we got the evidence all hid away tidy and if there's ever any talk of me and Soapy being 'rehabilitated' we'll lay it out conspicuous.

"Well, so long, chum. Tomorrow's my morning for Remedial Repose so I daresay you'll be off before I get down. Come back soon."

"I hope so," said Miles and turned alone into his own room.

He stood briefly at the window and gazed his last on the cobbled yard. He made a good figure of a man, for he came of handsome parents and all his life had been carefully fed and doctored and exercised; well clothed too. He wore the drab serge dress that was the normal garb of the period—only certified homosexuals wore colors—but there were differences of fit and condition among these uniforms. Miles displayed the handiwork of tailor and valet. He belonged to a privileged class.

The State had made him.

No clean-living, God-fearing, Victorian gentleman, he; no complete man of the renaissance; no gentil knight nor dutiful pagan nor, even, noble savage. All that succession of past worthies had gone its way, content to play a prelude to Miles. He was the Modern Man.

His history, as it appeared in multuplet in the filing cabinets of numberless State departments, was typical of a thousand others. Before his birth the politicians had succeeded in bringing down his father and mother to penury; they, destitute, had thrown themselves into the simple diversions of the very poor and thus, between one war and the next, set in motion a chain-reaction of divorces which scattered them and their various associates in forlorn couples all over the Free World. The aunt on whom the infant Miles had been quartered was conscriped for work in a factory and shortly afterwards died of boredom at the conveyer-belt. The child was put to safety in an orphanage.

Huge sums were thenceforward spent upon him; sums which, fifty years earlier, would have sent whole quiversful of boys to Winchester and New College and established them in the learned professions. In halls adorned with Picassos and Legers he yawned through long periods of Constructive Play. He never lacked the requisite cubic feet of air. His diet was balanced and on the first Friday of every month he was psychoanalyzed. Every detail of his adolescence was recorded and microfilmed and filed, until at the appropriate age he was transferred to the Air Force.

There were no airplanes at the station to which he was posted. It was an institution to train instructors to train instructors to train instructors in Personal Recreation.

There for some weeks he tended a dish-washing machine and tended it, as his adjutant testified at his trial, in an exemplary fashion. The work in itself lacked glory, but

it was the normal novitiate. Men from the orphanages provided the hard core of the Forces, a caste apart which united the formidable qualities of Janissary and Junker. Miles had been picked early for high command. Dish-washing was only the beginning. The adjutant, an Orphan too, had himself washed both dishes and officers' underclothes, he testified, before rising to his present position.

Courts Martial had been abolished some years before this. The Forces handed their defaulters over to the civil arm for treatment. Miles came up at quarter sessions. It was plain from the start, when Arson, Wilful Damage, Manslaughter, Prejudicial Conduct and Treason were struck out of the Indictment and the whole reduced to a simple charge of Antisocial Activity, that the sympathies of the Court were with the prisoner.

The Station Psychologist gave his opinion that an element of incendiarism was inseparable from adolescence. Indeed, if checked, it might produce morbid neuroses. For his part he thought the prisoner had performed a perfectly normal act and, moreover, had shown more than normal intelligence in its execution.

At this point some widows, mothers and orphans of the incinerated airmen set up an outcry from the public gallery and were sharply reminded from the Bench that this was a Court of Welfare and not a meeting of the Housewives' Union.

The case developed into a concerted eulogy of the accused. An attempt by the prosecution to emphasize the extent of the damage was rebuked from the Bench.

"The jury," he said, "will expunge from their memories these sentimental details which have been most improperly introduced."

"May be a detail to you," said a voice from the gallery. "He was a good husband to me."

"Arrest that woman," said the Judge.

Order was restored and the panegyrics continued.

At last the Bench summed up. He reminded the jury that it was a first principle of the New Law that no man could be held responsible for the consequences of his own acts. The jury must dismiss from their minds the consideration that much valuable property and many valuable lives had been lost and the cause of Personal Recreation gravely retarded. They had merely to decide whether in fact the prisoner had arranged inflammable material at various judiciously selected points in the Institution and had ignited them. If he had done so, and the evidence plainly indicated that he had, he contravened the Standing Orders of the Institution and was thereby liable to the appropriate penalties.

Thus directed the jury brought in a verdict of guilty coupled with a recommendation of mercy towards the various bereaved persons who from time to time in the course of the hearing had been committed for contempt. The Bench reprimanded the jury for presumption and impertinence in the matter of the prisoners held in contempt, and sentenced Miles to residence during the State's pleasure at Mountjoy Castle (the ancestral seat of a maimed V.C. of the Second World War, who had been sent to a Home for the Handicapped when the place was converted into a jail).

The State was capricious in her pleasures. For nearly two years Miles enjoyed her particular favors. Every agreeable remedial device was applied to him and applied, it was now proclaimed, successfully. Then without warning a few days back, while he lay dozing under a mulberry tree, the unexpected blow had fallen; they had come to him, the Deputy Chief-Guide and the sub-Deputy, and told him bluntly and brutally that he was rehabilitated.

Now on this last night he knew he was to wake tomorrow on a harsh world. Nevertheless he slept and was gently awoken for the last time to the familiar scent of china tea on his bed table, the thin bread and butter, the curtains drawn above the luggage porch, the sunlit kitchen-yard and the stable clock just visible behind the cut-leaf copper beech.

He breakfasted late and alone. The rest of the household were already engaged in the first community-songs of the day. Presently he was called to the Guidance Office.

Since his first day at Mountjoy, when with other entrants Miles had been addressed at length by the Chief Guide on the Aims and Achievements of the New Penology, they had seldom met. The Chief Guide was almost always away addressing penological conferences.

The Guidance Office was the former housekeeper's room stripped now of its plush and patriotic pictures; sadly tricked out instead with standard civil-service equipment, class A.

It was full of people.

"This is Miles Plastic," said the Chief Guide. "Sit down, Miles. You can see from the presence of our visitors this morning what an important occasion this is."

Miles took a chair and looked and saw seated beside the Chief Guide two elderly men whose faces were familiar from the television screen as prominent colleagues in the Coalition Government. They wore open flannel shirts, blazers with numerous pens and pencils protruding from the breast pocket, and baggy trousers. This was the dress of very high politicians.

"The Minister of Welfare and the Minister of Rest and Culture," continued the Chief Guide. "The stars to which we have hitched our wagon. Have the press got the hand-out?"

"Yes, Chief."

"And the photographers are all ready?"

"Yes, Chief."

"Then I can proceed."

He proceeded as he had done at countless congresses, at countless spas and university cities. He concluded, as he always did: "In the New Britain which we are building, there are no criminals. There are only the victims of inadequate social services."

The Minister of Welfare, who had not reached his present eminence without the help of a certain sharpness in debate, remarked: "But I understood that Plastic is from one of our own Orphanages. . . ."

"Plastic is recognized as a Special Case," said the Chief Guide.

The Minister of Rest and Culture, who in the old days had more than once done time himself, said: "Well, Plastic, lad, from all they do say I reckon you've been uncommon smart."

"Exactly," said the Chief Guide. "Miles is our first success, the vindication of the Method."

"Of all the new prisons established in the first glorious wave of Reform, Mountjoy alone has produced a complete case of rehabilitation," the Minister of Welfare said. "You may or may not be aware that the Method has come in for a good deal of criticism both in Parliament and outside. There are a lot of young hot-heads who take their inspiration from our Great Neighbor in the East. You can quote the authorities to them till you're black in the face but they are always pressing for the all latest gadgets of capital and corporal punishment, for chain gangs and solitary confinement, bread and water, the cat-o'-nine-tails, the rope and the block, and all manner of new-fangled nonsense. They think we're a lot of old fogeys. Thank goodness we've still got the solid sense of the people behind us, but we're on the defensive now. We have to show results. That's why we're here this morning. To show them results. *You* are our Result!"

These were solemn words and Miles in some measure responded to the occasion. He gazed before him blankly with an expression that might seem to be awe.

"You'd best watch your step now, lad," said the Minister of Rest and Culture.

"Photographs," said the Minister of Welfare, "Yes, shake my hand. Turn towards the cameras. Try to smile."

Bulbs flashed all over the dreary little room.

"Give us a paw, lad," said the Minister of Rest and Culture, taking Miles's hand in his turn. "And no funny business, mind."

Then the politicians departed.

"The Deputy-Chief will attend to all the practical matters," said the Chief wearily. "Go and see him now."

Miles went.

"Well, Miles, from now on I must call you Mr. Plastic," said the Deputy-Chief. "In less than a minute you become a Citizen. This little pile of papers is *You*. When I stamp them, Miles the Problem ceases to exist and Mr. Plastic the Citizen is born. We are sending you to Satellite City, the nearest Population Center, where you will be attached to the Ministry of Welfare as a sub-official. In view of your special training you are not being classified as a Worker. The immediate material rewards, of course, are not as great. But you are definitely in the Service. We have set your foot on the bottom rung of the non-competitive ladder."

The Deputy Chief Guide picked up the rubber stamp and proceeded to his work of creation. Flip-thump, flip-thump the papers were turned and stained.

"There you are, Mr. Plastic," said the Deputy-Chief handing Miles, as it were, the baby.

At last Miles spoke: "What must I do to get back here?" he asked.

"Come, come, you're rehabilitated now, remember. It is your turn to give back to the State some of the service the State has given you. You will report this morning to the Area Progressive. Transport has been laid on. State be with you, Mr. Plastic. Be careful, that's your Certificate of Human Personality you've dropped—a *vital* document."

II

Satellite City, one of a hundred such grand conceptions, was not yet in its teens but already the Dome of Security showed signs of wear. This was the name of the great municipal edifice about which the city was planned. The eponymous dome had looked well enough in the architect's model, shallow certainly but amply making up in girth what it lacked in height, the daring exercise of some new trick of construction. But to the surprise of all, when the building arose and was seen from the ground, the dome blandly vanished. It was hidden forever among the roofs and butting shoulders of the ancillary wings and was never seen again from the outside except by airmen and steeplejacks. Only the name remained. On the day of its dedication, among massed politicians and People's Choirs the great lump of building materials had shone fine as a factory in all its brilliance of glass and new concrete. Since then, during one of the rather frequent week-ends of international panic, it had been camouflaged and its windows blackened. Cleaners were few and usually on strike. So the Dome of Security remained blotched and dingy, the sole permanent building of Satellite City. There were no workers' flats, no officials' garden suburbs, no parks, no playgrounds yet. These were all on the drawing-boards in the surveyor's office, tattered at the edges, ringed by tea cups; their designer long cremated and his ashes scattered among the docks and nettles. Thus the Dome of Security comprised, even more than had been intended, all the aspirations and amenities of the city.

The officials subsisted in perpetual twilight. Great sheets of glass planned to "trap" the sun, admitted few gleams from scratches in their coat of tar. At evening when the electric light came on, there was faint glow, here and there. When, as often, the power-station was "shedding its load" the officials stopped work early and groped their way back to their darkened huts where in the useless refrigerators their tiny rations were quietly putrefying. On working days the officials, male and female, trudged through cigarette ends round and round, up and down what had once been lift-shafts, in a silent, shabby, shadowy procession.

Among these pilgrims of the dusk, in the weeks that followed his discharge from Mountjoy, moved the exiled Miles Plastic.

He was in a key department.

Euthanasia had not been part of the original 1945 Health Service; it was a Tory measure designed to attract votes from the aged and the mortally sick. Under the Bevan-Eden Coalition the Service came into general use and won instant popularity. The Union of Teachers was pressing for its application to difficult children. Foreigners came in such numbers to take advantage of the service that immigration authorities now turned back the bearers of single tickets.

Miles recognised the importance of his appointment even before he began work. On his first evening in the hostel his fellow sub-officials gathered round to question him.

"Euthanasia? I say, you're in luck. They work you jolly hard, of course, but it's the one department that's expanding."

"You'll get promoted before you know your way about."

"Great State! You *must* have pull. Only the very bright boys get posted to Euthanasia."

"I've been in Contraception for five years. It's a blind alley."

"They say that in a year or two Euthanasia will have taken over Pensions."

"You must be an Orphan."

"Yes, I am."

"That accounts for it. Orphans get all the plums. I had a Full Family Life, State help me."

It was gratifying, of course, this respect and envy. It was well to have fine prospects; but for the time being Miles's duties were humble enough.

He was junior sub-official in a staff of half a dozen. The Director was an elderly man called Dr. Beamish, a man whose character had been formed in the nervous '30s, now much embittered, like many of his contemporaries, by the fulfilment of his early hopes. He had signed manifestos in his hot youth, had raised his fist in Barcelona and had painted abstractedly for *Horizon;* he had stood beside Spender at great concourses of Youth, and written "publicity" for the Last Viceroy. Now his reward had come to him. He held the most envied post in Satellite City and, sardonically, he was making the worst of it. Dr. Beamish rejoiced in every attenuation of official difficulties.

Satellite City was said to be the worst served Euthanasia Center in the State. Dr. Beamish's patients were kept waiting so long that often they died natural deaths before he found it convenient to poison them.

His small staff respected Dr. Beamish. They were all of the official class, for it was part of the grim little game which Dr. Beamish played with the higher authorities to economize extravagantly. His department, he maintained, could not, on its present allotment, afford workers. Even the furnace-man and the girl who dispatched unwanted false teeth to the Dental Redistribution Center were sub-officials.

Sub-officials were cheap and plentiful. The Universities turned them out in thousands every year. Indeed, ever since the Incitement to Industry Act of 1955, which exempted workers from taxation—that great and popular measure of reform which had consolidated the now permanent Coalition Government—there had been a nefarious one-way traffic of expensively State-educated officials "passing," as it was called, into the ranks of the workers.

Miles's duties required no special skill. Daily at ten the Service opened its doors to welfare-weary citizens. Miles was the man who opened them, stemmed the too eager rush and admitted the first half-dozen; then he closed the doors on the waiting multitude until a Higher Official gave the signal for the admission of another batch.

Once inside they came briefly under his charge; he set them in order, saw that they did not press ahead of their turn, and adjusted the television set for their amusement. A Higher Official interviewed them, checked their papers and arranged for the confiscation of their property. Miles never passed the door through which they were finally one by one conducted. A faint whiff of cyanide sometimes gave a hint of the mysteries beyond. Meanwhile he swept the waiting room, emptied the wastepaper basket and brewed tea—a worker's job, for which the refinements of Mountjoy proved a too rich apprenticeship.

In his hostel the same reproductions of Leger and Picasso as had haunted his childhood still stared down on him. At the cinema, to which he could afford, at the best, a weekly visit, the same films as he had seen free at Orphanage, Air Force station and prison, flickered and drawled before him. He was a child of Welfare, strictly schooled to a life of boredom, but he had known better than this. He had known the tranquil melancholy of the gardens at Mountjoy. He had known ecstasy when the Air Force Training School had whirled to the stars in a typhoon of flame. And as he moved sluggishly between Dome and hostel there rang in his ears the words of the old lag: "You didn't give enough trouble."

Then one day, in the least expected quarter, in his own drab department, hope appeared.

Miles later remembered every detail of that morning. It had started in the normal way; rather below normal indeed, for they were reopening after a week's enforced idleness. There had been a strike among the coal miners and Euthanasia had been at a standstill. Now the necessary capitulations had been signed, the ovens glowed again, and the queue at the patients' entrance stretched halfway round the dome. Dr. Beamish squinted at the waiting crowd through the periscope and said with some satisfaction: "It will take months to catch up on the waiting list now. We shall have to start making a charge for the service. It's the only way to keep down the demand."

"The Ministry will never agree to that, surely, sir?"

"Damned sentimentalists. My father and mother hanged themselves in their own backyard with their own clothes-line. Now no one will lift a finger to help himself. There's something wrong in the system, Plastic. There are still rivers to drown in, trains—every now and then—to put your head under; gas-fires in some of the huts. The country is full of the natural resources of death, but everyone has to come to us."

It was not often he spoke so frankly before his subordinates. He had overspent during the week's holiday, drunk too much at his hostel with other unemployed colleagues. Always after a strike the senior officials returned to work in low spirits.

"Shall I let the first batch in, sir?"

"Not for the moment," said Dr. Beamish. "There's a priority case to see first, sent over with a pink chit from Drama. She's in the private waiting-room now. Fetch her in."

Miles went to the room reserved for patients of importance. All one wall was of glass. Pressed to it a girl was standing, turned away from him, looking out at the glum queue below. Miles stood, the light in his eyes, conscious only of a shadow which stirred at the sound of the latch and turned, still a shadow merely but of exquisite grace, to meet him. He stood at the door, momentarily struck silent at this blind glance of beauty. Then he said: "We're quite ready for you now, miss."

The girl came nearer. Miles' eyes adjusted themselves to the light. The shadow took form. The full vision was all that the first glance had hinted; more than all, for every slight movement revealed perfection. One feature only broke the canon of pure beauty; a long, silken, corn-gold beard.

She said, with a deep, sweet tone, all unlike the flat conventional accent of the age: "Let it be quite understood that I don't want anything done to me. I consented to come here. The Director of Drama and the Director of Health were so pathetic about it all that I thought it was the least I could do. I said I was quite willing to hear about your service, but I do *not* want anything *done*."

"Better tell him inside," said Miles.

He led her to Dr. Beamish's room.

"Great State!" said Dr. Beamish, with eyes for the beard alone.

"Yes," she said. "It is a shock, isn't it? I've got used to it by now but I can understand how people feel seeing it for the first time."

"Is it real?"

"Pull."

"It *is* strong. Can't they do anything about it?"

"Oh they've tried everything."

Dr. Beamish was so deeply interested that he forgot Miles's presence. "Klugmann's Operation, I suppose?"

"Yes."

"It does go wrong like that every now and then. They had two or three cases at Cambridge."

"I never wanted it done. I never want anything done. It was the Head of the Ballet. He insists on all the girls being sterilized. Apparently you can never dance really well again after you've had a baby. And I did want to dance really well. Now this is what's happened."

"Yes," said Dr. Beamish. "Yes. They're far too slap-dash. They had to put down those girls at Cambridge, too. There was no cure. Well, we'll attend to you, young lady. Have you any arrangements to make or shall I take you straight away?"

"But I don't want to be put down. I told your assistant here, I've simply consented to come at all, because the Director of Drama cried so, and he's rather a darling. I've not the smallest intention of letting you kill me."

While she spoke, Dr. Beamish's geniality froze. He looked at her with hatred, not speaking. Then he picked up the pink form. "Then this no longer applies?"

"No."

"Then for State's sake," said Dr. Beamish, very angry, "What are you wasting my time for? I've got more than a hundred urgent cases waiting outside and you come in here to tell me that the Director of Drama is a darling. I know the Director of Drama. We live side by side in the same ghastly hostel. He's a pest. And I'm going to write a report to the Ministry about this tomfoolery which will make him and the lunatic who thinks he can perform a Klugmann, come round to me begging for extermination. And then I'll put them at the bottom of the queue. Get her out of here, Plastic, and let some sane people in."

Miles led her into the public waiting-room. "What an old beast," she said. "What a perfect beast. I've never been spoken to like that before even in the ballet-school. He seemed so nice at first."

"It's his professional feeling," said Miles. "He was naturally put out at losing such an attractive patient."

She smiled. Her beard was not so thick as quite to obscure her delicate ovoid of cheek and chin. She might have been peeping at him over ripe heads of barley.

Her smiles started in her wide grey eyes. Her lips under her golden moustachios were unpainted, tactile. A line of pale down sprang below them and ran through the center of the chin, spreading and thickening and growing richer in color till it met the full flow of the whiskers, but leaving on either side, clear and tender, two symmetrical zones, naked and provocative. So might have smiled some carefree deacon in the colonnaded school of fifth-century Alexandria and struck dumb the heresiarchs.

"I think your beard is beautiful."

"Do you really? I can't help liking it too. I can't help liking anything about myself, can you?"

"Yes. Oh, yes."

"That's not natural."

Clamor at the outer door interrupted the talk. Like gulls around a lighthouse the impatient victims kept up an irregular flap and slap on the panels.

"We're all ready, Plastic," said a senior official. "What's going on this morning?"

What was going on? Miles could not answer. Turbulent sea birds seemed to be dashing themselves against the light in his own heart.

"Don't go," he said to the girl. "Please, I shan't be a minute."

"Oh, I've nothing to take me away. My department all think I'm half dead by now."

Miles opened the door and admitted an indignant half-dozen. He directed them to their chairs, to the registry. Then he went back to the girl who had turned away slightly from the crowd and drawn a scarf peasantwise round her head, hiding her beard.

"I still don't quite like people staring," she said.

"Our patients are far too busy with their

own affairs to notice anyone else," said Miles. "Besides you'd have been stared at all right if you'd stayed on in ballet."

Miles adjusted the television but few eyes in the waiting-room glanced towards it; all were fixed on the registrar's table and the doors beyond.

"Think of them all coming here," said the bearded girl.

"We give them the best service we can," said Miles.

"Yes, of course, I know you do. Please don't think I was finding fault. I only meant, fancy wanting to die."

"One or two have good reasons."

"I suppose you would say that I had. Everyone has been trying to persuade me, since my operation. The medical officials were the worst. They're afraid they may get into trouble for doing it wrong. And then the ballet people were almost as bad. They are so keen on Art that they say: 'You were the best of your class. You can never dance again. How can life be worth living?' What I try to explain is that it's just because I could dance that I *know* life is worth living. That's what Art means to me. Does that sound silly?"

"It sounds unorthodox."

"Ah, but you're not an artist."

"Oh, I've danced all right. Twice a week all through my time at the Orphanage."

"Therapeutic dancing?"

"That's what they called it."

"But, you see, that's quite different from Art."

"Why?"

"Oh," she said with a sudden full intimacy, with fondness, "Oh what a lot you don't know."

The dancer's name was Clara.

III

Courtship was free and easy in this epoch but Miles was Clara's first lover. The strenuous exercises of her training, the austere standards of the corps-de-ballet and her devotion to her art had kept her body and soul unencumbered.

For Miles, child of the State, Sex had been part of the curriculum at every stage of his education; first in diagrams, then in demonstrations, then in application, he had mastered all the antics of procreation. Love was a word seldom used except by politicians and by them only in moments of pure fatuity. Nothing that he had been taught prepared him for Clara.

Once in drama, always in drama. Clara now spent her days mending ballet shoes and helping neophytes on the wall bars. She had a cubicle in a Nissen hut and it was there that she and Miles spent most of their evenings. It was unlike anyone else's quarters in Satellite City.

Two little paintings hung on the walls, unlike any paintings Miles had seen before, unlike anything approved by the Ministry of Art. One represented a goddess of antiquity, naked and rosy, fondling a peacock on a bank of flowers; the other a vast, tree-fringed lake and a party in spreading silken clothes embarking in a pleasure boat under a broken arch. The gilt frames were much chipped but what remained of them was elaborately foliated.

"They're French," said Clara. "More than two hundred years old. My mother left them to me."

All her possessions had come from her mother, nearly enough of them to furnish the little room—a looking glass framed in porcelain flowers, a gilt, irregular clock. She and Miles drank their sad, officially compounded coffee out of brilliant, riveted cups.

"It reminds me of prison," said Miles when he was first admitted there.

It was the highest praise he knew.

On the first evening among this delicate bric-a-brac his lips found the bare twin spaces of her chin.

"I knew it would be a mistake to let the beastly doctor poison me," said Clara complacently.

Full summer came. Another moon waxed over these rare lovers. Once they sought coolness and secrecy among the high cow-parsley and willow-herb of the waste building sites. Clara's beard was all silvered like a patriarch's in the midnight radiance.

"On such a night as this," said Miles, supine, gazing into the face of the moon, "on such a night as this I burned an Air Force Station and half its occupants."

Clara sat up and began lazily smoothing her whiskers, then more vigorously tugged the comb through the thicker, tangled growth of her head, dragging it from her forehead; re-ordered the clothing which their embraces had loosed. She was full of womanly content and ready to go home. But Miles, all male, *post coitum tristis,* was struck by a chill sense of loss. No demonstration or exercise had pre-pared him for this strange new experience of the sudden loneliness that follows requited love.

Walking home they talked casually and rather crossly.

"You never go to the ballet now."

"No."

"Won't they give you seats?"

"I suppose they would."

"Then why don't you go?"

"I don't think I should like it. I see them often rehearsing. I don't like it."

"But you lived for it."

"Other interests now."

"Me?"

"Of course."

"You love me more than the ballet?"

"I am very happy."

"Happier than if you were dancing?"

"I can't tell, can I? You're all I've got now."

"But if you could change?"

"I can't."

"If?"

"There's no 'if.' "

"Damn."

"Don't fret, darling. It's only the moon."

And they parted in silence.

November came, a season of strikes; leisure for Miles, unsought and unvalued; lonely peri-ods when the ballet school worked on and the death house stood cold and empty.

Clara began to complain of ill health. She was growing stout.

"Just contentment," she said at first, but the change worried her. "Can it be that beastly operation?" she asked. "I heard the reason they put down one of the Cambridge girls was that she kept growing fatter and fatter."

"She weighed nineteen stone," said Miles. "I know because Dr. Beamish mentioned it. He has strong professional objections to the Klug-mann operation."

"I'm going to see the Director of Medicine. There's a new one now."

When she returned from her appointment, Miles, still left idle by the strikers, was waiting for her among her pictures and china. She sat beside him on the bed.

"Let's have a drink," she said.

They had taken to drinking wine together, very rarely because of the expense. The State chose and named the vintage. This month the issue was "Progress Port." Clara kept it in a crimson, white-cut, Bohemian flagon. The glasses were modern, unbreakable and un-sightly.

"What did the doctor say?"

"He's very sweet."

"Well?"

"Much cleverer than the one before."

"Did he say it was anything to do with your operation?"

"Oh, yes. Everything to do with it."

"Can he put you right?"

"Yes, he thinks so."

"Good."

They drank their wine.

"That first doctor did make a mess of the operation, didn't he?"

"Such a mess. The new doctor says I'm a unique case. You see, I'm pregnant."

"Clara."

"Yes, it is a surprise, isn't it?"

"This needs thinking about," said Miles.

He thought.

He refilled their glasses.

He said: "It's hard luck on the poor little beast not being an Orphan. Not much oppor-tunity for it. If he's a boy we must try and get him registered as a worker. Of course it might be a girl. Then," brightly, "we could make her a dancer."

"Oh, don't mention dancing," cried Clara, and suddenly began weeping. "Don't speak to me of dancing."

Her tears fell fast. No tantrum this, but deep uncontrolled inconsolable sorrow.

And next day she disappeared.

IV

Santa-Claus-tide was near. Shops were full of shoddy little dolls. Children in the schools sang old ditties about peace and goodwill. Strikers went back to work in order to qualify for their seasonal bonus. Electric bulbs were hung in the conifers and the furnaces in the Dome of Security roared again. Miles had been promoted. He now sat beside the assistant registrar and helped stamp and file the documents of the dead. It was harder work than he was used to and Miles was hungry for Clara's company. The lights were going out in the Dome and on the Goodwill Tree in the car park. He walked the half-mile of hutments to Clara's quarters. Other girls were waiting for their consorts or setting out to find them in the Recreatorium, but Clara's door was locked. A note, pinned to it read: *Miles, Going away for a bit. C.* Angry and puzzled he returned to his hostel.

Clara, unlike himself, had uncles and cousins scattered about the country. Since her operation she had been shy of visiting them. Now, Miles supposed, she was taking cover among them. It was the manner of her flight, so unlike her gentle ways, that tortured him. For a busy week he thought of nothing else. His reproaches sang in his head as the undertone to all the activities of the day and at night he lay sleepless repeating in his mind every word spoken between them and every act of intimacy.

After a week the thought of her became spasmodic and regular. The subject bored him unendurably. He strove to keep it out of his mind as a man might strive to control an attack of hiccups, and as impotently. Spasmodically, mechanically, the thought of Clara returned. He timed it and found that it came every seven and one-half minutes. He went to sleep thinking of her, he woke up thinking of her. But between times he slept. He consulted the departmental psychiatrist who told him that he was burdened by the responsibility of parentage. But it was not Clara the mother who haunted him, but Clara the betrayer.

Next week he thought of her every twenty minutes. The week after that he thought of her irregularly, though often; only when something outside himself reminded him of her. He began to look at other girls and considered himself cured.

He looked hard at other girls as he passed them in the dim corridors of the Dome and they looked boldly back at him. Then one of them stopped him and said: "I've seen you before with Clara" and at the mention of her name all interest in the other girl ceased in pain. "I went to visit her yesterday."

"Where?"

"In hospital, of course. Didn't you know?"

"What's the matter with her?"

"She won't say. Nor will anyone else at the hospital. She's top secret. If you ask me she's been in an accident and there's some politician involved. I can't think of any other reason for all the fuss. She's covered in bandages and gay as a lark."

Next day, December 25th, was Santa Claus Day; no holiday in the department of Euthanasia, which was an essential service. At dusk Miles walked to the hospital, one of the unfinished edifices, all concrete and steel and glass in front and a jumble of huts behind. The hall porter was engrossed in the television, which was performing an old obscure folk play which past generations had performed on Santa Claus Day, and was now revived and revised as a matter of historical interest.

It was of professional interest to the porter for it dealt with maternity services before the days of Welfare. He gave the number of Clara's room without glancing up from the strange spectacle of an ox and an ass, an old man with a lantern, and a young mother. "People here are always complaining," he said. "They ought to realize what things were like before Progress."

The corridors were loud with relayed music. Miles found the hut he sought. It was marked "Experimental Surgery. Health Officers Only." He found the cubicle. He found Clara sleeping, the sheet pulled up to her eyes, her hair loose on the pillow. She had brought some of her property with her. An old shawl lay across the bed-table. A painted fan stood against the television set. She awoke, her eyes full of frank welcome and pulled the sheet higher, speaking through it.

"Darling, you shouldn't have come. I was keeping it for a surprise."

Miles sat by the bed and thought of nothing to say except: "How are you?"

"Wonderful. They've taken the bandages off today. They won't let me have a looking glass yet but they say everything has been a tremendous success. I'm something very special, Miles —a new chapter in surgical progress."

"But what has happened to you. Is it something to do with the baby?"

"Oh no. At least, it was. That was the first

operation. But that's all over now."

"You mean our child?"

"Yes, that had to go. I should never have been able to dance afterwards. I told you all about it. That was why I had the Klugmann operation, don't you remember?"

"But you gave up dancing."

"That's where they've been so clever. Didn't I tell you about the sweet, clever new medical director? He's cured all that."

"Your dear beard."

"Quite gone. An operation the new director invented himself. It's going to be named after him or even perhaps after me. He's so unselfish he wants to call it the Clara Operation. He's taken off all the skin and put on a wonderful new substance, a sort of synthetic rubber that takes grease-paint perfectly. He says the color isn't perfect but that it will never show on the stage. Look, feel it."

She sat up in bed, joyful and proud.

Her eyes and brow were all that was left of the loved face. Below it something quite inhuman, a tight, slippery mask, salmon pink.

Miles stared. In the television screen by the bed further characters had appeared—Food Production Workers. They seemed to declare a sudden strike, left their sheep and ran off at the bidding of some kind of shop-steward in fantastic dress. The machine by the bedside broke into song, an old, forgotten ditty: "O tidings of comfort and joy."

Miles retched unobtrusively. The ghastly face regarded him with fondness and pride. At length the right words came to him; the trite, the traditional sentence uttered by countless lips of generations of baffled and impassioned Englishmen: "I think I shall go for a short walk."

But first he walked only as far as his hostel. There he lay down until the moon moved to his window and fell across his sleepless face. Then he set out, walking far into the fields, out of sight of the Dome of Security, for two hours until the moon was near setting.

He had traveled at random but now the white rays fell on a signpost and he read: "Mountjoy ¾." He strode on with only the stars to light his way till he came to the Castle gates.

They stood open as always, gracious symbol of the new penology. He followed the drive.

The whole lightless face of the old house stared at him silently, without rebuke. He knew now what was needed. He carried in his pocket a cigarette lighter which often worked. It worked for him now.

No need for oil here. The dry old silk of the drawing-room curtains lit like paper. Paint and paneling, plaster and tapestry and gilding bowed to the embrace of the leaping flames. He stepped outside. Soon it was too hot on the terrace and he retreated further, to the marble temple at the end of the long walk. The murderers were leaping from the first story windows but the sexual offenders, trapped above, set up a wail of terror. He heard the chandeliers fall and saw the boiling lead cascading from the roof. This was something altogether finer than the strangulation of a few peacocks. He watched exultant as minute by minute the scene disclosed fresh wonders. Great timbers crashed within; outside the lily-pond hissed with falling brands; a vast ceiling of smoke shut out the stars and under it tongues of flame floated away into the tree tops.

Two hours later when the first engine arrived, the force of the fiery storm was already spent. Miles rose from his marble throne and began the long walk home. But he was no longer at all fatigued. He strode out cheerfully with his shadow, cast by the dying blaze, stretching before him along the lane.

On the main road a motorist stopped him and asked: "What's that over there? A house on fire?"

"It was," said Miles. "It's almost out now."

"Looks like a big place. Only Government property, I suppose?"

"That's all," said Miles.

"Well hop in if you want a lift."

"Thanks," said Miles, "I'm walking for pleasure."

v

Miles rose after two hours in bed. The hostel was alive with all the normal activity of morning. The wireless was playing; the sub-officials were coughing over their wash-basins; the reek of State sausages frying in State grease filled the asbestos cubicle. He was slightly stiff after his long walk and slightly footsore, but his mind was as calm and empty as the sleep from which he had awoken. The scorched-earth policy had succeeded. He had made a desert in his imagination which he might call peace. Once before he had burned his childhood. Now his brief adult life lay in ashes; the enchantments that surrounded Clara were one with the splendors of Mountjoy; her great golden beard, one with the tongues of flame that had leaped and expired among the stars; her fans and pictures and scraps of old embroidery, one with the gilded cornices and silk hangings, black, cold and sodden. He ate his sausage with keen appetite and went to work.

All was quiet too at the Department of Euthanasia.

The first announcement of the Mountjoy disaster had been on the early news. Its proximity to Satellite City gave it a special poignancy there.

"It is a significant phenomenon," said Dr. Beamish, "that any bad news has an immediate effect on our service. You see it whenever there is an international crisis. Sometimes I think people only come to us when they have nothing to talk about. Have you looked at our queue today?"

Miles turned to the periscope. Only one man waited outside, old Parsnip, a poet of the '30s who came daily but was usually jostled to the back of the crowd. He was a comic character in the department, this veteran poet. Twice in Miles's short term he had succeeded in gaining admission but on both occasions had suddenly taken fright and bolted.

"It's a lucky day for Parsnip," said Miles.

"Yes. He deserves some luck. I knew him well once, him and his friend Pimpernell. *New Writing*, the Left Book Club, they were all the rage. Pimpernell was one of my first patients. Hand Parsnip in and we'll finish him off."

So old Parsnip was summoned and that day his nerve stood firm. He passed fairly calmly through the gas chamber on his way to rejoin Pimpernell.

"We might as well knock off for the day," said Dr. Beamish. "We shall be busy again soon when the excitement dies down."

But the politicians seemed determined to keep the excitement up. All the normal features of television were interrupted and curtailed to give place to Mountjoy. Survivors appeared on the screen, among them Soapy, who described how long practice as a cat burglar had enabled him to escape. Mr. Sweat, he remarked with respect, had got clear away. The ruins were surveyed by the apparatus. A sexual maniac with broken legs gave audience from his hospital bed. The Minister of Welfare, it was announced, would make a special appearance that evening to comment on the disaster.

Miles dozed intermittently beside the hostel set and at dusk rose, still calm and free; so purged of emotion that he made his way once more to the hospital and called on Clara.

She had spent the afternoon with looking-glass and make-up box. The new substance of her face fulfilled all the surgeon's promises. It took paint to perfection. Clara had given herself a full mask as though for the lights of the stage; an even creamy white with sudden high spots of crimson on the cheek bones, huge hard crimson lips, eyebrows extended and turned up catwise, the eyes shaded all around with ultramarine and dotted at the corners with crimson.

"You're the first to see me," she said. "I was half-afraid you wouldn't come. You seemed cross yesterday."

"I wanted to see the television," said Miles. "It's so crowded in the hostel."

"So dull today. Nothing except this prison that has been burned down."

"I was there myself. Don't you remember? I often talked of it."

"Did you, Miles? Perhaps so. I've such a bad memory for things that don't concern me. Do you really want to hear the Minister? It would be much cozier to talk."

"It's him I've come for."

And presently the Minister appeared, open-necked as always but without his usual smile; grave to the verge of tears. He spoke for twenty minutes. ". . . The great experiment must go on . . . the martyrs of maladjustment shall not have died in vain. . . . A greater, new Mountjoy shall rise from the ashes of the old. . . ." Eventually tears came—real tears for he held an invisible onion—and trickled down his cheeks. So the speech ended.

"That's all I came for," said Miles, and left Clara to her cocoa-butter and face-towel.

Next day all the organs of public information were still piping the theme of Mountjoy. Two or three patients, already bored with the entertainment, presented themselves for extermination and were happily dispatched. Then a message came from the Regional Director, official-in-chief of Satellite City. He required the immediate presence of Miles in his office.

"I have a move order for you, Mr. Plastic. You are to report to the Ministers of Welfare and Rest and Culture. You will be issued with a Grade A hat, umbrella and brief case for the journey. My congratulations."

Equipped with these insignia of sudden, dizzy promotion, Miles traveled to the capital leaving behind a domeful of sub-officials chattering with envy.

At the terminus an official met him. Together in an official car they drove to Whitehall.

"Let me carry your brief case, Mr. Plastic."

"There's nothing in it."

Miles's escort laughed obsequiously at this risqué joke.

At the Ministry the lifts were in working order. It was a new and alarming experience to enter the little cage and rise to the top of the great building.

"Do they always work here?"

"Not *always,* but very very often."

Miles realized that he was indeed at the heart of things.

"Wait here. I will call you when the Ministers are ready."

Miles looked from the waiting room window at the slow streams of traffic. Just below him stood a strange, purposeless obstruction of stone. A very old man, walking by, removed his hat to it as though saluting an acquaintance. Why? Miles wondered. Then he was summoned to the politicians.

They were alone in their office save for a gruesome young woman. The Minister of Rest and Culture said: "Ease your feet, lad," and indicated a large leatherette armchair.

"Not such a happy occasion, alas, as our last meeting," said the Minister of Welfare.

"Oh, I don't know," said Miles. He was enjoying the outing.

"The tragedy at Mountjoy Castle was a grievous loss to the cause of penology."

"But the great work of Rehabilitation will continue," said the gruesome young woman.

"A greater Mountjoy will arise from the ashes," said the Minister.

"Those noble criminal lives have not been lost in vain."

"Their memory will inspire us."

"Yes," said Miles. "I heard the broadcast."

"Exactly," said the Minister. "Precisely. Then you appreciate, perhaps, what a change the occurrence makes in your own position. From being, as we hoped, the first of a continuous series of successes, you are our only one. It would not be too much to say that the whole future of penology is in your hands. The destruction of Mountjoy Castle by itself was merely a set-back. A sad one, of course, but something which might be described as the growing pains of a great movement. But there is a darker side. I told you, I think, that our great experiment had been made only against considerable opposition. Now—I speak confidentially—that opposition has become vocal and unscrupulous. There is, in fact, a whispering campaign that the fire was no accident but the act of one of the very men whom we were seeking to serve. That campaign must be scotched."

"They can't do us down as easy as they think," said the Minister of Rest and Culture. "Us old dogs know a trick or two."

"Exactly. Counter-propaganda. You are our Exhibit A. The irrefutable evidence of the triumph of our system. We are going to send you up and down the country to lecture. My colleagues have already written your speech. You will be accompanied by Miss Flower here, who will show and explain the model of the new Mountjoy. Perhaps you will care to see it yourself. Miss Flower, the model please."

All the time they were speaking Miles had been aware of a bulky, sheeted object on a table in the window. Miss Flower now unveiled it. Miles gazed in awe.

The object displayed was a familiar, standard packing-case, set on end.

"A rush job," said the Minister of Welfare. "You will be provided with something more elaborate for your tour."

Miles gazed at the box.

It fitted. It fell into place precisely in the void of his mind, satisfying all the needs for which his education had prepared him. The conditioned personality recognized its proper pre-ordained environment. All else was insubstantial; the gardens of Mountjoy, Clara's cracked Crown Derby and her enveloping beard were trophies of a fading dream.

The Modern Man was home.

"There is one further point," continued the Minister of Welfare. "A domestic one but not as irrelevant as it may seem. Have you by any chance formed an attachment in Satellite City? Your dossier suggests that you have."

"Any woman trouble?" explained the Minister of Rest and Culture.

"Oh, yes," said Miles. "Great trouble. But that is over."

"You see, perfect rehabilitation, complete citizenship should include marriage."

"It has not," said Miles.

"That should be rectified."

"Folks like a bloke to be spliced," said the Minister of Rest and Culture. "With a couple of kids."

"There is hardly time for *them,*" said the Minister of Welfare. "But we think that psychologically you will have more appeal if you have a wife by your side. Miss Flower here has every qualification."

"Looks are only skin deep, lad," said the Minister of Rest and Culture.

"So if you have no preferable alternative to offer . . . ?"

"None," said Miles.

"Spoken like an Orphan. I see a splendid career ahead of the pair of you."

"When can we get divorced?"

"Come, come Plastic. You musn't look too far ahead. First things first. You have already obtained the necessary leave from your Director, Miss Flower?"

"Yes, Minister."

"Then off you both go. And State be with you."

In perfect peace of heart Miles followed Miss Flower to the Registrar's office.

Then the mood veered.

Miles felt ill at ease during the ceremony and fidgeted with something small and hard which he found in his pocket. It proved to be his cigarette-lighter, a most uncertain apparatus. He pressed the catch and instantly, surprisingly there burst out a tiny flame—gemlike, hymeneal, auspicious.

Questions

1. Describe the setting of the opening and discuss its significance.

2. What are the characteristics of the "Modern Man"? How does he differ from men of the past?

3. One of the problems of indirect satire, in which there is no direct spokesman for the author, is to discover what the author's values are, the standards by which he is implicitly measuring the persons and world of his story. Go through "Love Among the Ruins" and see if you can describe the techniques Waugh uses to remind us of the cultural and personal ideals which are being destroyed in his "Utopia." Is Waugh's moral attitude consistent throughout the story?

4. Discuss the character of Miles Plastic. How does the use of this type of character contribute to the meaning of the satire? Of what significance is Miles's pyromania? Does Miles change in any way during the story?

5. During the course of even so short a story as this, Waugh manages to attack a great many aspects of the modern world. Make a representative collection of ideas, persons, institutions, and activities which are attacked, and then see if you can discover any common element. Is Waugh ultimately attacking many things at random, or one thing with many manifestations?

6. Discuss the significance of Clara's beard.

7. What does the description of the politicians add to the story?

Inflexible Logic

Russell Maloney's "Inflexible Logic," which first appeared in the *New Yorker* some twenty years ago—and which has by now become a minor classic—is an amusing, but ultimately quite serious, attack on the modern belief in the value of probability theory. Briefly, the probability theory assumes that, while we cannot predict accurately what will happen on any particular occasion, we can predict on the basis of past observation the percentage of times that a given event will occur. For example, we cannot know for certain whether on the fifth or fiftieth spin of a roulette wheel the ball will fall in a black or a red hole. But if the wheel is true and the black and red holes are equal in number, then it is probable that in the long run—in one hundred or one thousand or ten thousand spins—the ball will fall in the red and the black holes an equal number of times. The law, however, operates only over the long run, and there is—though most of us would bet against it—no reason why red should not win the first five thousand or five million times in a row.

When the six chimpanzees came into his life, Mr. Bainbridge was thirty-eight years old. He was a bachelor and lived comfortably in a remote part of Connecticut, in a large old house with a carriage drive, a conservatory, a tennis court, and a well-selected library. His income was derived from impeccably situated real estate in New York City, and he spent it soberly, in a manner which could give offence to nobody. Once a year, late in April, his tennis court was resurfaced, and after that anybody in the neighborhood was welcome to use it; his monthly statement from Brentano's seldom ran below seventy-five dollars; every third year, in November, he turned in his old

Cadillac coupé for a new one; he ordered his cigars, which were mild and rather moderately priced, in shipments of one thousand from a tobacconist in Havana; because of the international situation he had cancelled arrangements to travel abroad, and after due thought had decided to spend his travelling allowance on wines, which seemed likely to get scarcer and more expensive if the war lasted. On the whole, Mr. Bainbridge's life was deliberately, and not too unsuccessfully, modelled after that of an English country gentleman of the late eighteenth century, a gentleman interested in the arts and in the expansion of science, and so sure of himself that he didn't care if some people thought him eccentric.

Mr. Bainbridge had many friends in New York, and he spent several days of the month in the city, staying at his club and looking around. Sometimes he called up a girl and took her out to a theatre and a night club. Sometimes he and a couple of classmates got a little tight and went to a prizefight. Mr. Bainbridge also looked in now and then at some of the conservative art galleries, and liked occasionally to go to a concert. And he liked cocktail parties, too, because of the fine footling conversation and the extraordinary number of pretty girls who had nothing else to do with the rest of their evening. It was at a New York cocktail party, however, that Mr. Bainbridge kept his preliminary appointment with doom. At one of the parties given by Hobie Packard, the stockbroker, he learned about the theory of the six chimpanzees.

It was almost six-forty. The people who had intended to have one drink and go had already gone, and the people who intended to stay were fortifying themselves with slightly dried canapés and talking animatedly. A group of stage and radio people had coagulated in one corner, near Packard's Capehart, and were wrangling about various methods of cheating the Collector of Internal Revenue. In another corner was a group of stockbrokers, talking about the greatest stockbroker of them all, Gauguin. Little Marcia Lupton was sitting with a young man, saying earnestly, "Do you really want to know what my greatest ambition is? I want to be myself," and Mr. Bainbridge smiled gently, thinking of the time Marcia had said that to him. Then he heard the voice of Bernard Weiss, the critic, saying, "Of course he wrote one good novel. It's not surprising. After all, we know that if six chimpanzees were set to work pounding six typewriters at random, they would, in a million years, write all the books in the British Museum."

Mr. Bainbridge drifted over to Weiss and was introduced to Weiss's companion, a Mr. Noble. "What's this about a million chimpanzees, Weiss?" he asked.

"Six chimpanzees," Mr. Weiss said. "It's an old cliché of the mathematicians. I thought everybody was told about it in school. Law of averages, you know, or maybe it's permutation and combination. The six chimps, just pounding away at the typewriter keys, would be

bound to copy out all the books ever written by man. There are only so many possible combinations of letters and numerals, and they'd produce all of them—see? Of course they'd also turn out a mountain of gibberish, but they'd work the books in, too. All the books in the British Museum."

Mr. Bainbridge was delighted; this was the sort of talk he liked to hear when he came to New York. "Well, but look here," he said, just to keep up his part in the foolish conversation, "what if one of the chimpanzees finally did duplicate a book, right down to the last period, but left that off? Would that count?"

"I suppose not. Probably the chimpanzee would get around to doing the book again, and put the period in."

"What nonsense!" Mr. Noble cried.

"It may be nonsense, but Sir James Jeans believes it," Mr. Weiss said, huffily. "Jeans or Lancelot Hogben. I know I ran across it quite recently."

Mr. Bainbridge was impressed. He read quite a bit of popular science, and both Jeans and Hogben were in his library. "Is that so?" he murmured, no longer feeling frivolous. "Wonder if it has ever actually been tried? I mean, has anybody ever put six chimpanzees in a room with six typewriters and a lot of paper?"

Mr. Weiss glanced at Mr. Bainbridge's empty cocktail glass and said drily, "Probably not."

Nine weeks later, on a winter evening, Mr. Bainbridge was sitting in his study with his friend James Mallard, an assistant professor of mathematics at New Haven. He was plainly nervous as he poured himself a drink and said, "Mallard, I've asked you to come here— Brandy? Cigar?—for a particular reason. You remember that I wrote you some time ago, asking your opinion of . . . of a certain mathematical hypothesis or supposition."

"Yes," Professor Mallard said, briskly. "I remember perfectly. About the six chimpanzees and the British Museum. And I told you it was a perfectly sound popularization of a principle known to every schoolboy who had studied the science of probabilities."

"Precisely," Mr. Bainbridge said. "Well, Mallard, I made up my mind . . . It was not difficult for me, because I have, in spite of that fellow in the White House, been able to give something every year to the Museum of Natural History, and they were naturally glad to oblige me. . . . And after all, the only contribution a layman can make to the progress of science is to assist with the drudgery of experiment. . . . In short, I—"

"I suppose you're trying to tell me that you have procured six chimpanzees and set them to work at typewriters in order to see whether they will eventually write all the books in the British Museum. Is that it?"

"Yes, that's it," Mr. Bainbridge said. "What a mind you have, Mallard. Six fine young males, in perfect condition. I had a—I suppose you'd call it a dormitory—built out in back of the stable. The typewriters are in the conservatory. It's light and airy in there, and I moved most of the plants out. Mr. North, the man who owns the circus, very obligingly let me engage one of his best animal men. Really, it was no trouble at all."

Professor Mallard smiled indulgently. "After all, such a thing is not unheard of," he said. "I seem to remember that a man at some university put his graduate students to work flipping coins, to see if heads and tails came up an equal number of times. Of course they did."

Mr. Bainbridge looked at his friend very queerly. "Then you believe that any such principle of the science of probabilities will stand up under an actual test?"

"Certainly."

"You had better see for yourself." Mr. Bainbridge led Professor Mallard downstairs, along a corridor, through a disused music room, and into a large conservatory. The middle of the floor had been cleared of plants and was occupied by a row of six typewriter tables, each one supporting a hooded machine. At the left of each typewriter was a neat stack of yellow copy paper. Empty wastebaskets were under each table. The chairs were the unpadded, spring-backed kind favored by experienced stenographers. A large bunch of ripe bananas was hanging in one corner, and in another stood a Great Bear water-cooler and a rack of Lily cups. Six piles of typescript, each about a foot high, were ranged along the wall on an improvised shelf. Mr. Bainbridge picked up

one of the piles, which he could just conveniently lift, and set it on a table before Professor Mallard. "The output to date of Chimpanzee A, known as Bill," he said simply.

"'"Oliver Twist," by Charles Dickens,'" Professor Mallard read out. He read the first and second pages of the manuscript, then feverishly leafed through to the end. "You mean to tell me," he said, "that this chimpanzee has written—"

"Word for word and comma for comma," said Mr. Bainbridge. "Young, my butler, and I took turns comparing it with the edition I own. Having finished 'Oliver Twist,' Bill is, as you see, starting the sociological works of Vilfredo Pareto, in Italian. At the rate he has been going, it should keep him busy for the rest of the month."

"And all the chimpanzees"—Professor Mallard was pale, and enunciated with difficulty—"they aren't all—"

"Oh, yes, all writing books which I have every reason to believe are in the British Museum. The prose of John Donne, some Anatole France, Conan Doyle, Galen, the collected plays of Somerset Maugham, Marcel Proust, the memoirs of the late Marie of Rumania, and a monograph by a Dr. Wiley on the marsh grasses of Maine and Massachusetts. I can sum it up for you, Mallard, by telling you that since I started this experiment, four weeks and some days ago, none of the chimpanzees has spoiled a single sheet of paper."

Professor Mallard straightened up, passed his handkerchief across his brow, and took a deep breath. "I apologize for my weakness," he said. "It was simply the sudden shock. No, looking at the thing scientifically—and I hope I am at least as capable of that as the next man—there is nothing marvellous about the situation. These chimpanzees, or a succession of similar teams of chimpanzees, would in a million years write all the books in the British Museum. I told you some time ago that I believed that statement. Why should my belief be altered by the fact that they produced some of the books at the very outset? After all, I should not be very much surprised if I tossed a coin a hundred times and it came up heads every time. I know that if I kept at it long enough, the ratio would reduce itself to an exact fifty per cent. Rest assured, these chimpanzees will begin to compose gibberish quite soon. It is bound to happen. Science tells us so. Meanwhile, I advise you to keep this experiment secret. Uninformed people might create a sensation if they knew."

"I will, indeed," Mr. Bainbridge said. "And I'm very grateful for your rational analysis. It reassures me. And now, before you go, you must hear the new Schnabel records that arrived today."

During the succeeding three months, Professor Mallard got into the habit of telephoning Mr. Bainbridge every Friday afternoon at five-thirty, immediately after leaving his seminar room. The Professor would say, "Well?," and Mr. Bainbridge would reply, "They're still at it, Mallard. Haven't spoiled a sheet of paper yet." If Mr. Bainbridge had to go out on Friday afternoon, he would leave a written message with his butler, who would read it to Professor Mallard: "Mr. Bainbridge says we now have Trevelyan's 'Life of Macaulay,' the Confessions of St. Augustine, 'Vanity Fair,' part of Irving's 'Life of George Washington,' the Book of the Dead, and some speeches delivered in Parliament in opposition to the Corn Laws, sir." Professor Mallard would reply, with a hint of a snarl in his voice, "Tell him to remember what I predicted," and hang up with a clash.

The eleventh Friday that Professor Mallard telephoned, Mr. Bainbridge said, "No change. I have had to store the bulk of the manuscript in the cellar. I would have burned it, except that it probably has some scientific value."

"How dare you talk of scientific value?" The voice from New Haven roared faintly in the receiver. "Scientific value! You—you—chimpanzee!" There were further inarticulate sputterings, and Mr. Bainbridge hung up with a disturbed expression. "I am afraid Mallard is overtaxing himself," he murmured.

Next day, however, he was pleasantly surprised. He was leafing through a manuscript that had been completed the previous day by Chimpanzee D, Corky. It was the complete diary of Samuel Pepys, and Mr. Bainbridge

was chuckling over the naughty passages, which were omitted in his own edition, when Professor Mallard was shown into the room. "I have come to apologize for my outrageous conduct on the telephone yesterday," the Professor said.

"Please don't think of it any more. I know you have many things on your mind," Mr. Bainbridge said. "Would you like a drink?"

"A large whiskey, straight, please," Professor Mallard said. "I got rather cold driving down. No change, I presume?"

"No, none. Chimpanzee F, Dinty, is just finishing John Florio's translation of Montaigne's essays, but there is no other news of interest."

Professor Mallard squared his shoulders and tossed off his drink in one astonishing gulp. "I should like to see them at work," he said. "Would I disturb them, do you think?"

"Not at all. As a matter of fact, I usually look in on them around this time of day. Dinty may have finished his Montaigne by now, and it is always interesting to see them start a new work. I would have thought that they would continue on the same sheet of paper, but they don't, you know. Always a fresh sheet, and the title in capitals."

Professor Mallard, without apology, poured another drink and slugged it down. "Lead on," he said.

It was dusk in the conservatory, and the chimpanzees were typing by the light of student lamps clamped to their desks. The keeper lounged in a corner, eating a banana and reading *Billboard*. "You might as well take an hour or so off," Mr. Bainbridge said. The man left.

Professor Mallard, who had not taken off his overcoat, stood with his hands in his pockets, looking at the busy chimpanzees. "I wonder if you know, Bainbridge, that the science of probabilities takes everything into account," he said, in a queer, tight voice. "It is certainly almost beyond the bounds of credibility that these chimpanzees should write books without a single error, but that abnormality may be corrected by—*these!*" He took his hands from his pockets, and each one held a .38 revolver. "Stand back out of harm's way!" he shouted.

"Mallard! Stop it!" The revolvers barked,

first the right hand, then the left, then the right. Two chimpanzees fell, and a third reeled into a corner. Mr. Bainbridge seized his friend's arm and wrested one of the weapons from him.

"Now I am armed, too, Mallard, and I advise you to stop!" he cried. Professor Mallard's answer was to draw a bead on Chimpanzee E and shoot him dead. Mr. Bainbridge made a rush, and Professor Mallard fired at him. Mr. Bainbridge, in his quick death agony, tightened his finger on the trigger of his revolver. It went off, and Professor Mallard went down. On his hands and knees he fired at the two chimpanzees which were still unhurt, and then collapsed.

There was nobody to hear his last words. "The human equation . . . always the enemy of science . . ." he panted. "This time . . .

vice versa . . . I, a mere mortal . . . savior of science . . . deserve a Nobel . . ."

When the old butler came running into the conservatory to investigate the noises, his eyes were met by a truly appalling sight. The student lamps were shattered, but a newly risen moon shone in through the conservatory windows on the corpses of the two gentlemen, each clutching a smoking revolver. Five of the chimpanzees were dead. The sixth was Chimpanzee F. His right arm disabled, obviously bleeding to death, he was slumped before his typewriter. Painfully, with his left hand, he took from the machine the completed last page of Florio's Montaigne. Groping for a fresh sheet, he inserted it, and typed with one finger, "UNCLE TOM'S CABIN, by Harriet Beecher Stowe. Chapte . . ." Then he, too, was dead.

Questions

1. How does Maloney establish the fashionable ordinariness of Mr. Bainbridge's life and the society he moves in? Why is it important for the meaning of the story that the events take place in the world of the ordinary?

2. This is a story about "probability" or "the law of averages," and the fact that outside the laboratory the law often does not work. Describe the various kinds of probability Maloney has woven into his story and the ways in which the improbable makes its appearance.

3. What is the meaning of the term "the human equation"?

4. Why does Mallard carry *two* revolvers when he comes to kill the chimpanzees?

SHIRLEY JACKSON

The Lottery

Shirley Jackson (b. 1919) is the author of a large number of short stories and several novels, but "The Lottery," which first appeared in the *New Yorker* in 1948, is her most famous piece of work. Her great strength as a writer has always been her ability to portray simultaneously the normal surface of life and the primitive cruelties and fears which lie just below that surface.

In the satires placed before "The Lottery" in this volume, it has been perfectly clear from the very beginning of each work that the satirist is attacking something. But here it is not until the end of the piece is reached that we even become aware of the satiric charge. This particular satiric technique, which Jonathan Swift claimed to have "refined," is known as "extended irony," and you will want to ponder the effectiveness of this particular strategy and compare it to the methods of such writers as Wylie and Waugh. The discussion of irony included in the critical selections from David Worcester's *The Art of Satire* will be most helpful in understanding Miss Jackson's ironic technique.

The morning of June 27th was clear and sunny, with the fresh warmth of a full-summer day; the flowers were blossoming profusely and the grass was richly green. The people of the village began to gather in the square, between the post office and the bank, around ten o'clock; in some towns there were so many people that the lottery took two days and had to be started on June 26th, but in this village, where there were only about three hundred people, the whole lottery took less than two hours, so it could begin at ten o'clock in the morning and still be through in time to allow the villagers to get home for noon dinner.

The children assembled first, of course. School was recently over for the summer, and the feeling of liberty sat uneasily on most of them; they tended to gather together quietly for a while before they broke into boisterous play, and their talk was still of the classroom and the teacher, of books and reprimands. Bobby Martin had already stuffed his pockets full of stones, and the other boys soon followed his example, selecting the smoothest and roundest stones; Bobby and Harry Jones and Dickie Delacroix—the villagers pronounced this name "Dellacroy"—eventually made a great pile of stones in one corner of the square and guarded it against

REPRINTED FROM *The Lottery* by Shirley Jackson, by permission of Farrar, Straus & Cudahy, Inc. Copyright 1948 by The New Yorker Magazine, copyright 1949 by Shirley Jackson.

the raids of the other boys. The girls stood aside, talking among themselves, looking over their shoulders at the boys, and the very small children rolled in the dust or clung to the hands of their older brothers or sisters.

Soon the men began to gather, surveying their own children, speaking of planting and rain, tractors and taxes. They stood together, away from the pile of stones in the corner, and their jokes were quiet and they smiled rather than laughed. The women, wearing faded house dresses and sweaters, came shortly after their menfolk. They greeted one another and exchanged bits of gossip as they went to join their husbands. Soon the women, standing by their husbands, began to call to their children, and the children came reluctantly, having to be called four or five times. Bobby Martin ducked under his mother's grasping hand and ran, laughing, back to the pile of stones. His father spoke up sharply, and Bobby came quickly and took his place between his father and his oldest brother.

The lottery was conducted—as were the square dances, the teen-age club, the Halloween program—by Mr. Summers, who had time and energy to devote to civic activities. He was a round-faced, jovial man and he ran the coal business, and people were sorry for him, because he had no children and his wife was a scold. When he arrived in the square, carrying the black wooden box, there was a murmur of conversation among the villagers, and he waved and called, "Little late today, folks." The postmaster, Mr. Graves, followed him, carrying a three-legged stool, and the stool was put in the center of the square and Mr. Summers set the black box down on it. The villagers kept their distance, leaving a space between themselves and the stool, and when Mr. Summers said, "Some of you fellows want to give me a hand?" there was a hesitation before two men, Mr. Martin and his oldest son, Baxter, came forward to hold the box steady on the stool while Mr. Summers stirred up the papers inside it.

The original paraphernalia for the lottery had been lost long ago, and the black box now resting on the stool had been put into use even before Old Man Warner, the oldest man in town, was born. Mr. Summers spoke frequently to the villagers about making a new box, but no one liked to upset even as much tradition as was represented by the black box. There was a story that the present box had been made with some pieces of the box that had preceded it, the one that had been constructed when the first people settled down to make a village here. Every year, after the lottery, Mr. Summers began talking again about a new box, but every year the subject was allowed to fade off without anything's being done. The black box grew shabbier each year; by now it was no longer completely black but splintered badly along one side to show the original wood color, and in some places faded or stained.

Mr. Martin and his oldest son, Baxter, held the black box securely on the stool until Mr. Summers had stirred the papers thoroughly with his hand. Because so much of the ritual had been forgotten or discarded, Mr. Summers had been successful in having slips of paper substituted for the chips of wood that had been used for generations. Chips of wood, Mr. Summers had argued, had been all very well when the village was tiny, but now that the population was more than three hundred and likely to keep on growing, it was necessary to use something that would fit more easily into the black box. The night before the lottery, Mr. Summers and Mr. Graves made up the slips of paper and put them in the box, and it was then taken to the safe of Mr. Summers' coal company and locked up until Mr. Summers was ready to take it to the square next morning. The rest of the year, the box was put away, sometimes one place, sometimes another; it had spent one year in Mr. Graves's barn and another year underfoot in the post office, and sometimes it was set on a shelf in the Martin grocery and left there.

There was a great deal of fussing to be done before Mr. Summers declared the lottery open. There were the lists to make up—of heads of families, heads of households in each family, members of each household in each family. There was the proper swearing-in of Mr. Summers by the postmaster, as the official of the lottery; at one time, some people remembered, there had been a recital of some sort, performed by the official of the lottery, a perfunctory, tuneless chant that had been rattled off duly each year; some people believed that the official of the lottery used to stand just so when he said or sang it, others believed that he was supposed to walk among the people, but years and years ago this part of the ritual had been allowed to lapse. There had been, also, a ritual salute, which the official of the lottery had had to use in addressing each person who came up to draw from the box, but this also had changed with time, until now it was felt necessary only for the official to speak to each person approaching. Mr. Summers was very good at all this; in his clean white shirt and blue jeans, with one hand resting carelessly on the black box, he seemed very proper and important as he talked interminably to Mr. Graves and the Martins.

Just as Mr. Summers finally left off talking and turned to the assembled villagers, Mrs. Hutchinson came hurriedly along the path to the square, her sweater thrown over her shoulders, and slid into place in the back of the crowd. "Clean forgot what day it was," she said to Mrs. Delacroix, who stood next to her, and they both laughed softly. "Thought my old man was out back stacking wood," Mrs. Hutchinson went on, "and then I looked out the window and the kids was gone, and then I remembered it was the twenty-seventh and came a-running." She dried her hands on her apron, and Mrs. Delacroix said, "You're in time, though. They're still talking away up there."

Mrs. Hutchinson craned her neck to see through the crowd and found her husband and children standing near the front. She tapped Mrs. Delacroix on the arm as a farewell and began to make her way through the crowd. The people separated good-humoredly to let her through; two or three people said, in voices just loud enough to be heard across the crowd, "Here comes your Missus, Hutchinson," and "Bill, she made it after all." Mrs. Hutchinson reached her husband, and Mr. Summers, who had been waiting, said cheerfully, "Thought we were going to have to get on without you, Tessie." Mrs. Hutchinson said, grinning, "Wouldn't have me leave m'dishes in the sink, now, would you, Joe?," and soft laughter ran through the crowd as the people stirred back into position after Mrs. Hutchinson's arrival.

"Well, now," Mr. Summers said soberly, "guess we better get started, get this over with, so's we can go back to work. Anybody ain't here?"

"Dunbar," several people said. "Dunbar, Dunbar."

Mr. Summers consulted his list. "Clyde Dunbar," he said. "That's right. He's broke his leg, hasn't he? Who's drawing for him?"

"Me, I guess," a woman said, and Mr. Summers turned to look at her. "Wife draws for her husband," Mr. Summers said. "Don't you have a grown boy to do it for you, Janey?" Although Mr. Summers and everyone else in the village knew the answer perfectly well, it was the business of the official of the lottery to ask such questions formally. Mr. Summers waited with an expression of polite interest while Mrs. Dunbar answered.

"Horace's not but sixteen yet," Mrs. Dunbar said regretfully. "Guess I gotta fill in for the old man this year."

"Right," Mr. Summers said. He made a note on the list he was holding. Then he asked, "Watson boy drawing this year?"

A tall boy in the crowd raised his hand. "Here," he said. "I'm drawing for m'mother and me." He blinked his eyes nervously and ducked his head as several voices in the crowd said things like "Good fellow, Jack," and "Glad to see your mother's got a man to do it."

"Well," Mr. Summers said, "guess that's everyone. Old Man Warner make it?"

"Here," a voice said, and Mr. Summers nodded.

A sudden hush fell on the crowd as Mr. Summers cleared his throat and looked at the list. "All ready?" he called. "Now, I'll read the names—heads of families first—and the men come up and take a paper out of the box. Keep the paper folded in your hand without looking at it until everyone has had a turn. Everything clear?"

The people had done it so many times that they only half listened to the directions; most of them were quiet, wetting their lips, not looking around. Then Mr. Summers raised one hand high and said, "Adams." A man disengaged himself from the crowd and came forward. "Hi, Steve," Mr. Summers said, and Mr. Adams said, "Hi, Joe." They grinned at one another humorlessly and nervously. Then Mr. Adams reached into the black box and took out a folded paper. He held it firmly by one corner as he turned and went hastily back to his place in the crowd, where he stood a little apart from his family, not looking down at his hand.

"Allen," Mr. Summers said. "Anderson. . . . Bentham."

"Seems like there's no time at all between lotteries any more," Mrs. Delacroix said to Mrs. Graves in the back row. "Seems like we got through with the last one only last week."

"Time sure goes fast," Mrs. Graves said.

"Clark. . . . Delacroix."

"There goes my old man," Mrs. Delacroix said. She held her breath while her husband went forward.

"Dunbar," Mr. Summers said, and Mrs. Dunbar went steadily to the box while one of the women said, "Go on, Janey," and another said, "There she goes."

"We're next," Mrs. Graves said. She watched while Mr. Graves came around from the side of the box, greeted Mr. Summers gravely, and selected a slip of paper from the box. By now, all through the crowd there were men holding the small folded papers in their large hands, turning them over and over nervously. Mrs. Dunbar and her two sons stood together, Mrs. Dunbar holding the slip of paper.

"Harburt. . . . Hutchinson."

"Get up there, Bill," Mrs. Hutchinson said, and the people near her laughed.

"Jones."

"They do say," Mr. Adams said to Old Man Warner, who stood next to him, "that over in the north village they're talking of giving up the lottery."

Old Man Warner snorted. "Pack of crazy fools," he said. "Listening to the young folks, nothing's good enough for *them*. Next thing you know, they'll be wanting to go back to living in caves, nobody work any more, live *that* way for a while. Used to be a saying about 'Lottery in June, corn be heavy soon.' First thing you know, we'd all be eating stewed chickweed and acorns. There's *always* been a lottery," he added petulantly. "Bad enough to see young Joe Summers up there joking with everybody."

"Some places have already quit lotteries," Mrs. Adams said.

"Nothing but trouble in *that*," Old Man Warner said stoutly. "Pack of young fools."

"Martin." And Bobby Martin watched his father go forward. "Overdyke. . . . Percy."

"I wish they'd hurry," Mrs. Dunbar said to her older son. "I wish they'd hurry."

"They're almost through," her son said.

"You get ready to run tell Dad," Mrs. Dunbar said.

Mr. Summers called his own name and then stepped forward precisely and selected a slip from the box. Then he called, "Warner."

"Seventy-seventh year I been in the lottery," Old Man Warner said as he went through the crowd. "Seventy-seventh time."

"Watson." The tall boy came awkwardly through the crowd. Someone said, "Don't be nervous, Jack," and Mr. Summers said, "Take your time, son."

"Zanini."

After that, there was a long pause, a breathless pause, until Mr. Summers, holding his slip of paper in the air, said, "All right, fellows." For a minute, no one moved, and then all the slips of paper were opened. Suddenly, all the women began to speak at once, saying, "Who is it?," "Who's got it?," "Is it the Dunbars?," "Is it the Watsons?" Then the voices began to say, "It's Hutchinson. It's Bill," "Bill Hutchinson's got it."

"Go tell your father," Mrs. Dunbar said to her older son.

People began to look around to see the Hutchinsons. Bill Hutchinson was standing quiet, staring down at the paper in his hand. Suddenly, Tessie Hutchinson shouted to Mr. Summers, "You didn't give him time enough to take any paper he wanted. I saw you. It wasn't fair!"

"Be a good sport, Tessie," Mrs. Delacroix called, and Mrs. Graves said, "All of us took the same chance."

"Shut up, Tessie," Bill Hutchinson said.

"Well, everyone," Mr. Summers said, "that was done pretty fast, and now we've got to be hurrying a little more to get done in time." He consulted his next list. "Bill," he said, "you draw for the Hutchinson family. You got any other households in the Hutchinsons?"

"There's Don and Eva," Mrs. Hutchinson yelled. "Make *them* take their chance!"

"Daughters draw with their husbands' families, Tessie," Mr. Summers said gently. "You know that as well as anyone else."

"It wasn't *fair*," Tessie said.

"I guess not, Joe," Bill Hutchinson said regretfully. "My daughter draws with her husband's family, that's only fair. And I've got no other family except the kids."

"Then, as far as drawing for families is concerned, it's you," Mr. Summers said in explanation, "and as far as drawing for households is concerned, that's you, too. Right?"

"Right," Bill Hutchinson said.

"How many kids, Bill?" Mr. Summers asked formally.

"Three," Bill Hutchinson said. "There's Bill, Jr., and Nancy, and little Dave. And Tessie and me."

"All right, then," Mr. Summers said. "Harry, you got their tickets back?"

Mr. Graves nodded and held up the slips of paper. "Put them in the box, then," Mr. Summers directed. "Take Bill's and put it in."

"I think we ought to start over," Mrs. Hutchinson said, as quietly as she could. "I tell you it wasn't *fair*. You didn't give him time enough to choose. *Every*body saw that."

Mr. Graves had selected the five slips and put them in the box, and he dropped all the papers but those onto the ground, where the breeze caught them and lifted them off.

"Listen, everybody," Mrs. Hutchinson was saying to the people around her.

"Ready, Bill?" Mr. Summers asked, and Bill Hutchinson, with one quick glance around at his wife and children, nodded.

"Remember," Mr. Summers said, "take the slips and keep them folded until each person has taken one. Harry, you help little Dave." Mr. Graves took the hand of the little boy, who came willingly with him up to the box. "Take a paper out of the box, Davy," Mr. Summers said. Davy put his hand into the box and laughed. "Take just *one* paper," Mr. Summers said. "Harry, you hold it for him." Mr. Graves took the child's hand and removed the folded paper from the tight fist and held it while little Dave stood next to him and looked up at him wonderingly.

"Nancy next," Mr. Summers said. Nancy was twelve, and her school friends breathed heavily as she went forward, switching her skirt, and took a slip daintily from the box. "Bill, Jr.," Mr. Summers said, and Billy, his face red and his feet overlarge, nearly knocked the box over as he got a paper out. "Tessie," Mr. Summers said. She hesitated for a minute, looking around defiantly, and then set her lips and went up to the box. She snatched a paper out and held it behind her.

"Bill," Mr. Summers said, and Bill Hutchinson reached into the box and felt around, bringing his hand out at last with the slip of paper in it.

The crowd was quiet. A girl whispered, "I hope it's not Nancy," and the sound of the whisper reached the edges of the crowd.

"It's not the way it used to be," Old Man Warner said clearly. "People ain't the way they used to be."

"All right," Mr. Summers said. "Open the papers. Harry, you open little Dave's."

Mr. Graves opened the slip of paper and there was a general sigh through the crowd as he held it up and everyone could see that it was blank. Nancy and Bill, Jr., opened theirs at the same time, and both beamed and laughed, turning around to the crowd and holding their slips of paper above their heads.

"Tessie," Mr. Summers said. There was a pause, and then Mr. Summers looked at Bill Hutchinson, and Bill unfolded his paper and showed it. It was blank.

"It's Tessie," Mr. Summers said, and his voice was hushed. "Show us her paper, Bill."

Bill Hutchinson went over to his wife and forced the slip of paper out of her hand. It had a black spot on it, the black spot Mr. Summers had made the night before with the heavy pencil in the coal-company office. Bill Hutchinson held it up, and there was a stir in the crowd.

"All right, folks," Mr. Summers said. "Let's finish quickly."

Although the villagers had forgotten the ritual and lost the original black box, they still remembered to use stones. The pile of stones the boys had made earlier was ready; there were stones on the ground with the blowing scraps of paper that had come out of the box. Mrs. Delacroix selected a stone so large she had to pick it up with both hands and turned to Mrs. Dunbar. "Come on," she said. "Hurry up."

Mrs. Dunbar had small stones in both hands, and she said, gasping for breath, "I can't run at all. You'll have to go ahead and I'll catch up with you."

The children had stones already, and someone gave little Davy Hutchinson a few pebbles.

Tessie Hutchinson was in the center of a cleared space by now, and she held her hands out desperately as the villagers moved in on her. "It isn't fair," she said. A stone hit her on the side of the head.

Old Man Warner was saying, "Come on, come on, everyone." Steve Adams was in the front of the crowd of villagers, with Mrs. Graves beside him.

"It isn't fair, it isn't right," Mrs. Hutchinson screamed, and then they were upon her.

Questions

1. It was a custom among certain peoples—for example, some of the ancient Greeks and Hebrews—to select once a year, usually in the spring, an animal or a man to be loaded with all the moral guilt of the people and either killed or driven forth into the wilderness. The purpose of this ritual was to rid the community of its sins and, some authorities say, to ensure the growth of the new crops. The Old Testament suggests that the Jews merely drove a goat into the wilds: "And Aaron shall lay both his hands upon the head of the live goat and confess over him all the iniquities of the children of Israel . . . putting them upon the head of the goat, and shall send him away by the hand of a fit man into the wilderness. And the goat shall bear upon him all their iniquities unto a land not inhabited." (Leviticus 16:21-22) There is, however, considerable evidence that even so civilized a people as the Greeks chose their scapegoats (*pharmakoi*) from the offscourings of their citizens and then beat and executed them. How is the ritual of the scapegoat introduced into "The Lottery," and what use is made of it?

2. What is the significance of the fact that the villagers have forgotten the origin of the custom that they still cling to?

3. What is Mrs. Hutchinson's attitude toward the crucial day, and of what significance to the story is this attitude?

4. How is the atmosphere of a small, friendly, rather ordinary town built up in the story? Why is this atmosphere important to the story?

5. Select several statements or situations which seem ordinary enough but become charged with sinister meaning when we know what is going to happen.

6. There have been, of course, no American towns which actually chose an annual scapegoat, but Shirley Jackson is not merely spinning a fantastic tale. She is writing a satire on life as we live it in the twentieth century. What contemporary practices and events do you think she is mirroring in the story? Does it provide any clues to what kind of attitudes and actions are being satirized?

7. Discuss the ways in which the structure of the story, the long train of apparently trivial events leading up to the sudden climax, contributes to its meaning.

8. Discuss the use of objects as symbols in the story.

The Madwoman of Chaillot

This fellow's wise enough to play the fool.

Twelfth Night

When the Delphic Oracle declared that no man was wiser than Socrates, Socrates interpreted the oracle to mean, "He, O men, is the wisest who, like Socrates, knows that his wisdom is in truth worth nothing." Since that day the wise fools, in literature and life, have continued to reveal the folly of the wise. Few satiric devices have been so effective as that in which the learned, the powerful, the eminent, the great men of the world are exposed by the humble comments and the sly questionings of a rustic simpleton who naïvely believes a few obvious truths or holds a few plain moral values.

The Madwoman of Chaillot (La Folle de Chaillot) is perhaps the most successful instance of the use of the wise fool as a satiric instrument in our century. It was first produced in Paris in 1945, a year after the death of the author, Jean Giraudoux. Giraudoux was himself one of the great men of the world. He held the post of Commissioner General for Information in France from the beginning of World War II until his death, and combined the profession of diplomat and writer during most of his life. The English adaptation printed here is that of Maurice Valency.

ACT I

SCENE: *The café terrace at* Chez Francis, *on the Place de l'Alma in Paris. The Alma is in the stately quarter of Paris known as Chaillot, between the Champs Élysées and the Seine, across the river from the Eiffel Tower.* Chez Francis *has several rows of tables set out under its awning, and, as it is lunch time, a good many of them are occupied. At a table, downstage, a somewhat obvious* BLONDE *with ravishing legs is sipping a vermouth-cassis and trying hard to engage the attention of the* PROSPECTOR, *who sits at an adjacent table taking little sips of water and rolling them over his tongue with the air of a connoisseur. Downstage right, in front of the tables on the sidewalk, is the usual Paris bench, a stout and uncomfortable affair provided by the municipality for the benefit of those who prefer to sit without drinking. A* POLICEMAN *lounges about, keeping the peace without unnecessary exertion.*

TIME: *It is a little before noon in the Spring of next year.*

AT RISE: *The* PRESIDENT *and the* BARON *enter with importance, and are ushered to a front table by the* WAITER.

THE PRESIDENT.   Baron, sit down. This is a historic occasion. It must be properly celebrated. The waiter is going to bring out my special port.

THE BARON.   Splendid.

THE PRESIDENT [*offers his cigar case*].   Cigar? My private brand.

THE BARON.   Thank you. You know, this all gives me the feeling of one of those enchanted mornings in the *Arabian Nights* when thieves foregather in the market place. Thieves—pashas . . .

[*He sniffs the cigar judiciously, and begins lighting it.*]

THE PRESIDENT [*chuckles*].   Tell me about yourself.

THE BARON.   Well, where shall I begin?

[*The* STREET SINGER *enters. He takes off a battered black felt with a flourish and begins singing an ancient mazurka.*]

STREET SINGER [*sings*].

Do you hear, Mademoiselle,
Those musicians of hell?

THE PRESIDENT.   Waiter! Get rid of that man.

WAITER.   He is singing *La Belle Polonaise*.

THE PRESIDENT.   I didn't ask for the program. I asked you to get rid of him. [*The* WAITER *doesn't budge. The* SINGER *goes by himself.*] As you were saying, Baron . . . ?

THE BARON.   Well, until I was fifty . . . [*the*

FLOWER GIRL *enters through the café door, center*] my life was relatively uncomplicated. It consisted of selling off one by one the various estates left me by my father. Three years ago, I parted with my last farm. Two years ago, I lost my last mistress. And now—all that is left me is . . .

THE FLOWER GIRL [*to the* BARON].   Violets, sir?

THE PRESIDENT.   Run along.

[*The* FLOWER GIRL *moves on.*]

THE BARON [*staring after her*].   So that, in short, all I have left now is my name.

THE PRESIDENT.   Your name is precisely the name we need on our board of directors.

THE BARON [*with an inclination of his head*].   Very flattering.

THE PRESIDENT.   You will understand when I tell you that mine has been a very different experience. I came up from the bottom. My mother spent most of her life bent over a washtub in order to send me to school. I'm eternally grateful to her, of course, but I must confess that I no longer remember her face. It was no doubt beautiful—but when I try to recall it, I see only the part she invariably showed me—her rear.

THE BARON.   Very touching.

THE PRESIDENT.   When I was thrown out of school for the fifth and last time, I decided to find out for myself what makes the world go round. I ran errands for an editor, a movie star, a financier. . . . I began to understand a little what life is. Then, one day, in the subway, I saw a face. . . . My rise in life dates from that day.

THE BARON.   Really?

THE PRESIDENT.   One look at that face, and I knew. One look at mine, and he knew. And so I made my first thousand—passing a boxful of counterfeit notes. A year later, I saw another such face. It got me a nice berth in the narcotics business. Since then, all I do is to look out for such faces. And now here I am—president of eleven corporations, director of fifty-two companies, and, beginning today, chairman of the board of the international combine in which you have been so good as to accept a post. [*The* RAGPICKER *passes, sees something under the* PRESIDENT's *table, and stoops to pick it up.*] Looking for something?

THE RAGPICKER.   Did you drop this?

THE PRESIDENT. I never drop anything.

THE RAGPICKER. Then this hundred-franc note isn't yours?

THE PRESIDENT. Give it here.

[*The* RAGPICKER *gives him the note, and goes out.*]

THE BARON. Are you sure it's yours?

THE PRESIDENT. All hundred-franc notes, Baron, are mine.

THE BARON. Mr. President, there's something I've been wanting to ask you. What exactly is the purpose of our new company? Or is that an indiscreet question . . . ?

THE PRESIDENT. Indiscreet? Not a bit. Merely unusual. As far as I know, you're the first member of a board of directors ever to ask such a question.

THE BARON. Do we plan to exploit a commodity? A utility?

THE PRESIDENT. My dear sir, I haven't the faintest idea.

THE BARON. But if you don't know—who does?

THE PRESIDENT. Nobody. And at the moment, it's becoming just a trifle embarrassing. Yes, my dear Baron, since we are now close business associates, I must confess that for the time being we're in a little trouble.

THE BARON. I was afraid of that. The stock issue isn't going well?

THE PRESIDENT. No, no—on the contrary. The stock issue is going beautifully. Yesterday morning at ten o'clock we offered 500,000 shares to the general public. By 10:05 they were all snapped up at par. By 10:20, when the police finally arrived, our offices were a shambles. . . . Windows smashed—doors torn off their hinges—you never saw anything so beautiful in your life! And this morning our stock is being quoted over the counter at 124 with no sellers, and the orders are still pouring in.

THE BARON. But in that case—what is the trouble?

THE PRESIDENT. The trouble is we have a tremendous capital, and not the slightest idea of what to do with it.

THE BARON. You mean all those people are fighting to buy stock in a company that has no object?

THE PRESIDENT. My dear Baron, do you imagine that when a subscriber buys a share of stock, he has any idea of getting behind a counter or digging a ditch? A stock certificate is not a tool, like a shovel, or a commodity, like a pound of cheese. What we sell a customer is not a share in a business, but a view of the Elysian Fields. A financier is a creative artist. Our function is to stimulate the imagination. We are poets!

THE BARON. But in order to stimulate the imagination, don't you need some field of activity?

THE PRESIDENT. Not at all. What you need for that is a name. A name that will stir the pulse like a trumpet call, set the brain awhirl like a movie star, inspire reverence like a cathedral. *United General International Consolidated!* Of course that's been used. That's what a corporation needs.

THE BARON. And do we have such a name?

THE PRESIDENT. So far we have only a blank space. In that blank space a name must be printed. This name must be a masterpiece. And if I seem a little nervous today, it's because—somehow—I've racked my brains, but it hasn't come to me. Oho! Look at that! Just like the answer to a prayer . . . ! [*The* BARON *turns and stares in the direction of the prospector.*] You see? There's one. And what a beauty!

THE BARON. You mean that girl?

THE PRESIDENT. No, no, not the girl. That face. You see . . . ? The one that's drinking water.

THE BARON. You call that a face? That's a tombstone.

THE PRESIDENT. It's a milestone. It's a signpost. But is it pointing the way to steel, or wheat, or phosphates? That's what we have to find out. Ah! He sees me. He understands. He will be over.

THE BARON. And when he comes . . . ?

THE PRESIDENT. He will tell me what to do.

THE BARON. You mean business is done this way? You mean, you would trust a stranger with a matter of this importance?

THE PRESIDENT. Baron, I trust neither my wife, nor my daughter, nor my closest friend. My confidential secretary has no idea where I live. But a face like that I would trust with my inmost secrets. Though we have never laid eyes on each other before, that man and I know each other to the depths of our souls.

He's no stranger—he's my brother, he's myself. You'll see. He'll be over in a minute. [*The* DEAF MUTE *enters and passes slowly among the tables, placing a small envelope before each customer. He comes to the* PRESIDENT's *table.*] What is this anyway? A conspiracy? We don't want your envelopes. Take them away. [*The* DEAF MUTE *makes a short but pointed speech in sign language.*] Waiter, what the devil's he saying?

WAITER.   Only Irma understands him.

THE PRESIDENT.   Irma? Who's Irma?

WAITER [*calls*].   Irma! It's the waitress inside, sir. Irma!

[IRMA *comes out. She is twenty. She has the face and figure of an angel.*]

IRMA.   Yes?

WAITER.   These gentlemen would . . .

THE PRESIDENT.   Tell this fellow to get out of here, for God's sake! [*The* DEAF MUTE *makes another manual oration.*] What's he trying to say, anyway?

IRMA.   He says it's an exceptionally beautiful morning, sir . . .

THE PRESIDENT.   Who asked him?

IRMA.   But, he says, it was nicer before the gentleman stuck his face in it.

THE PRESIDENT.   Call the manager!

[IRMA *shrugs. She goes back into the restaurant. The* DEAF MUTE *walks off, Left. Meanwhile a* SHOELACE PEDDLER *has arrived.*]

PEDDLER.   Shoelaces? Postcards?

THE BARON.   I think I could use a shoelace.

THE PRESIDENT.   No, no . . .

PEDDLER.   Black? Tan?

THE BARON [*showing his shoes*].   What would you recommend?

PEDDLER.   Anybody's guess.

THE BARON.   Well, give me one of each.

THE PRESIDENT [*putting a hand on the* BARON's *arm*].   Baron, although I am your chairman, I have no authority over your personal life—none, that is, except to fix the amount of your director's fees, and eventually to assign a motor car for your use. Therefore, I am asking you, as a personal favor to me, not to purchase anything from this fellow.

THE BARON.   How can I resist so gracious a request? [*The* PEDDLER *shrugs, and passes on.*] But I really don't understand . . . What difference would it make?

THE PRESIDENT.   Look here, Baron. Now

that you're with us, you must understand that between this irresponsible riff-raff and us there is an impenetrable barrier. *We* have no dealings whatever with *them.*

THE BARON.   But without us, the poor devil will starve.

THE PRESIDENT.   No, he won't. He expects nothing from us. He has a clientele of his own. He sells shoelaces exclusively to those who have no shoes. Just as the necktie peddler sells only to those who wear no shirts. And that's why these street hawkers can afford to be insolent, disrespectful and independent. They don't need us. They have a world of their own. Ah! My broker. Splendid. He's beaming.

[*The* BROKER *walks up and grasps the* PRESIDENT's *hand with enthusiasm.*]

BROKER.   Mr. President! My heartiest congratulations! What a day! What a day!

[*The* STREET JUGGLER *appears, Right. He removes his coat, folds it carefully, and puts it on the bench. Then he opens a suitcase, from which he extracts a number of colored clubs.*]

THE PRESIDENT [*presenting the* BROKER]. Baron Tommard, of our Board of Directors. My broker. [*The* BROKER *bows. So does the* JUGGLER. *The* BROKER *sits down and signals for a drink. The* JUGGLER *prepares to juggle.*] What's happened?

BROKER.   Listen to this. Ten o'clock this morning. The market opens. [*As he speaks, the* JUGGLER *provides a visual counterpart to the* BROKER's *lines, his clubs rising and falling in rhythm to the* BROKER's *words.*] Half million shares issued at par, par value a hundred, quoted on the curb at 124 and we start buying at 126, 127, 129—and it's going up—up—up—[*the* JUGGLER's *clubs rise higher and higher*]—132—133—138—141—141—141—141 . . .

THE BARON.   May I ask . . . ?

THE PRESIDENT.   No, no—any explanation would only confuse you.

BROKER.   Ten forty-five we start selling short on rumors of a Communist plot, market bearish. . . . 141—138—133—132—and it's down—down—down—102—and we start buying back at 93. Eleven o'clock, rumors denied—95—98—101—106—124—141—and by 11:30 we've got it all back—net profit three and a half million francs.

THE PRESIDENT. Classical. Pure. [*The* JUG-GLER *bows again. A* LITTLE MAN *leans over from a near-by table, listening intently, and trembling with excitement.*] And how many shares do we reserve to each member of the board?

BROKER. Fifty, as agreed.

THE PRESIDENT. Bit stingy, don't you think?

BROKER. All right—three thousand.

THE PRESIDENT. That's a little better. [*To the* BARON.] You get the idea?

THE BARON. I'm beginning to get it.

BROKER. And now we come to the exciting part . . . [*The* JUGGLER *prepares to juggle with balls of fire.*] Listen carefully: With 35 percent of our funded capital under Section 32 I buy 50,000 United at 36 which I im-mediately reconvert into 32,000 National Amalgamated two's preferred which I set up as collateral on 150,000 General Consols which I deposit against a credit of fifteen billion to buy Eastern Hennequin which I immediately turn into Argentine wheat realizing 136 per-cent of the original investment which natu-rally accrues as capital gain and not as cor-porate income thus saving twelve millions in taxes, and at once convert the 25 percent cotton reserve into lignite, and as our people swing into action in London and New York, I beat up the price on greige goods from 26 to 92—114—203—306—[*the* JUGGLER *by now is juggling his fireballs in the sky. The balls no longer return to his hands*] 404 . . .

[*The* LITTLE MAN *can stand no more. He rushes over and dumps a sackful of money on the table.*]

LITTLE MAN. Here—take it—please, take it!

BROKER [*frigidly*]. Who is this man? What is this money?

LITTLE MAN. It's my life's savings. Every cent. I put it all in your hands.

BROKER. Can't you see we're busy?

LITTLE MAN. But I beg you . . . It's my only chance . . . Please don't turn me away.

BROKER. Oh, all right. [*He sweeps the money into his pocket.*] Well?

LITTLE MAN. I thought—perhaps you'd give me a little receipt. . . .

THE PRESIDENT. My dear man, people like us don't give receipts for money. We take them.

LITTLE MAN. Oh, pardon. Of course. I was confused. Here it is. [*Scribbles a receipt.*] Thank you—thank you—thank you.

[*He rushes off joyfully. The* STREET SINGER *reappears.*]

STREET SINGER [*sings*].
Do you hear, Mademoiselle,
Those musicians of hell!

THE PRESIDENT. What, again? Why does he keep repeating those two lines like a parrot?

WAITER. What else can he do? He doesn't know any more and the song's been out of print for years.

THE BARON. Couldn't he sing a song he knows?

WAITER. He likes this one. He hopes if he keeps singing the beginning someone will turn up to teach him the end.

THE PRESIDENT. Tell him to move on. We don't know the song.

[*The* PROFESSOR *strolls by, swinging his cane. He overhears.*]

PROFESSOR [*stops and addresses the* PRESI-DENT *politely*]. Nor do I, my dear sir. Nor do I. And yet, I'm in exactly the same predica-ment. I remember just two lines of my favorite song, as a child. A mazurka also, in case you're interested. . . .

THE PRESIDENT. I'm not.

PROFESSOR. Why is it, I wonder, that one always forgets the words of a mazurka? I sup-pose they just get lost in that damnable rhythm. All I remember is: [*He sings.*]
From England to Spain
I have drunk, it was bliss . . .

STREET SINGER [*walks over, and picks up the tune*].
Red wine and champagne
And many a kiss.

PROFESSOR. Oh, God! It all comes back to me . . . ! [*He sings.*]
Red lips and white hands I have known
Where the nightingales dwell. . . .

THE PRESIDENT [*holding his hands to his ears*]. Please—please . . .

STREET SINGER.
And to each one I've whispered, "My own,"
And to each one, I've murmured:

"Farewell."

THE PRESIDENT. Farewell. Farewell.

STREET SINGER, PROFESSOR [duo]. But there's one I shall never forget. . . .

THE PRESIDENT. This isn't a café. It's a circus!

[The two go off, still singing: "There is one that's engraved in my heart." The PROSPECTOR gets up slowly and walks toward the PRESIDENT'S table. He looks down without a word. There is a tense silence.]

PROSPECTOR. Well?

THE PRESIDENT. I need a name.

PROSPECTOR [nods, with complete comprehension]. I need fifty thousand.

THE PRESIDENT. For a corporation.

PROSPECTOR. For a woman.

THE PRESIDENT. Immediately.

PROSPECTOR. Before evening.

THE PRESIDENT. Something . . .

PROSPECTOR. Unusual?

THE PRESIDENT. Something . . .

PROSPECTOR. Provocative?

THE PRESIDENT. Something . . .

PROSPECTOR. Practical.

THE PRESIDENT. Yes.

PROSPECTOR. Fifty thousand. Cash.

THE PRESIDENT. I'm listening.

PROSPECTOR. *International Substrate of Paris, Inc.*

THE PRESIDENT [snaps his fingers]. That's it! [To the BROKER.] Pay him off. [The BROKER pays with the LITTLE MAN'S money.] Now— what does it mean?

PROSPECTOR. It means what it says. I'm a prospector.

THE PRESIDENT [rises]. A prospector! Allow me to shake your hand. Baron, you are in the presence of one of nature's noblemen. Shake his hand. This is Baron Tommard. [They shake hands.] It is this man, my dear Baron, who smells out in the bowels of the earth those deposits of metal or liquid on which can be founded the only social unit of which our age is capable—the corporation. Sit down, please. [They all sit.] And now that we have a name . . .

PROSPECTOR. You need a property.

THE PRESIDENT. Precisely.

PROSPECTOR. I have one.

THE PRESIDENT. A claim?

PROSPECTOR. Terrific.

THE PRESIDENT. Foreign?

PROSPECTOR. French.

THE BARON. In Indo-China?

BROKER. Morocco?

THE PRESIDENT. In France?

PROSPECTOR [matter of fact]. In Paris.

THE PRESIDENT. In Paris? You've been prospecting in Paris?

THE BARON. For women, no doubt.

THE PRESIDENT. For art?

BROKER. For gold?

PROSPECTOR. Oil.

BROKER. He's crazy.

THE PRESIDENT. Sh! He's inspired.

PROSPECTOR. You think I'm crazy. Well, they thought Columbus was crazy.

THE BARON. Oil in Paris?

BROKER. But how is it possible?

PROSPECTOR. It's not only possible. It's certain.

THE PRESIDENT. Tell us.

PROSPECTOR. You don't know, my dear sir, what treasures Paris conceals. Paris is the least prospected place in the world. We've gone over the rest of the planet with a fine-tooth comb. But has anyone ever thought of looking for oil in Paris? Nobody. Before me, that is.

THE PRESIDENT. Genius!

PROSPECTOR. No. Just a practical man. I use my head.

THE BARON. But why has nobody ever thought of this before?

PROSPECTOR. The treasures of the earth, my dear sir, are not easy to find nor to get at. They are invariably guarded by dragons. Doubtless there is some reason for this. For once we've dug out and consumed the internal ballast of the planet, the chances are it will shoot off on some irresponsible tangent and smash itself up in the sky. Well, that's the risk we take. Anyway, that's not my business. A prospector has enough to worry about.

THE BARON. I know—snakes—tarantulas— fleas . . .

PROSPECTOR. Worse than that, sir. Civilization.

THE PRESIDENT. Does that annoy you?

PROSPECTOR. Civilization gets in our way all the time. In the first place, it covers the earth with cities and towns which are damned awkward to dig up when you want to see what's

underneath. It's not only the real-estate people—you can always do business with them—
it's human sentimentality. How do you do
business with that?

THE PRESIDENT.   I see what you mean.

PROSPECTOR.   They say that where we pass,
nothing ever grows again. What of it? Is a
park any better than a coal mine? What's a
mountain got that a slag pile hasn't? What
would you rather have in your garden—an
almond tree or an oil well?

THE PRESIDENT.   Well . . .

PROSPECTOR.   Exactly. But what's the use of
arguing with these fools? Imagine the choicest
place you ever saw for an excavation, and
what do they put there? A playground for
children! Civilization!

THE PRESIDENT.   Just show us the point
where you want to start digging. We'll do the
rest. Even if it's in the middle of the Louvre.
Where's the oil?

PROSPECTOR.   Perhaps you think it's easy to
make an accurate fix in an area like Paris
where everything conspires to put you off the
scent? Women—perfume—flowers—history. You
can talk all you like about geology, but an oil
deposit, gentlemen, has to be smelled out. I
have a good nose. I go further. I have a phenomenal nose. But the minute I get the right
whiff—the minute I'm on the scent—a fra-
grance rises from what I take to be the spiritual
deposits of the past—and I'm completely at
sea. Now take this very point, for example,
this very spot.

THE BARON.   You mean—right here in
Chaillot?

PROSPECTOR.   Right under here.

THE PRESIDENT.   Good heavens!

[He looks under his chair.]

PROSPECTOR.   It's taken me months to locate
the spot.

THE BARON.   But what in the world makes
you think . . . ?

PROSPECTOR.   Do you know this place,
Baron?

THE BARON.   Well, I've been sitting here for
thirty years.

PROSPECTOR.   Did you ever taste the water?

THE BARON.   The water? Good God, no!

PROSPECTOR.   It's plain to see that you are
no prospector! A prospector, Baron, is addicted
to water as a drunkard to wine. Water, gentle-

men, is the one substance from which the
earth can conceal nothing. It sucks out its
innermost secrets and brings them to our very
lips. Well—beginning at Notre Dame, where I
first caught the scent of oil three months ago,
I worked my way across Paris, glassful by glassful, sampling the water, until at last I came
to this café. And here—just two days ago—I
took a sip. My heart began to thump. Was it
possible that I was deceived? I took another,
a third, a fourth, a fifth. I was trembling like
a leaf. But there was no mistake. Each time
that I drank, my taste-buds thrilled to the
most exquisite flavor known to a prospector
—the flavor of—[With utmost lyricism.] Petro-
leum!

THE PRESIDENT.   Waiter! Some water and
four glasses. Hurry. This round, gentlemen,
is on me. And as a toast—I shall propose International Substrate of Paris, Incorporated. [The
WAITER brings a decanter and the glasses. The
PRESIDENT pours out the water amid profound silence. They taste it with the air of
connoisseurs savoring something that has
never before passed human lips. Then they
look at each other doubtfully. The PROSPEC-
TOR pours himself a second glass and drinks
it off.] Well . . .

BROKER.   Ye-es . . .

THE BARON.   Mm . . .

PROSPECTOR.   Get it?

THE BARON.   Tastes queer.

PROSPECTOR.   That's it. To the unpracticed
palate it tastes queer. But to the taste-buds of
the expert—ah!

THE BARON.   Still, there's one thing I don't
quite understand . . .

PROSPECTOR.   Yes?

THE BARON.   This café doesn't have its own
well, does it?

PROSPECTOR.   Of course not. This is Paris
water.

BROKER.   Then why should it taste different here than anywhere else?

PROSPECTOR.   Because, my dear sir, the pipes
that carry this water pass deep through the
earth, and the earth just here is soaked with
oil, and this oil permeates the pores of the
iron and flavors the water it carries. Ever so
little, yes—but quite enough to betray its
presence to the sensitive tongue of the specialist.

THE BARON. I see.

PROSPECTOR. I don't say everyone is capable of tasting it. No. But I—I can detect the presence of oil in water that has passed within fifteen miles of a deposit. Under special circumstances, twenty.

THE PRESIDENT. Phenomenal!

PROSPECTOR. And so here I am with the greatest discovery of the age on my hands—but the blasted authorities won't let me drill a single well unless I show them the oil! Now how can I show them the oil unless they let me dig? Completely stymied! Eh?

THE PRESIDENT. What? A man like you?

PROSPECTOR. That's what they think. That's what they want. Have you noticed the strange glamor of the women this morning? And the quality of the sunshine? And this extraordinary convocation of vagabonds buzzing about protectively like bees around a hive? Do you know why it is? Because they know. It's a plot to distract us, to turn us from our purpose. Well, let them try. I know there's oil here. And I'm going to dig it up, even if I . . . [*He smiles.*] Shall I tell you my little plan?

THE PRESIDENT. By all means.

PROSPECTOR. Well . . . For heaven's sake, what's that?

[*At this point, the* MADWOMAN *enters. She is dressed in the grand fashion of 1885, a taffeta skirt with an immense train—which she has gathered up by means of a clothespin—ancient button shoes, and a hat in the style of Marie Antoinette. She wears a lorgnette on a chain, and an enormous cameo pin at her throat. In her hand she carries a small basket. She walks in with great dignity, extracts a dinner bell from the bosom of her dress, and rings it sharply.* IRMA *appears.*]

COUNTESS. Are my bones ready, Irma?

IRMA. There won't be much today, Countess. We had broilers. Can you wait? While the gentleman inside finishes eating?

COUNTESS. And my gizzard?

IRMA. I'll try to get it away from him.

COUNTESS. If he eats my gizzard, save me the giblets. They will do for the tomcat that lives under the bridge. He likes a few giblets now and again.

IRMA. Yes, Countess.

[IRMA *goes back into the café. The* COUNTESS *takes a few steps and stops in front of the* PRESIDENT's *table. She examines him with undisguised disapproval.*]

THE PRESIDENT. Waiter. Ask that woman to move on.

WAITER. Sorry, sir. This is her café.

THE PRESIDENT. Is she the manager of the café?

WAITER. She's the Madwoman of Chaillot.

THE PRESIDENT. A Madwoman? She's mad?

WAITER. Who says she's mad?

THE PRESIDENT. You just said so yourself.

WAITER. Look, sir. You asked me who she was. And I told you. What's mad about her? She's the Madwoman of Chaillot.

THE PRESIDENT. Call a policeman.

[*The* COUNTESS *whistles through her fingers. At once, the* DOORMAN *runs out of the café. He has three scarves in his hands.*]

COUNTESS. Have you found it? My feather boa?

DOORMAN. Not yet, Countess. Three scarves. But no boa.

COUNTESS. It's five years since I lost it. Surely you've had time to find it.

DOORMAN. Take one of these, Countess. Nobody's claimed them.

COUNTESS. A boa like that doesn't vanish, you know. A feather boa nine feet long!

DOORMAN. How about this blue one?

COUNTESS. With my pink ruffle and my green veil? You're joking! Let me see the yellow. [*She tries it on.*] How does it look?

DOORMAN. Terrific.

[*With a magnificent gesture, she flings the scarf about her, upsetting the* PRESIDENT's *glass and drenching his trousers with water. She stalks off without a glance at him.*]

THE PRESIDENT. Waiter! I'm making a complaint.

WAITER. Against whom?

THE PRESIDENT. Against her! Against you! The whole gang of you! That singer! That shoelace peddler! That female lunatic! Or whatever you call her!

THE BARON. Calm yourself, Mr. President.

THE PRESIDENT. I'll do nothing of the sort! Baron, the first thing we have to do is to get rid of these people! Good heavens, look at them! Every size, shape, color and period of history imaginable. It's utter anarchy! I tell you, sir, the only safeguard of order and discipline in the modern world is a standardized worker with interchangeable parts. That would solve the entire problem of management. Here, the manager . . . And there—one composite drudge grunting and sweating all over the world. Just we two. Ah, how beautiful! How easy on the eyes! How restful for the conscience!

THE BARON. Yes, yes—of course.

THE PRESIDENT. Order. Symmetry. Balance. But instead of that, what? Here in Chaillot, the very citadel of management, these insolent phantoms of the past come to beard us with their raffish individualism—with the right of the voiceless to sing, of the dumb to make speeches, of trousers to have no seats and bosoms to have dinner bells!

THE BARON. But, after all, do these people matter?

THE PRESIDENT. My dear sir, wherever the poor are happy, and the servants are proud, and the mad are respected, our power is at an end. Look at that. That waiter! That madwoman! That flower girl! Do I get that sort of service? And suppose that I—president of twelve corporations and ten times a millionaire—were to stick a gladiolus in my buttonhole and start yelling—[*He tinkles his spoon in a glass violently, yelling.*] Are my bones ready, Irma?

THE BARON [*reprovingly*]. Mr. President . . .

[*People at the adjoining tables turn and stare with raised eyebrows. The* WAITER *starts to come over.*]

THE PRESIDENT. You see? Now.

PROSPECTOR. We were discussing my plan.

THE PRESIDENT. Ah yes, your plan. [*He glances in the direction of the* MADWOMAN'S *table.*] Careful—she's looking at us.

PROSPECTOR. Do you know what a bomb is?

THE PRESIDENT. I'm told they explode.

PROSPECTOR. Exactly. You see that white building across the river. Do you happen to know what that is?

THE PRESIDENT. I do not.

PROSPECTOR. That's the office of the City Architect. That man has stubbornly refused to give me a permit to drill for oil anywhere within the limits of the city of Paris. I've tried everything with him—influence, bribes, threats. He says I'm crazy. And now . . .

THE PRESIDENT. Oh, my God! What is this one trying to sell us?

[*A little* OLD MAN *enters left, and doffs his hat politely. He is somewhat ostentatiously respectable—gloved, pomaded, and carefully dressed, with a white handkerchief peeping out of his breast pocket.*]

DR. JADIN. Nothing but health, sir. Or rather the health of the feet. But remember—as the foot goes, so goes the man. May I present myself . . . ? Dr. Gaspard Jadin, French Navy, retired. Former specialist in the extraction of ticks and chiggers. At present specializing in the extraction of bunions and corns. In case of sudden emergency, Martial the waiter will furnish my home address. My office is here, second row, third table, week days, twelve to five. Thank you very much.

[*He sits at his table.*]

WAITER. Your vermouth, Doctor?

DR. JADIN. My vermouth. My vermouths. How are your gallstones today, Martial?

WAITER. Fine. They rattle like anything.

DR. JADIN. Splendid. [*He spies the* COUNTESS.] Good morning, Countess. How's the floating kidney? Still afloat? [*She nods graciously.*] Splendid. Splendid. So long as it floats, it can't sink.

THE PRESIDENT. This is impossible! Let's go somewhere else.

PROSPECTOR. No. It's nearly noon.

THE PRESIDENT. Yes. It is. Five to twelve.

PROSPECTOR. In five minutes' time you're going to see that City Architect blown up, building and all—boom!

BROKER. Are you serious?

PROSPECTOR. That imbecile has no one to blame but himself. Yesterday noon, he got my ultimatum—he's had twenty-four hours to think it over. No permit? All right. Within two minutes my agent is going to drop a little package in his coal bin. And three minutes after that, precisely at noon . . .

THE BARON. You prospectors certainly use modern methods.

PROSPECTOR. The method may be modern. But the idea is old. To get at the treasure, it has always been necessary to slay the dragon. I guarantee that after this, the City Architect will be more reasonable. The new one, I mean.

THE PRESIDENT.   Don't you think we're sitting a little close for comfort?

PROSPECTOR.   Oh no, no. Don't worry. And, above all, don't stare. We may be watched. [*A clock strikes.*] Why, that's noon. Something's wrong! Good God! What's this? [*A POLICEMAN staggers in bearing a lifeless body on his shoulders in the manner prescribed as "The Fireman's Lift."*] It's Pierre! My agent! [*He walks over with affected nonchalance.*] I say, Officer, what's that you've got?

POLICEMAN.   Drowned man.

[*He puts him down on the bench.*]

WAITER.   He's not drowned. His clothes are dry. He's been slugged.

POLICEMAN.   Slugged is also correct. He was just jumping off the bridge when I came along and pulled him back. I slugged him, naturally, so he wouldn't drag me under. Life Saving Manual, Rule 5: "In cases where there is danger of being dragged under, it is necessary to render the subject unconscious by means of a sharp blow." He's had that.

[*He loosens the clothes and begins applying artificial respiration.*]

PROSPECTOR.   The stupid idiot! What the devil did he do with the bomb? That's what comes of employing amateurs!

THE PRESIDENT.   You don't think he'll give you away?

PROSPECTOR.   Don't worry. [*He walks over to the policeman.*] Say, what do you think you're doing?

POLICEMAN.   Lifesaving. Artificial respiration. First aid to the drowning.

PROSPECTOR.   But he's not drowning.

POLICEMAN.   But he thinks he is.

PROSPECTOR.   You'll never bring him round that way, my friend. That's meant for people who drown in water. It's no good at all for those who drown without water.

POLICEMAN.   What am I supposed to do? I've just been sworn in. It's my first day on the beat. I can't afford to get in trouble. I've got to go by the book.

PROSPECTOR.   Perfectly simple. Take him back to the bridge where you found him and throw him in. Then you can save his life and you'll get a medal. This way, you'll get fined for slugging an innocent man.

POLICEMAN.   What do you mean, innocent?

He was just going to jump when I grabbed him.

PROSPECTOR.   Have you any proof of that?

POLICEMAN.   Well, I saw him.

PROSPECTOR.   Written proof? Witnesses?

POLICEMAN.   No, but . . .

PROSPECTOR.   Then don't waste time arguing. You're in trouble. Quick—before anybody notices—throw him in and dive after him. It's the only way out.

POLICEMAN.   But I don't swim.

THE PRESIDENT.   You'll learn how on the way down. Before you were born, did you know how to breathe?

POLICEMAN [*convinced*].   All right. Here we go.

[*He starts lifting the body.*]

DR. JADIN.   One moment, please. I don't like to interfere, but it's my professional duty to point out that medical science has definitely established the fact of intra-uterine respiration. Consequently, this policeman, even before he was born, knew not only how to breathe but also how to cough, hiccup and belch.

THE PRESIDENT.   Suppose he did—how does it concern you?

DR. JADIN.   On the other hand, medical science has never established the fact of intra-uterine swimming or diving. Under the circumstances, we are forced to the opinion, Officer, that if you dive in you will probably drown.

POLICEMAN.   You think so?

PROSPECTOR.   Who asked you for an opinion?

THE PRESIDENT.   Pay no attention to that quack, Officer.

DR. JADIN.   Quack, sir?

PROSPECTOR.   This is not a medical matter. It's a legal problem. The officer has made a grave error. He's new. We're trying to help him.

BROKER.   He's probably afraid of the water.

POLICEMAN.   Nothing of the sort. Officially, I'm afraid of nothing. But I always follow doctor's orders.

DR. JADIN.   You see, Officer, when a child is born . . .

PROSPECTOR. Now, what does he care about when a child is born? He's got a dying man on his hands. . . . Officer, if you want my advice . . .

POLICEMAN. It so happens, I care a lot about when a child is born. It's part of my duty to aid and assist any woman in childbirth or labor.

THE PRESIDENT. Can you imagine!

POLICEMAN. Is it true, Doctor, what they say, that when you have twins, the first born is considered to be the youngest?

DR. JADIN. Quite correct. And what's more, if the twins happen to be born at midnight on December 31st, the older is a whole year younger. He does his military service a year later. That's why you have to keep your eyes open. And that's the reason why a queen always gives birth before witnesses. . . .

POLICEMAN. God! The things a policeman is supposed to know! Doctor, what does it mean if, when I get up in the morning sometimes . . .

PROSPECTOR [nudging the PRESIDENT meanfully]. The old woman . . .

BROKER. Come on, Baron.

THE PRESIDENT. I think we'd better all run along.

PROSPECTOR. Leave him to me.

THE PRESIDENT. I'll see you later.

[The PRESIDENT steals off with the BROKER and the BARON.]

POLICEMAN [still in conference with DR. JADIN]. But what's really worrying me, Doctor, is this—don't you think it's a bit risky for a man to marry after forty-five?

[The BROKER runs in breathlessly.]

BROKER. Officer! Officer!

POLICEMAN. What's the trouble?

BROKER. Quick! Two women are calling for help—on the sidewalk—Avenue Wilson!

POLICEMAN. Two women at once? Standing up or lying down?

BROKER. You'd better go and see. Quick!

PROSPECTOR. You'd better take the Doctor with you.

POLICEMAN. Come along, Doctor, come along. . . . [Pointing to PIERRE.] Tell him to wait till I get back. Come along, Doctor.

[He runs out, the DOCTOR following. The PROSPECTOR moves over toward PIERRE, but IRMA crosses in front of him and takes the boy's hand.]

IRMA. How beautiful he is! Is he dead, Martial?

WAITER [handing her a pocket mirror]. Hold this mirror to his mouth. If it clouds over . . .

IRMA. It clouds over.

WAITER. He's alive.

[He holds out his hand for the mirror.]

IRMA. Just a sec—[She rubs it clean and looks at herself intently. Before handing it back, she fixes her hair and applies her lipstick. Meanwhile the PROSPECTOR tries to get around the other side, but the COUNTESS' eagle eye drives him off. He shrugs his shoulders and exits with the BARON.] Oh, look—he's opened his eyes!

[PIERRE opens his eyes, stares intently at IRMA and closes them again with the expression of a man who is among the angels.]

PIERRE [murmurs]. Oh! How beautiful!

VOICE [from within the café]. Irma!

IRMA. Coming. Coming.

[She goes in, not without a certain reluctance. The COUNTESS at once takes her place on the bench, and also the young man's hand. PIERRE sits up suddenly, and finds himself staring, not at IRMA, but into the very peculiar face of the COUNTESS. His expression changes.]

COUNTESS. You're looking at my iris? Isn't it beautiful?

PIERRE. Very.

[He drops back, exhausted.]

COUNTESS. The Sergeant was good enough to say it becomes me. But I no longer trust his taste. Yesterday, the flower girl gave me a lily, and he said it didn't suit me.

PIERRE [weakly]. It's beautiful.

COUNTESS. He'll be very happy to know that you agree with him. He's really quite sensitive. [She calls.] Sergeant!

PIERRE. No, please—don't call the police.

COUNTESS. But I must. I think I hurt his feelings.

PIERRE. Let me go, Madame.

COUNTESS. No, no. Stay where you are. Sergeant!

[PIERRE struggles weakly to get up.]

PIERRE. Please let me go.

COUNTESS. I'll do nothing of the sort. When you let someone go, you never see him again. I let Charlotte Mazumet go. I never saw her again.

PIERRE. Oh, my head.

COUNTESS. I let Adolphe Bertaut go. And I was holding him. And I never saw him again.

PIERRE. Oh, God!

COUNTESS. Except once. Thirty years later. In the market. He had changed a great deal—he didn't know me. He sneaked a melon from right under my nose, the only good one of the year. Ah, here we are. Sergeant!

[*The* POLICE SERGEANT *comes in with importance.*]

SERGEANT. I'm in a hurry, Countess.

COUNTESS. With regard to the iris. This young man agrees with you. He says it suits me.

SERGEANT [*going*]. There's a man drowning in the Seine.

COUNTESS. He's not drowning in the Seine. He's drowning here. Because I'm holding him tight—as I should have held Adolphe Bertaut. But if I let him go, I'm sure he will go and drown in the Seine. He's a lot better looking than Adolphe Bertaut, wouldn't you say?

[PIERRE *sighs deeply.*]

SERGEANT. How would I know?

COUNTESS. I've shown you his photograph. The one with the bicycle.

SERGEANT. Oh, yes. The one with the harelip.

COUNTESS. I've told you a hundred times! Adolphe Bertaut had no harelip. That was a scratch in the negative. [*The* SERGEANT *takes out his notebook and pencil.*] What are you doing?

SERGEANT. I am taking down the drowned man's name, given name and date of birth.

COUNTESS. You think that's going to stop him from jumping in the river? Don't be silly, Sergeant. Put that book away and try to console him.

SERGEANT. I should try and console him?

COUNTESS. When people want to die, it is your job as a guardian of the state to speak out in praise of life. Not mine.

SERGEANT. I should speak out in praise of life?

COUNTESS. I assume you have some motive for interfering with people's attempts to kill each other, and rob each other, and run each other over? If you believe that life has some value, tell him what it is. Go on.

SERGEANT. Well, all right. Now look, young man . . .

COUNTESS. His name is Roderick.

PIERRE. My name is not Roderick.

COUNTESS. Yes, it is. It's noon. At noon all men become Roderick.

SERGEANT. Except Adolphe Bertaut.

COUNTESS. In the days of Adolphe Bertaut, we were forced to change the men when we got tired of their names. Nowadays, we're more practical—each hour on the hour all names are automatically changed. The men remain the same. But you're not here to discuss Adolphe Bertaut, Sergeant. You're here to convince the young man that life is worth living.

PIERRE. It isn't.

SERGEANT. Quiet. Now then—what was the idea of jumping off the bridge, anyway?

COUNTESS. The idea was to land in the river. Roderick doesn't seem to be at all confused about that.

SERGEANT. Now how can I convince anybody that life is worth living if you keep interrupting all the time?

COUNTESS. I'll be quiet.

SERGEANT. First of all, Mr. Roderick, you have to realize that suicide is a crime against the state. And why is it a crime against the state? Because every time anybody commits suicide, that means one soldier less for the army, one taxpayer less for the . . .

COUNTESS. Sergeant, isn't there something about life that you really enjoy?

SERGEANT. That I enjoy?

COUNTESS. Well, surely, in all these years, you must have found something worth living for. Some secret pleasure, or passion. Don't blush. Tell him about it.

SERGEANT. Who's blushing? Well, naturally, yes—I have my passions—like everybody else. The fact is, since you ask me—I love—to play—casino. And if the gentleman would like to join me, by and by when I go off duty, we can sit down to a nice little game in the back room with a nice cold glass of beer. If he wants to kill an hour, that is.

COUNTESS. He doesn't want to kill an hour. He wants to kill himself. Well? Is that all the police force has to offer by way of earthly bliss?

SERGEANT. Huh? You mean—[*He jerks a thumb in the direction of the pretty* BLONDE, *who has just been joined by a* BRUNETTE *of the same stamp.*] Paulette?

[*The young man groans.*]

COUNTESS. You're not earning your salary, Sergeant. I defy anybody to stop dying on your account.

SERGEANT. Go ahead, if you can do any better. But you won't find it easy.

COUNTESS. Oh, this is not a desperate case at all. A young man who has just fallen in love with someone who has fallen in love with him!

PIERRE. She hasn't. How could she?

COUNTESS. Oh, yes, she has. She was holding your hand, just as I'm holding it, when all of a sudden . . . Did you ever know Marshal Canrobert's niece?

SERGEANT. How could he know Marshal Canrobert's niece?

COUNTESS. Lots of people knew her—when she was alive. [PIERRE begins to struggle energetically.] No, no, Roderick—stop—stop!

SERGEANT. You see? You won't do any better than I did.

COUNTESS. No? Let's bet. I'll bet my iris against one of your gold buttons. Right?— Roderick, I know very well why you tried to drown yourself in the river.

PIERRE. You don't at all.

COUNTESS. It's because that Prospector wanted you to commit a horrible crime.

PIERRE. How did you know that?

COUNTESS. He stole my boa, and now he wants you to kill me.

PIERRE. Not exactly.

COUNTESS. It wouldn't be the first time they've tried it. But I'm not so easy to get rid of, my boy, oh, no . . . Because . . .

[The DOORMAN rides in on his bicycle. He winks at the SERGEANT, who has now seated himself while the WAITER serves him a beer.]

DOORMAN. Take it easy, Sergeant.

SERGEANT. I'm busy saving a drowning man.

COUNTESS. They can't kill me because—I have no desire to die.

PIERRE. You're fortunate.

COUNTESS. To be alive is to be fortunate, Roderick. Of course, in the morning, when you first awake, it does not always seem so very gay. When you take your hair out of the drawer, and your teeth out of the glass, you are apt to feel a little out of place in this world. Especially if you've just been dreaming that you're a little girl on a pony looking for strawberries in the woods. But all you need to feel the call of life once more is a letter in your mail giving you your schedule for the day— your mending, your shopping, that letter to your grandmother that you never seem to get around to. And so, when you've washed your face in rosewater, and powdered it—not with this awful rice-powder they sell nowadays, which does nothing for the skin, but with a cake of pure white starch—and put on your pins, your rings, your brooches, bracelets, earrings and pearls—in short, when you are dressed for your morning coffee—and have had a good look at yourself—not in the glass naturally—it lies—but in the side of the brass gong that once belonged to Admiral Courbet—then, Roderick, then you're armed, you're strong, you're ready—you can begin again.

[PIERRE is listening now intently. There are tears in his eyes.]

PIERRE. Oh, Madame . . . ! Oh, Madame . . . !

COUNTESS. After that, everything is pure delight. First the morning paper. Not, of course, these current sheets full of lies and vulgarity. I always read the Gaulois, the issue of March 22, 1903. It's by far the best. It has some delightful scandal, some excellent fashion notes, and, of course, the last-minute bulletin on the death of Leonide Leblanc. She used to live next door, poor woman, and when I learn of her death every morning, it gives me quite a shock. I'd gladly lend you my copy, but it's in tatters.

SERGEANT. Couldn't we find him a copy in some library?

COUNTESS. I doubt it. And so, when you've taken your fruit salts—not in water, naturally —no matter what they say, it's water that gives you gas—but with a bit of spiced cake—then in sunlight or rain, Chaillot calls. It is time to dress for your morning walk. This takes much longer, of course—without a maid, impossible to do it under an hour, what with your corset, corset-cover and drawers all of which lace or button in the back. I asked Madame Lanvin, a while ago, to fit the drawers with zippers. She was quite charming, but she declined. She thought it would spoil the style.

[The DEAF MUTE comes in.]

WAITER. I know a place where they put zippers on anything.

[*The* RAGPICKER *enters.*]

COUNTESS. I think Lanvin knows best. But I really manage very well, Martial. What I do now is, I lace them up in front, then twist them around to the back. It's quite simple, really. Then you choose a lorgnette, and then the usual fruitless search for the feather boa that the prospector stole—I know it was he: he didn't dare look me in the eye—and then all you need is a rubber band to slip around your parasol—I lost the catch the day I struck the cat that was stalking the pigeon—it was worth it—ah, that day I earned my wages!

THE RAGPICKER. Countess, if you can use it, I found a nice umbrella catch the other day with a cat's eye in it.

COUNTESS. Thank you, Ragpicker. They say these eyes sometimes come to life and fill with tears. I'd be afraid . . .

PIERRE. Go on, Madame, go on . . .

COUNTESS. Ah! So life is beginning to interest you, is it? You see how beautiful it is?

PIERRE. What a fool I've been!

COUNTESS. Then, Roderick, I begin my rounds. I have my cats to feed, my dogs to pet, my plants to water. I have to see what the evil ones are up to in the district—those who hate people, those who hate plants, those who hate animals. I watch them sneaking off in the morning to put on their disguises—to the baths, to the beauty parlors, to the barbers. But they can't deceive me. And when they come out again with blonde hair and false whiskers, to pull up my flowers and poison my dogs, I'm there, and I'm ready. All you have to do to break their power is to cut across their path from the left. That isn't always easy. Vice moves swiftly. But I have a good long stride and I generally manage. . . . Right, my friends? [*The* WAITER *and the* RAGPICKER *nod their heads with evident approval.*] Yes, the flowers have been marvelous this year. And the butcher's dog on the Rue Bizet, in spite of that wretch that tried to poison him, is friskier than ever. . . .

SERGEANT. That dog had better look out. He has no license.

COUNTESS. He doesn't seem to feel the need of one.

THE RAGPICKER. The Duchess de la Rochefoucauld's whippet is getting awfully thin. . . .

COUNTESS. What can I do? She bought that dog full grown from a kennel where they didn't know his right name. A dog without his right name is bound to get thin.

THE RAGPICKER. I've got a friend who knows a lot about dogs—an Arab . . .

COUNTESS. Ask him to call on the Duchess. She receives. Thursdays, five to seven. You see then, Roderick. That's life. Does it appeal to you now?

PIERRE. It seems marvelous.

COUNTESS. Ah! Sergeant. My button. [*The* SERGEANT *gives her his button and goes off. At this point the* PROSPECTOR *enters.*] That's only the morning. Wait till I tell you about the afternoon!

PROSPECTOR. All right, Pierre. Come along now.

PIERRE. I'm perfectly all right here.

PROSPECTOR. I said, come along now.

PIERRE [*to the* COUNTESS]. I'd better go, Madame.

COUNTESS. No.

PIERRE. It's no use. Please let go my hand.

PROSPECTOR. Madame, will you oblige me by letting my friend go?

COUNTESS. I will not oblige you in any way.

PROSPECTOR. All right. Then I'll oblige you . . . !

[*He tries to push her away. She catches up a soda water siphon and squirts it in his face.*]

PIERRE. Countess . . .

COUNTESS. Stay where you are. This man isn't going to take you away. In the first place, I shall need you in a few minutes to take me home. I'm all alone here and I'm very easily frightened.

[*The* PROSPECTOR *makes a second attempt to drag* PIERRE *away. The* COUNTESS *cracks him over the skull with the siphon. They join battle. The* COUNTESS *whistles. The* DOORMAN *comes, then the other* VAGABONDS, *and lastly the* POLICE SERGEANT.]

PROSPECTOR. Officer! Arrest this woman!

SERGEANT. What's the trouble here?

PROSPECTOR. She refuses to let this man go.

SERGEANT. Why should she?

PROSPECTOR. It's against the law for a woman to detain a man on the street.

IRMA. Suppose it's her son whom she's found again after twenty years?

THE RAGPICKER [*gallantly*]. Or her long-lost brother? The Countess is not so old.

PROSPECTOR. Officer, this is a clear case of disorderly conduct.

[*The* DEAF MUTE *interrupts with frantic signals.*]

COUNTESS. Irma, what is the Deaf Mute saying?

IRMA [*interpreting*]. The young man is in danger of his life. He mustn't go with him.

PROSPECTOR. What does he know?

IRMA. He knows everything.

PROSPECTOR. Officer, I'll have to take your number.

COUNTESS. Take his number. It's 2133. It adds up to nine. It will bring you luck.

SERGEANT. Countess, between ourselves, what are you holding him for, anyway?

COUNTESS. I'm holding him because it's very pleasant to hold him. I've never really held anybody before, and I'm making the most of it. And because so long as *I* hold him, he's free.

PROSPECTOR. Pierre, I'm giving you fair warning. . . .

COUNTESS. And I'm holding him because Irma wants me to hold him. Because if I let him go, it will break her heart.

IRMA. Oh, Countess!

SERGEANT [*to the* PROSPECTOR]. All right, you—move on. Nobody's holding you. You're blocking traffic. Move on.

PROSPECTOR [*menacingly*]. I have your number. [*And murderously, to* PIERRE.] You'll regret this, Pierre.

[*Exit* PROSPECTOR.]

PIERRE. Thank you, Countess.

COUNTESS. They're blackmailing you, are they? [PIERRE *nods.*] What have you done? Murdered somebody?

PIERRE. No.

COUNTESS. Stolen something?

PIERRE. No.

COUNTESS. What then?

PIERRE. I forged a signature.

COUNTESS. Whose signature?

PIERRE. My father's. To a note.

COUNTESS. And this man has the paper, I suppose?

PIERRE. He promised to tear it up, if I did what he wanted. But I couldn't do it.

COUNTESS. But the man is mad! Does he really want to destroy the whole neighborhood?

PIERRE. He wants to destroy the whole city.

COUNTESS [*laughs*]. Fantastic.

PIERRE. It's not funny, Countess. He can do it. He's mad, but he's powerful, and he has friends. Their machines are already drawn up and waiting. In three months' time you may see the city covered by a forest of derricks and drills.

COUNTESS. But what are they looking for? Have they lost something?

PIERRE. They're looking for oil. They're convinced that Paris is sitting on a lake of oil.

COUNTESS. Suppose it is. What harm does it do?

PIERRE. They want to bring the oil to the surface, Countess.

COUNTESS [*laughs*]. How silly! Is that a reason to destroy a city? What do they want with this oil?

PIERRE. They want to make war, Countess.

COUNTESS. Oh, dear, let's forget about these horrible men. The world is beautiful. It's happy. That's how God made it. No man can change it.

WAITER. Ah, Countess, if you only knew . . .

COUNTESS. If I only knew what?

WAITER. Shall we tell her now? Shall we tell her?

COUNTESS. What is it you are hiding from me?

THE RAGPICKER. Nothing, Countess. It's you who are hiding.

WAITER. You tell her. You've been a pitchman. You can talk.

ALL. Tell her. Tell her. Tell her.

COUNTESS. You're frightening me, my friends. Go on. I'm listening.

THE RAGPICKER. Countess, there was a time when old clothes were as good as now—in fact, they were better. Because when people wore clothes, they gave something to them. You may not believe it, but right this minute, the highest-priced shops in Paris are selling clothes that were thrown away thirty years ago. They're selling them for new. That's how good they were.

COUNTESS. Well?

THE RAGPICKER. Countess, there was a

time when garbage was a pleasure. A garbage can was not what it is now. If it smelled a little strange, it was because it was a little confused —there was everything there—sardines, cologne, iodine, roses. An amateur might jump to a wrong conclusion. But to a professional—it was the smell of God's plenty.

COUNTESS. Well?

THE RAGPICKER. Countess, the world has changed.

COUNTESS. Nonsense. How could it change? People are the same, I hope.

THE RAGPICKER. No, Countess. The people are not the same. The people are different. There's been an invasion. An infiltration. From another planet. The world is not beautiful any more. It's not happy.

COUNTESS. Not happy? Is that true? Why didn't you tell me this before?

THE RAGPICKER. Because you live in a dream, Countess. And we don't like to disturb you.

COUNTESS. But how could it have happened?

THE RAGPICKER. Countess, there was a time when you could walk around Paris, and all the people you met were just like yourself. A little cleaner, maybe, or dirtier, perhaps, or angry, or smiling—but you knew them. They were you. Well, Countess, twenty years ago, one day, on the street, I saw a face in the crowd. A face, you might say, without a face. The eyes—empty. The expression—not human. Not a human face. It saw me staring, and when it looked back at me with its gelatine eyes, I shuddered. Because I knew that to make room for this one, one of us must have left the earth. A while after, I saw another. And another. And since then I've seen hundreds come in—yes—thousands.

COUNTESS. Describe them to me.

THE RAGPICKER. You've seen them yourself Countess. Their clothes don't wrinkle. Their hats don't come off. When they talk, they don't look at you. They don't perspire.

COUNTESS. Have they wives? Have they children?

THE RAGPICKER. They buy the models out of shop windows, furs and all. They animate them by a secret process. Then they marry them. Naturally, they don't have children.

COUNTESS. What work do they do?

THE RAGPICKER. They don't do any work. Whenever they meet, they whisper, and then they pass each other thousand-franc notes. You see them standing on the corner by the Stock Exchange. You see them at auctions—in the back. They never raise a finger—they just stand there. In theater lobbies, by the box office— they never go inside. They don't do anything, but wherever you see them, things are not the same. I remember well the time when a cabbage could sell itself just by being a cabbage. Nowadays it's no good being a cabbage—unless you have an agent and pay him a commission. Nothing is free any more to sell itself or give itself away. These days, Countess, every cabbage has its pimp.

COUNTESS. I can't believe that.

THE RAGPICKER. Countess, little by little, the pimps have taken over the world. They don't do anything, they don't make anything —they just stand there and take their cut. It makes a difference. Look at the shopkeepers. Do you ever see one smiling at a customer any more? Certainly not. Their smiles are strictly for the pimps. The butcher has to smile at the meat-pimp, the florist at the rose-pimp, the grocer at the fresh-fruit-and-vegetable pimp. It's all organized down to the slightest detail. A pimp for bird-seed. A pimp for fish-food. That's why the cost of living keeps going up all the time. You buy a glass of beer—it costs twice as much as it used to. Why? 10 percent for the glass-pimp, 10 percent for the beer-pimp, 20 percent for the glass-of-beer-pimp— that's where our money goes. Personally, I prefer the old-fashioned type. Some of those men at least were loved by the women they sold. But what feelings can a pimp arouse in a leg of lamb? Pardon my language, Irma.

COUNTESS. It's all right. She doesn't understand it.

THE RAGPICKER. So now you know, Countess, why the world is no longer happy. We are the last of the free people of the earth. You saw them looking us over today. Tomorrow, the street-singer will start paying the song-pimp, and the garbage-pimp will be after me. I tell you, Countess, we're finished. It's the end of free enterprise in this world!

COUNTESS. Is this true, Roderick?

PIERRE. I'm afraid it's true.

COUNTESS. Did you know about this, Irma?

IRMA. All I know is the doorman says that faith is dead.

DOORMAN. I've stopped taking bets over the phone.

JUGGLER. The very air is different, Countess. You can't trust it any more. If I throw my torches up too high, they go out.

THE RAGPICKER. The sky-pimp puts them out.

FLOWER GIRL. My flowers don't last over night now. They wilt.

JUGGLER. Have you noticed, the pigeons don't fly any more?

THE RAGPICKER. They can't afford to. They walk.

COUNTESS. They're a lot of fools and so are you! You should have told me at once! How can you bear to live in a world where there is unhappiness? Where a man is not his own master? Are you cowards? All we have to do is to get rid of these men.

PIERRE. How can we get rid of them? They're too strong.

[The SERGEANT walks up again.]

COUNTESS [smiling]. The Sergeant will help us.

SERGEANT. Who? Me?

IRMA. There are a great many of them, Countess. The Deaf Mute knows them all. They employed him once, years ago, because he was deaf. [The DEAF MUTE wigwags a short speech.] They fired him because he wasn't blind. [Another flash of sign language.] They're all connected like the parts of a machine.

COUNTESS. So much the better. We shall drive the whole machine into a ditch.

SERGEANT. It's not that easy, Countess. You never catch these birds napping. They change before your very eyes. I remember when I was in the detectives . . . You catch a president, pfft! He turns into a trustee. You catch him as trustee, and pfft! he's not a trustee—he's an honorary vice-chairman. You catch a Senator dead to rights: he becomes Minister of Justice. You get after the Minister of Justice—he is Chief of Police. And there you are—no longer in the detectives.

PIERRE. He's right, Countess. They have all the power. And all the money. And they're greedy for more.

COUNTESS. They're greedy? Ah, then, my friends, they're lost. If they're greedy, they're stupid. If they're greedy—don't worry, I know exactly what to do. Roderick, by tonight you will be an honest man. And, Juggler, your torches will stay lit. And your beer will flow freely again, Martial. And the world will be saved. Let's go to work.

THE RAGPICKER. What are you going to do?

COUNTESS. Have you any kerosene in the house, Irma?

IRMA. Yes. Would you like some?

COUNTESS. I want just a little. In a dirty bottle. With a little mud. And some mange-cure, if you have it. [To the DEAF MUTE.] Deaf Mute! Take a letter. [IRMA interprets in sign language. To the SINGER.] Singer, go and find Madame Constance.

[IRMA and the WAITER go into the café.]

SINGER. Yes, Countess.

COUNTESS. Ask her to be at my house by two o'clock. I'll be waiting for her in the cellar. You may tell her we have to discuss the future of humanity. That's sure to bring her.

SINGER. Yes, Countess.

COUNTESS. And ask her to bring Mademoiselle Gabrielle and Madame Josephine with her. Do you know how to get in to speak to Madame Constance? You ring twice, and then meow three times like a cat. Do you know how to meow?

SINGER. I'm better at barking.

COUNTESS. Better practise meowing on the way. Incidentally, I think Madame Constance knows all the verses of your mazurka. Remind me to ask her.

SINGER. Yes, Countess.

[Exit.]

[IRMA comes in. She is shaking the oily concoction in a little perfume vial, which she now hands the COUNTESS.]

IRMA. Here you are, Countess.

COUNTESS. Thanks, Irma. [She assumes a presidential manner.] Deaf Mute! Ready?

[IRMA interprets in sign language. The WAITER has brought out a portfolio of letter paper and placed it on a table. The DEAF MUTE sits down before it, and prepares to write.]

IRMA [speaking for the DEAF MUTE]. I'm ready.

COUNTESS. My dear Mr.— What's his name?

[IRMA wigwags the question to the DEAF

MUTE, *who answers in the same manner. It is all done so deftly that is is as if the* DEAF MUTE *were actually speaking.*]

IRMA. They are all called Mr. President.

COUNTESS. My dear Mr. President: I have personally verified the existence of a spontaneous outcrop of oil in the cellar of Number 21 Rue de Chaillot, which is at present occupied by a dignified person of unstable mentality. [*The* COUNTESS *grins knowingly.*] This explains why, fortunately for us, the discovery has so long been kept secret. If you should wish to verify the existence of this outcrop for yourself, you may call at the above address at three P.M. today. I am herewith enclosing a sample so that you may judge the quality and consistency of the crude. Yours very truly. Roderick, can you sign the prospector's name?

PIERRE. You wish me to?

COUNTESS. One forgery wipes out the other.

[PIERRE *signs the letter. The* DEAF MUTE *types the address on an envelope.*]

IRMA. Who is to deliver this?

COUNTESS. The Doorman, of course. On his bicycle. And as soon as you have delivered it, run over to the prospector's office. Leave word that the President expects to see him at my house at three.

DOORMAN. Yes, Countess.

COUNTESS. I shall leave you now. I have many pressing things to do. Among others, I must press my red gown.

THE RAGPICKER. But this only takes care of two of them, Countess.

COUNTESS. Didn't the Deaf Mute say they are all connected like the works of a machine?

IRMA. Yes.

COUNTESS. Then, if one comes, the rest will follow. And we shall have them all. My boa, please.

DOORMAN. The one that's stolen, Countess?

COUNTESS. Naturally. The one the prospector stole.

DOORMAN. It hasn't turned up yet, Countess. But someone has left an ermine collar.

COUNTESS. Real ermine?

DOORMAN. Looks like it.

COUNTESS. Ermine and iris were made for each other. Let me see it.

DOORMAN. Yes, Countess. [*Exit* DOORMAN.]

COUNTESS. Roderick, you shall escort me.

You still look pale. I have some old Chartreuse at home. I always take a glass each year. Last year I forgot. You shall have it.

PIERRE. If there is anything I can do, Countess . . . ?

COUNTESS. There is a great deal you can do. There are all the things that need to be done in a room that no man has been in for twenty years. You can untwist the cord on the blind and let in a little sunshine for a change. You can take the mirror off the wardrobe door, and deliver me once and for all from the old harpy that lives in the mirror. You can let the mouse out of the trap. I'm tired of feeding it. [*To her friends.*] Each man to his post. See you later, my friends. [*The* DOORMAN *puts the ermine collar around her shoulder.*] Thank you, my boy. It's rabbit. [*One o'clock strikes.*] Your arm, Valentine.

PIERRE. Valentine?

COUNTESS. It's just struck one. At one, all men become Valentine.

PIERRE [*he offers his arm*]. Permit me.

COUNTESS. Or Valentino. It's obviously far from the same, isn't it, Irma? But they have that much choice.

[*She sweeps out majestically with* PIERRE. *The others disperse. All but* IRMA.]

IRMA [*clearing off the table*]. I hate ugliness. I love beauty. I hate meanness. I adore kindness. It may not seem so grand to some to be a waitress in Paris. I love it. A waitress meets all sorts of people. She observes life. I hate to be alone. I love people. But I have never said I love you to a man. Men try to make me say it. They put their arms around me—I pretend I don't see it. They pinch me— I pretend I don't feel it. They kiss me—I pretend I don't know it. They take me out in the evening and make me drink—but I'm careful, I never say it. If they don't like it, they can leave me alone. Because when I say I love you to Him, He will know just by looking in my eyes that many have held me and pinched me and kissed me, but I have never said I love you to anyone in the world before. Never. No. [*Looking off in the direction in which* PIERRE *has gone, she whispers softly:*] I love you.

VOICE [*from within the café*]. Irma!

IRMA. Coming. [*Exits.*]

CURTAIN

ACT II

SCENE: *The cellar of the* COUNTESS' *house. An ancient vault set deep in the ground, with walls of solid masonry, part brick and part great ashlars, mossy and sweating. A staircase of medieval pattern is built into the thickness of the wall, and leads up to the street level from a landing halfway down. In the corners of the cellar are piled casks, packing cases, bird-cages, and other odds and ends—the accumulation of centuries—the whole effect utterly fantastic.*

In the center of the vast underground room, some furniture has been arranged to give an impression of a sitting-room of the 1890's. There is a venerable chaise-longue piled with cushions that once were gay, three armchairs, a table with an oil lamp and a bowl of flowers, a shaggy rug. It is two P.M., *the same day.*

AT RISE: *The* COUNTESS *is sitting over a bit of mending, in one of the armchairs.* IRMA *appears on the landing and calls down.*

IRMA. Countess! The Sewer Man is here.

COUNTESS. Thank goodness, Irma. Send him down. [*The* SEWER MAN *enters. He carries his hip-boots in his hand.*] How do you do, Mr. Sewer Man? [*The* SEWER MAN *bows.*] But why do you have your boots in your hand instead of on your feet?

SEWER MAN. Etiquette, Countess. Etiquette.

COUNTESS. How very American! I'm told that Americans nowadays apologize for their gloves if they happen to take one's hand. As if the skin of a human were nicer to touch than the skin of a sheep! And particularly if they have sweaty hands . . . !

SEWER MAN. My feet never sweat, Countess.

COUNTESS. How very nice! But please don't stand on ceremony here. Put your boots on. Put them on.

SEWER MAN [*complying*]. Thanks very much, Countess.

COUNTESS [*while he draws on his boots*]. I'm sure you must have a very poor opinion of the upper world, from what you see of it. The way people throw their filth into your territory is absolutely scandalous! I burn all my refuse, and I scatter the ashes. All I ever throw in the drain is flowers. Did you happen to see a lily float by this morning? Mine. But perhaps you didn't notice?

SEWER MAN. We notice a lot more down there, Countess, than you might think. You'd be surprised the things we notice. There's lots of things come along that were obviously intended for us—little gifts you might call them—sometimes a brand-new shaving brush—sometimes, *The Brothers Karamazov* . . . Thanks for the lily, Countess. A very sweet thought.

COUNTESS. Tomorrow you shall have this iris. But now, let's come to the point. I have two questions to ask you.

SEWER MAN. Yes, Countess?

COUNTESS. First—and this has nothing to do with our problem—it's just something that has been troubling me. . . . Tell me, is it true that the sewer men of Paris have a king?

SEWER MAN. Oh, now, Countess, that's another of those fairy tales out of the Sunday supplements. It just seems those writers can't keep their minds off the sewers! It fascinates them. They keep thinking of us moving around in our underground canals like gondoliers in Venice, and it sends them into a fever of romance! The things they say about us! They say we have a race of girls down there who never see the light of day! It's completely fantastic! The girls naturally come out—every Christmas and Easter. And orgies by torchlight with gondolas and guitars! With troops of rats that dance as they follow the piper. What nonsense! The rats are not allowed to dance. No, no, no. Of course we have no king. Down in the sewers, you'll find nothing but good Republicans.

COUNTESS. And no queen?

SEWER MAN. No. We may run a beauty contest down there once in a while. Or crown a mermaid Queen of the May. But no queen what you'd call a queen. And, as for these swimming races they talk so much about . . . possibly once in a while—in the summer—in the dog days . . .

COUNTESS. I believe you. I believe you. And now tell me. Do you remember that night I found you here in my cellar—looking very pale and strange—you were half-dead as a matter of fact—and I gave you some brandy . . .

SEWER MAN. Yes, Countess.

COUNTESS. That night you promised if ever I should need it—you would tell me the secret of this room.

SEWER MAN. The secret of the moving stone?

COUNTESS. I need it now.

SEWER MAN. Only the King of the Sewer Men knows this secret.

COUNTESS. I'm sure of it. I know most secrets, of course. As a matter of fact, I have three magic words that will open any door that words can open. I have tried them all—in various tones of voice. They don't seem to work. And this is a matter of life and death.

SEWER MAN. Look, Countess.

[*He locates a brick in the masonry, and pushes it. A huge block of stone slowly pivots and uncovers a trap from which a circular staircase winds into the bowels of the earth.*]

COUNTESS. Good heavens! Where do those stairs lead?

SEWER MAN. Nowhere.

COUNTESS. But they must go somewhere.

SEWER MAN. They just go down.

COUNTESS. Let's go and see.

SEWER MAN. No, Countess. Never again. That time you found me, I had a pretty close shave. I kept going down and around, and down and around for an hour, a year—I don't know. There's no end to it, Countess. Once you start you can't stop. . . . Your head begins to turn—you're lost. No—once you start down, there's no coming up.

COUNTESS. You came up.

SEWER MAN. I—I am a special case. Besides, I had my tools, my ropes. And I stopped in time.

COUNTESS. You could have screamed—shouted.

SEWER MAN. You could fire off a cannon.

COUNTESS. Who could have built a thing like this?

SEWER MAN. Paris is old, you know. Paris is very old.

COUNTESS. You don't suppose, by any chance, there is oil down there?

SEWER MAN. There's only death down there.

COUNTESS. I should have preferred a little oil too—or a vein of gold—or emeralds. You're quite sure there is nothing?

SEWER MAN. Not even rats.

COUNTESS. How does one lower this stone?

SEWER MAN. To open, you press here. And to close, you push there. [*He presses the brick. The stone descends.*] Now there's two of us in the world that knows it.

COUNTESS. I won't remember long. Is it all right if I repeat my magic words while I press it?

SEWER MAN. It's bound to help.

[IRMA *enters.*]

IRMA. Countess, Madame Constance and Mademoiselle Gabrielle are here.

COUNTESS. Show them down, Irma. Thank you very much, Mr. Sewer Man.

SEWER MAN. Like that story about the steam laundry that's supposed to be running day and night in my sewer . . . I can assure you . . .

COUNTESS [*edging him toward the door*]. Thank you very much.

SEWER MAN. Pure imagination! They never work nights.

[*He goes off, bowing graciously.*]

[CONSTANCE, *the Madwoman of Passy, and* GABRIELLE, *the Madwoman of St. Sulpice, come down daintily.* CONSTANCE *is all in white. She wears an enormous hat graced with ostrich plumes, and a lavender veil.* GABRIELLE *is costumed with the affected simplicity of the 1880's. She is atrociously made up in a remorseless parody of blushing innocence, and she minces down the stairs with macabre coyness.*]

CONSTANCE. Aurelia! Don't tell us they've found your feather boa?

GABRIELLE. You don't mean Adolphe Bertaut has proposed at last! I knew he would.

COUNTESS. How are you, Constance? [*She shouts.*] How are you, Gabrielle?

GABRIELLE. You needn't shout today, my dear. It's Wednesday. Wednesdays, I hear perfectly.

CONSTANCE. It's Thursday.

GABRIELLE. Oh, dear. Well, never mind. I'm going to make an exception just this once.

CONSTANCE [*to an imaginary dog who has stopped on the landing*]. Come along, Dickie. Come along. And stop barking. What a racket you're making! Come on, darling—we've come to see the longest boa and the handsomest man in Paris. Come on.

COUNTESS. Constance, it's not a question of my boa today. Nor of poor Adolphe. It's a question of the future of the human race.

CONSTANCE. You think it has a future?

COUNTESS. Please don't make silly jokes. Sit down and listen to me. Today we must make a decision which may alter the fate of the world.

CONSTANCE. Couldn't we do it tomorrow? I want to wash my slippers. Now, Dickie—please!

COUNTESS. We haven't a moment to waste. Where is Josephine? Well, we'd best have our tea, and the moment Josephine comes . . .

GABRIELLE. Josephine is sitting on her bench in front of the palace waiting for President Wilson to come out. She says she's sorry, but she positively must see him today.

CONSTANCE. Dickie!

COUNTESS. What a pity! [*She gets the tea things from the side table, pours tea and serves cake and honey.*] I wish she were here to help us. She has a first-class brain.

CONSTANCE. Go ahead, dear. We're listening. [*To* DICKIE.] What is it, Dickie? You want to sit in Aunt Aurelia's lap. All right, darling. Go on. Jump, Dickie.

COUNTESS. Constance, we love you, as you know. And we love Dickie. But this is a serious matter. So let's stop being childish for once.

CONSTANCE. And what does that mean, if you please?

COUNTESS. It means Dickie. You know perfectly well that we love him and fuss over him just as if he were still alive. He's a sacred memory and we wouldn't hurt his feelings for the world. But please don't plump him in my lap when I'm settling the future of mankind. His basket is in the corner—he knows where it is, and he can just go and sit in it.

CONSTANCE. So you're against Dickie too! You too!

COUNTESS. Constance! I'm not in the least against Dickie! I adore Dickie. But you know as well as I that Dickie is only a convention with us. It's a beautiful convention—but it doesn't have to bark all the time. Besides, it's you that spoil him. The time you went to visit your niece and left him with me, we got on marvelously together. He didn't bark, he didn't tear things, he didn't even eat. But when you're with him, one can pay attention to nothing else. I'm not going to take Dickie in my lap at a solemn moment like this, no,

not for anything in the world. And that's that!

GABRIELLE [*very sweetly*]. Constance, dear, I don't mind taking him in my lap. He loves to sit in my lap, don't you, darling?

CONSTANCE. Kindly stop putting on angelic airs, Gabrielle. I know you very well. You're much too sweet to be sincere. There's plenty of times that I make believe that Dickie is here, when really I've left him home, and you cuddle and pet him just the same.

GABRIELLE. I adore animals.

CONSTANCE. If you adore animals, you shouldn't pet them when they're not there. It's a form of hypocrisy.

COUNTESS. Now, Constance, Gabrielle has as much right as you . . .

CONSTANCE. Gabrielle has no right to do what she does. Do you know what she does? She invites *people* to come to tea with us. *People* whom we know nothing about. *People* who exist only in her imagination.

COUNTESS. You think that's not an existence?

GABRIELLE. I don't invite them at all. They come by themselves. What can I do?

CONSTANCE. You might introduce us.

COUNTESS. If you think they're only imaginary, there's no point in your meeting them, is there?

CONSTANCE. Of course they're imaginary. But who likes to have imaginary people staring at one? Especially strangers.

GABRIELLE. Oh, they're really very nice. . . .

CONSTANCE. Tell me just one thing, Gabrielle—are they here now?

COUNTESS. Am I to be allowed to speak? Or is this going to be the same as the argument about inoculating Josephine's cat, when we didn't get to the subject at all!

CONSTANCE. Never! Never! Never! I'll never give my consent to that. [*To* DICKIE.] I'd never do a thing like that to you, Dickie sweet. . . . Oh, no! Oh, no!

[*She begins to weep softly.*]

COUNTESS. Good heavens! Now we have her in tears. What an impossible creature! With the fate of humanity hanging in the balance! All right, all right, stop crying. I'll take him in my lap. Come, Dickie, Dickie.

CONSTANCE. No. He won't go now. Oh, how can you be so cruel? Don't you suppose

I know about Dickie? Don't you think I'd rather have him here alive and woolly and frisking around the way he used to? You have your Adolphe, Gabrielle has her birds. But I have only Dickie. Do you think I'd be so silly about him if it wasn't that it's only by pretending that he's here all the time that I get him to come sometimes, really? Next time I won't bring him!

COUNTESS. Now let's not get ourselves worked up over nothing. Come here, Dickie. . . . Irma is going to take you for a nice walk. [*She rings her bell.*] Irma!

[IRMA *appears on the landing.*]

CONSTANCE. No. He doesn't want to go. Besides, I didn't bring him today. So there!

COUNTESS. Very well, then. Irma, make sure the door is locked.

IRMA. Yes, Countess.

[IRMA *exits.*]

CONSTANCE. What do you mean? Why locked? Who's coming?

COUNTESS. If you'd let me get a word in, you'd know by now. A terrible thing has happened. This morning, this very morning, exactly at noon . . .

CONSTANCE [*thrilled*]. Oh, how exciting!

COUNTESS. Be quiet. This morning, exactly at noon, thanks to a young man who'd drowned himself in the Seine . . . Oh, yes, while I think of it—do you know a mazurka called *La Belle Polonaise?*

CONSTANCE. Yes, Aurelia.

COUNTESS. Could you sing it now? This very minute?

CONSTANCE. Yes, Aurelia.

COUNTESS. All of it?

CONSTANCE. Yes, Aurelia. But who's interrupting now, Aurelia?

COUNTESS. You're right. Well, this morning, exactly at noon, I discovered a horrible plot. There is a group of men who intend to tear down the whole city!

CONSTANCE. Is that all?

GABRIELLE. But I don't understand, Aurelia. Why should men want to tear down the city? It was they themselves who put it up.

COUNTESS. You are so innocent, my poor Gabrielle. There are people in the world who want to destroy everything. They have the fever of destruction. Even when they pretend that they're building, it is only in order to

destroy. When they put up a new building, they quietly knock down two old ones. They build cities so that they can destroy the countryside. They destroy space with telephones and time with airplanes. Humanity is now dedicated to the task of universal destruction. I am speaking, of course, primarily of the male sex.

GABRIELLE [*shocked*]. Oh . . . !

CONSTANCE. Aurelia! Must you talk sex in front of Gabrielle?

COUNTESS. There are *two* sexes.

CONSTANCE. Gabrielle is a virgin, Aurelia!

COUNTESS. Oh, she can't be as innocent as all that. She keeps canaries.

GABRIELLE. I think you're being very cruel about men, Aurelia. Men are big and beautiful, and as loyal as dogs. I preferred not to marry, it's true. But I hear excellent reports from friends who have had an opportunity to observe them closely.

COUNTESS. My poor darling! You are still living in a dream. But one day, you will wake up as I have, and then you will see what is happening in the world! The tide has turned, my dear. Men are changing back into beasts. They know it. They no longer try to hide it. There was once such a thing as manners. I remember a time when the hungriest was the one who took the longest to pick up his fork. The one with the broadest grin was the one who needed most to go to the . . . It was such fun to keep them grinning like that for hours. But now they no longer pretend. Just look at them—snuffling their soup like pigs, tearing their meat like tigers, crunching their lettuce like crocodiles! A man doesn't take your hand nowadays. He gives you his paw.

CONSTANCE. Would that trouble you so much if they turned into animals? Personally, I think it's a good idea.

GABRIELLE. Oh, I'd love to see them like that. They'd be sweet.

CONSTANCE. It might be the salvation of the human race.

COUNTESS [*to* CONSTANCE]. You'd make a fine rabbit, wouldn't you?

CONSTANCE. I?

COUNTESS. Naturally. You don't think it's only the men who are changing? You change along with them. Husbands and wives together. We're all one race, you know.

CONSTANCE. You think so? And why would my poor husband have to be a rabbit if he were alive?

COUNTESS. Remember his front teeth? When he nibbled his celery?

CONSTANCE. I'm happy to say, I remember absolutely nothing about him. All I remember on that subject is the time that Father Lacordaire tried to kiss me in the park.

COUNTESS. Yes, yes, of course.

CONSTANCE. And what does that mean, if you please, "Yes, yes, of course?"

COUNTESS. Constance, just this once, look us in the eye and tell us truly—did that really happen or did you read about it in a book?

CONSTANCE. Now I'm being insulted!

COUNTESS. We promise you faithfully that we'll believe it all over again afterwards, won't we, Gabrielle? But tell us the truth this once.

CONSTANCE. How dare you question my memories? Suppose I said your pearls were false!

COUNTESS. They were.

CONSTANCE. I'm not asking what they were. I'm asking what they are. Are they false or are they real?

COUNTESS. Everyone knows that little by little, as one wears pearls, they become real.

CONSTANCE. And isn't it exactly the same with memories?

COUNTESS. Now do not let us waste time. I must go on.

CONSTANCE. I think Gabrielle is perfectly right about men. There are still plenty who haven't changed a bit. There's an old Senator who bows to Gabrielle every day when he passes her in front of the palace. And he takes off his hat each time.

GABRIELLE. That's perfectly true, Aurelia. He's always pushing an empty baby carriage, and he always stops and bows.

COUNTESS. Don't be taken in, Gabrielle. It's all make-believe. And all we can expect from these make-believe men is itself make-believe. They give us facepowder made of stones, sausages made of sawdust, shirts made of glass, stockings made of milk. It's all a vulgar pretence. And if that is the case, imagine what passes, these days, for virtue, sincerity, generosity and love! I warn you, Gabrielle, don't let this Senator with the empty baby carriage pull the wool over your eyes.

GABRIELLE. He's really the soul of courtesy. He seems very correct.

COUNTESS. Those are the worst. Gabrielle, beware! He'll make you put on black riding boots, while he dances the can-can around you, singing God knows what filth at the top of his voice. The very thought makes one's blood run cold!

GABRIELLE. You think that's what he has in mind?

COUNTESS. Of course. Men have lost all sense of decency. They are all equally disgusting. Just look at them in the evening, sitting at their tables in the café, working away in unison with their toothpicks, hour after hour, digging up roast beef, veal, onion . . .

CONSTANCE. They don't harm anyone that way.

COUNTESS. Then why do you barricade your door, and make your friends meow before you let them come up? Incidentally, we must make an interesting sight, Gabrielle and I, yowling together on your doorstep like a couple of tomcats!

CONSTANCE. There's no need at all for you to yowl together. One would be quite enough. And you know perfectly well why I have to do it. It's because there are murderers.

COUNTESS. I don't quite see what prevents murderers from meowing like anybody else. But why are there murderers?

CONSTANCE. Why? Because there are thieves.

COUNTESS. And why are there thieves? Why is there almost nothing but thieves?

CONSTANCE. Because they worship money. Because money is king.

COUNTESS. Ah—now we've come to it. Because we live in the reign of the Golden Calf. Did you realize that, Gabrielle? Men now publicly worship the Golden Calf!

GABRIELLE. How awful! Have the authorities been notified?

COUNTESS. The authorities do it themselves, Gabrielle.

GABRIELLE. Oh! Has anyone talked to the bishop?

COUNTESS. Nowadays only money talks to the bishop. And so you see why I asked you to come here today. The world has gone out of its mind. Unless we do something, humanity is doomed! Constance, have you any suggestions?

CONSTANCE. I know what I always do in a case like this. . . .

COUNTESS. You write to the Prime Minister.

CONSTANCE. He always does what I tell him.

COUNTESS. Does he ever answer your letters?

CONSTANCE. He knows I prefer him not to. It might excite gossip. Besides, I don't always write. Sometimes I wire. The time I told him about the Archbishop's frigidaire, it was by wire. And they sent a new one the very next day.

COUNTESS. There was probably a commission in it for someone. And what do you suggest, Gabrielle?

CONSTANCE. Now, how can she tell you until she's consulted her voices?

GABRIELLE. I could go right home and consult them, and we could meet again after dinner.

COUNTESS. There's no time for that. Besides, your voices are not real voices.

GABRIELLE [furious]. How dare you say a thing like that?

COUNTESS. Where do your voices come from? Still from your sewing-machine?

GABRIELLE. Not at all. They've passed into my hot-water bottle. And it's much nicer that way. They don't chatter any more. They gurgle. But they haven't been a bit nice to me lately. Last night they kept telling me to let my canaries out. "Let them out. Let them out. Let them out."

CONSTANCE. Did you?

GABRIELLE. I opened the cage. They wouldn't go.

COUNTESS. I don't call that voices. Objects talk—everyone knows that. It's the principle of the phonograph. But to ask a hot-water bottle for advice is silly. What does a hot-water bottle know? No, all we have to consult here is our own judgment.

CONSTANCE. Very well then, tell us what you have decided. Since you're asking our opinion, you've doubtless made up your mind.

COUNTESS. Yes, I've thought the whole thing out. All I really needed to discover was the source of the infection. Today I found it.

CONSTANCE. Where?

COUNTESS. You'll see soon enough. I've baited a trap. In just a few minutes, the rats will be here.

GABRIELLE [in alarm]. Rats!

COUNTESS. Don't be alarmed. They're still in human form.

GABRIELLE. Heavens! What are you going to do with them?

COUNTESS. That's just the question. Suppose I get these wicked men all here at once—in my cellar—have I the right to exterminate them?

GABRIELLE. To kill them?

[COUNTESS nods.]

CONSTANCE. That's not a question for us. You'll have to ask Father Bridet.

COUNTESS. I have asked him. Yes. One day, in confession, I told him frankly that I had a secret desire to destroy all wicked people. He said: "By all means, my child. And when you're ready to go into action, I'll lend you the jawbone of an ass."

CONSTANCE. That's just talk. You get him to put that in writing.

GABRIELLE. What's your scheme, Aurelia?

COUNTESS. That's a secret.

CONSTANCE. It's not so easy to kill them. Let's say you had a tank full of vitriol all ready for them. You could never get them to walk into it. There's nothing so stubborn as a man when you want him to do something.

COUNTESS. Leave that to me.

CONSTANCE. But if they're killed, they're bound to be missed, and then we'll be fined. They fine you for every little thing these days.

COUNTESS. They won't be missed.

GABRIELLE. I wish Josephine were here. Her sister's husband was a lawyer. She knows all about these things.

COUNTESS. Do you miss a cold when it's gone? Or the germs that caused it? When the world feels well again, do you think it will regret its illness? No, it will stretch itself joyfully, and it will smile—that's all.

CONSTANCE. Just a moment! Gabrielle, are they here now? Yes or no?

COUNTESS. What's the matter with you now?

CONSTANCE. I'm simply asking Gabrielle if her friends are in the room or not. I have a right to know.

GABRIELLE. I'm not allowed to say.

CONSTANCE. I know very well they are. I'm sure of it. Otherwise you wouldn't be making faces.

COUNTESS. May I ask what difference it makes to you if her friends are in the room?

CONSTANCE. Just this: If they're here, I'm not going to say another word! I'm certainly not going to commit myself in a matter involving the death sentence in the presence of third parties, whether they exist or not.

GABRIELLE. That's not being very nice to my guests, is it?

COUNTESS. Constance, you must be mad! Or are you so stupid as to think that just because we're alone, there's nobody with us? Do you consider us so boring or repulsive that of all the millions of beings, imaginary or otherwise, who are prowling about in space, there's not one who might possibly enjoy spending a little time with us? On the contrary, my dear—my house is full of guests always. They know that here they have a place in the universe where they can come when they're lonely and be sure of a welcome. For my part, I'm delighted to have them.

GABRIELLE. Thank you, Aurelia.

CONSTANCE. You know perfectly well, Aurelia . . .

COUNTESS. I know perfectly well that at this moment the whole universe is listening to us—and that every word we say echoes to the remotest star. To pretend otherwise is the sheerest hypocrisy.

CONSTANCE. Then why do you insult me in front of everybody? I'm not mean. I'm shy. I feel timid about giving an opinion in front of such a crowd. Furthermore, if you think I'm so bad and so stupid, why did you invite me, in the first place?

COUNTESS. I'll tell you. And I'll tell you why, disagreeable as you are, I always give you the biggest piece of cake and my best honey. It's because when you come there's always someone with you—and I don't mean Dickie—I mean someone who resembles you like a sister, only she's young and lovely, and she sits modestly to one side and smiles at me tenderly all the time you're bickering and quarreling, and never says a word. That's the Constance to whom I give the cake that you gobble, and it's because of her that you're here today, and it's her vote that I'm asking

you to cast in this crucial moment. And not yours, which is of no importance whatever.

CONSTANCE. I'm leaving.

COUNTESS. Be so good as to sit down. I can't let her go yet.

CONSTANCE [crossing toward the stairs]. No. This is too much. I'm taking her with me.

[IRMA enters.]

IRMA. Madame Josephine.

COUNTESS. Thank heaven!

GABRIELLE. We're saved.

[JOSEPHINE, the Madwoman of La Concorde, sweeps in majestically in a get-up somewhere between the regal and the priestly.]

JOSEPHINE. My dear friends, today once again, I waited for President Wilson—but he didn't come out.

COUNTESS. You'll have to wait quite a while longer before he does. He's been dead since 1924.

JOSEPHINE. I have plenty of time.

COUNTESS. In anyone else, Josephine, these extravagances might seem a little childish. But a person of your judgment doubtless has her reasons for wanting to talk to a man to whom no one would listen when he was alive. We have a legal problem for you. Suppose you had all the world's criminals here in this room. And suppose you had a way of getting rid of them forever. Would you have the right to do it?

JOSEPHINE. Why not?

COUNTESS. Exactly my point.

GABRIELLE. But, Josephine, so many people!

JOSEPHINE. *De minimis non curat lex!* The more there are, the more legal it is. It's impersonal. It's even military. It's the cardinal principle of battle—you get all your enemies in one place, and you kill them all together at one time. Because if you had to track them down one by one in their houses and offices, you'd get tired, and sooner or later you'd stop. I believe your idea is very practical, Aurelia. I can't imagine why we never thought of it before.

GABRIELLE. Well, if you think it's all right to do it. . . .

JOSEPHINE. By all means. Your criminals have had a fair trial, I suppose?

COUNTESS. Trial?

JOSEPHINE. Certainly. You can't kill anybody without a trial. That's elementary. "No man shall be deprived of his life, liberty and property without due process of law."

COUNTESS.   They deprive us of ours.

JOSEPHINE.   That's not the point. You're not accused of anything. Every accused—man, woman or child—has the right to defend himself at the bar of justice. Even animals. Before the Deluge, you will recall, the Lord permitted Noah to speak in defense of his fellow mortals. He evidently stuttered. You know the result. On the other hand, Captain Dreyfus was not only innocent—he was defended by a marvelous orator. The result was precisely the same. So you see, in having a trial, you run no risk whatever.

COUNTESS.   But if I give them the slightest cause for suspicion—I'll lose them.

JOSEPHINE.   There's a simple procedure prescribed in such cases. You can summon the defendants by calling them three times—mentally, if you like. If they don't appear, the court may designate an attorney who will represent them. This attorney can then argue their case to the court, *in absentia,* and a judgment can then be rendered, *in contumacio.*

COUNTESS.   But I don't know any attorneys. And we have only ten minutes.

GABRIELLE.   Hurry, Josephine, hurry!

JOSEPHINE.   In case of emergency, it is permissible for the court to order the first passer-by to act as attorney for the defense. A defense is like a baptism. Absolutely indispensable, but you don't have to know anything to do it. Ask Irma to get you somebody. Anybody.

COUNTESS.   The Deaf-Mute?

JOSEPHINE.   Well—that's getting it down a bit fine. That might be questionable on appeal.

COUNTESS [*calls*].   Irma! What about the Police Sergeant?

JOSEPHINE.   He won't do. He's under oath to the state.

[IRMA *appears.*]

IRMA.   Yes, Countess?

COUNTESS.   Who's out there, Irma?

IRMA.   All our friends, Countess. There's the Ragpicker and . . .

COUNTESS.   Send down the Ragpicker.

CONSTANCE.   Do you think it's wise to have all those millionaires represented by a ragpicker?

JOSEPHINE.   It's a first-rate choice. Crimi-

nals are always represented by their opposites. Murderers, by someone who obviously wouldn't hurt a fly. Rapists, by a member of the League for Decency. Experience shows it's the only way to get an acquittal.

COUNTESS.   But we must not have an acquittal. That would mean the end of the world!

JOSEPHINE.   Justice is justice, my dear.

[*The* RAGPICKER *comes down, with a stately air. Behind him, on the landing, appear the other* VAGABONDS.]

THE RAGPICKER.   Greetings, Countess. Greetings, ladies. My most sincere compliments.

COUNTESS.   Has Irma told you . . . ?

THE RAGPICKER.   She said something about a trial.

COUNTESS.   You have been appointed attorney for the defense.

THE RAGPICKER.   Terribly flattered, I'm sure.

COUNTESS.   You realize, don't you, how much depends on the outcome of this trial?

JOSEPHINE.   Do you know the defendants well enough to undertake the case?

THE RAGPICKER.   I know them to the bottom of their souls. I go through their garbage every day.

CONSTANCE.   And what do you find there?

THE RAGPICKER.   Mostly flowers.

GABRIELLE.   It's true, you know, the rich are always surrounded with flowers.

CONSTANCE.   How beautiful!

COUNTESS.   Are you trying to prejudice the court?

THE RAGPICKER.   Oh no, Countess, no.

COUNTESS.   We want a completely impartial defense.

THE RAGPICKER.   Of course, Countess, of course. Permit me to make a suggestion.

COUNTESS.   Will you preside, Josephine?

THE RAGPICKER.   Instead of speaking as attorney, suppose you let me speak directly as defendant. It will be more convincing, and I can get into it more.

JOSEPHINE.   Excellent idea. Motion granted.

COUNTESS.   We don't want you to be too convincing, remember.

THE RAGPICKER.   Impartial, Countess, impartial.

JOSEPHINE.   Well? Have you prepared your case?

THE RAGPICKER. How rich am I?

JOSEPHINE. Millions. Billions.

THE RAGPICKER. How did I get them? Theft? Murder? Embezzlement?

COUNTESS. Most likely.

THE RAGPICKER. Do I have a wife? A mistress?

COUNTESS. Everything.

THE RAGPICKER. All right. I'm ready.

GABRIELLE. Will you have some tea?

THE RAGPICKER. Is that good?

CONSTANCE. Very good for the voice. The Russians drink nothing but tea. And they talk like anything.

THE RAGPICKER. All right. Tea.

JOSEPHINE [to the VAGABONDS]. Come in. Come in. All of you. You may take places. Trial is public. [The VAGABONDS dispose themselves on the steps and elsewhere.] Your bell, if you please, Aurelia.

COUNTESS. But what if I should need to ring for Irma?

JOSEPHINE. Irma will sit here, next to me. If you need her, she can ring for herself. [To the POLICE SERGEANT and the POLICEMAN.] Conduct the accused to the bar. [The officers conduct the RAGPICKER to a bar improvised with a rocking chair and a packing case marked FRAGILE. The RAGPICKER mounts the box. She rings the bell.] The court is now in session. [All sit.] Counsel for the defense, you may take the oath.

THE RAGPICKER. I swear to tell the truth, the whole truth, and nothing but the truth, so help me God.

JOSEPHINE. Nonsense! You're not a witness. You're an attorney. It's your duty to lie, conceal and distort everything, and slander everybody.

THE RAGPICKER. All right. I swear to lie, conceal and distort everything, and slander everybody.

[JOSEPHINE rings stridently.]

JOSEPHINE. Quiet! Begin.

THE RAGPICKER. May it please the honorable, august and elegant Court . . .

JOSEPHINE. Flattery will get you nowhere. That will do. The defense has been heard. Cross-examination.

COUNTESS. Mr. President . . .

THE RAGPICKER [bowing with dignity]. Madame.

COUNTESS. Do you know what you are charged with?

THE RAGPICKER. I can't for the life of me imagine. My life is an open book. My ways are known to all. I am a pillar of the church and the sole support of the Opera. My hands are spotless.

COUNTESS. What an atrocious lie! Just look at them!

CONSTANCE. You don't have to insult the man. He's only lying to please you.

COUNTESS. Be quiet, Constance! You don't get the idea at all. [To the RAGPICKER.] You are charged with the crime of worshipping money.

THE RAGPICKER. Worshipping money? Me?

JOSEPHINE. Do you plead guilty or not guilty? Which is it?

THE RAGPICKER. Why, Your Honor . . .

JOSEPHINE. Yes or no?

THE RAGPICKER. Yes or no? No! I don't worship money, Countess. Heavens, no! Money worships me. It adores me. It won't let me alone. It's damned embarrassing, I can tell you.

JOSEPHINE. Kindly watch your language.

COUNTESS. Defendant, tell the Court how you came by your money.

THE RAGPICKER. The first time money came to me, I was a mere boy, a little golden-haired child in the bosom of my dear family. It came to me suddenly in the guise of a gold brick which, in my innocence, I picked out of a garbage can one day while playing. I was horrified, as you can imagine. I immediately tried to get rid of it by swapping it for a little rundown one-track railroad which, to my consternation, at once sold itself for a hundred times its value. In a desperate effort to get rid of this money, I began to buy things. I bought the Northern Refineries, the Galeries Lafayette, and the Schneider-Creusot Munition Works. And now I'm stuck with them. It's a horrible fate—but I'm resigned to it. I don't ask for your sympathy, I don't ask for your pity—all I ask for is a little common human understanding. . . .

[He begins to cry.]

COUNTESS. I object. This wretch is trying to play on the emotions of the Court.

JOSEPHINE. The Court has no emotions.

THE RAGPICKER. Everyone knows that the

poor have no one but themselves to blame for their poverty. It's only just that they should suffer the consequences. But how is it the fault of the rich if they're rich?

COUNTESS. Dry your tears. You're deceiving nobody. If, as you say, you're ashamed of your money, why is it you hold onto it with such a death-grip?

THE RAGPICKER. Me?

STREET PEDDLER. You never part with a franc!

JUGGLER. You wouldn't even give the poor Deaf-Mute a sou!

THE RAGPICKER. Me, hold onto money? What slander! What injustice! What a thing to say to me in the presence of this honorable, august and elegant Court! I spend all my time trying to spend my money. If I have tan shoes, I buy black ones. If I have a bicycle, I buy a motor car. If I have a wife, I buy . . .

JOSEPHINE [rings]. Order!

THE RAGPICKER. I dispatch a plane to Java for a bouquet of flowers. I send a steamer to Egypt for a basket of figs. I send a special representative to New York to fetch me an ice-cream cone. And if it's not just exactly right, back it goes. But no matter what I do, I can't get rid of my money! If I play a hundred to one shot, the horse comes in by twenty lengths. If I throw a diamond in the Seine, it turns up in the trout they serve me for lunch. Ten diamonds—ten trout. Well, now, do you suppose I can get rid of forty millions by giving a sou to a deaf-mute? Is it even worth the effort?

CONSTANCE. He's right.

THE RAGPICKER. Ah! You see, my dear? At last, there is somebody who understands me! Somebody who is not only beautiful, but extraordinarily sensitive and intelligent.

COUNTESS. I object!

JOSEPHINE. Overruled!

THE RAGPICKER. I should be delighted to send you some flowers, Miss—directly I'm acquitted. What flowers do you prefer?

CONSTANCE. Roses.

THE RAGPICKER. You shall have a bale every morning for the next five years. Money means nothing to me.

CONSTANCE. And amaryllis.

THE RAGPICKER. I'll make a note of the name. [In his best lyrical style.] The lady understands, ladies and gentlemen. The lady is no fool. She's been around and she knows what's what. If I gave the Deaf-Mute a franc, twenty francs, twenty million francs—I still wouldn't make a dent in the forty times a thousand million francs that I'm afflicted with! Right, little lady?

CONSTANCE. Right.

JOSEPHINE. Proceed.

THE RAGPICKER. Like on the Stock Exchange. If you buy a stock, it sinks at once like a plummet. But if I buy a stock, it turns around and soars like an eagle. If I buy it at 33 . . .

PEDDLER. It goes up to a thousand.

THE RAGPICKER. It goes to twenty thousand! That's how I bought my twelve chateaux, my twenty villas, my 234 farms. That's how I endow the Opera and keep my twelve ballerinas.

FLOWER GIRL. I hope every one of them deceives you every moment of the day!

THE RAGPICKER. How can they deceive me? Suppose they try to deceive me with the male chorus, the general director, the assistant electrician or the English horn—I own them all, body and soul. It would be like deceiving me with my big toe.

CONSTANCE. Don't listen, Gabrielle.

GABRIELLE. Listen to what?

THE RAGPICKER. No. I am incapable of jealousy. I have all the women—or I can have them, which is the same thing. I get the thin ones with caviar—the fat ones with pearls . . .

COUNTESS. So you think there are no women with morals?

THE RAGPICKER. I mix morals with mink —delicious combination. I drip pearls into protests. I adorn resistance with rubies. My touch is jeweled; my smile, a motor car. What woman can withstand me? I lift my little finger—and do they fall?—Like leaves in autumn—like tin cans from a second-story window.

CONSTANCE. That's going a little too far!

COUNTESS. You see where money leads.

THE RAGPICKER. Of course. When you have no money, nobody trusts you, nobody believes you, nobody likes you. Because to have money is to be virtuous, honest, beautiful and witty. And to be without is to be ugly and boring and stupid and useless.

COUNTESS. One last question. Suppose you find this oil you're looking for. What do you propose to do with it?

THE RAGPICKER. I propose to make war! I propose to conquer the world!

COUNTESS. You have heard the defense, such as it is. I demand a verdict of guilty.

THE RAGPICKER. What are you talking about? Guilty? I? I am never guilty!

JOSEPHINE. I order you to keep quiet.

THE RAGPICKER. I am never quiet!

JOSEPHINE. Quiet, in the name of the law!

THE RAGPICKER. I am the law. When I speak, that is the law. When I present my backside, it is etiquette to smile and to apply the lips respectfully. It is more than etiquette—it is a cherished national privilege, guaranteed by the Constitution.

JOSEPHINE. That's contempt of court. The trial is over.

COUNTESS. And the verdict?

ALL. Guilty!

JOSEPHINE. Guilty as charged.

COUNTESS. Then I have full authority to carry out the sentence?

ALL. Yes!

COUNTESS. I can do what I like with them?

ALL. Yes!

COUNTESS. I have the right to exterminate them?

ALL. Yes!

JOSEPHINE. Court adjourned!

COUNTESS [to the RAGPICKER]. Congratulations, Ragpicker. A marvelous defense. Absolutely impartial.

THE RAGPICKER. Had I known a little before, I could have done better. I could have prepared a little speech, like the time I used to sell the Miracle Spot Remover. . . .

JOSEPHINE. No need for that. You did very well, extempore. The likeness was striking and the style reminiscent of Clemenceau. I predict a brilliant future for you. Good-bye, Aurelia. I'll take our little Gabrielle home.

CONSTANCE. I'm going to walk along the river. [To DICKIE.] Oh! So here you are. And your ear all bloody! Dickie! Have you been fighting again? Oh, dear . . . !

COUNTESS [To the RAGPICKER]. See that she gets home all right, won't you? She loses everything on the way. And in the queerest

places. Her prayer book in the butcher shop. And her corset in church.

THE RAGPICKER [bowing and offering his arm]. Permit me, Madame.

STREET SINGER. Oh, Countess—my mazurka. Remember?

COUNTESS. Oh, yes. Constance, wait a moment. [To the SINGER.] Well? Begin.

SINGER [sings].
　　Do you hear, Mademoiselle,
　　Those musicians of hell?

CONSTANCE. Why, of course, it's La Belle Polonaise. . . .

[She sings.]
　　From Poland to France
　　Comes this marvelous dance,
　　　So gracious,
　　　Audacious,
　　Will you foot it, perchance?

SINGER. I'm saved!

JOSEPHINE [reappearing at the head of the stairs].
　　Now my arm I entwine
　　Round these contours divine,
　　So pure, so impassioned,
　　Which Cupid has fashioned. . . .

GABRIELLE [reappearing also, she sings a quartet with the others].
　　Come, let's dance the mazurka, that
　　　devilish measure,
　　'Tis a joy that's reserved to the gods
　　　for their pleasure—
　　　Let's gallop, let's hop,
　　　With never a stop,
　　　My blonde Polish miss,
　　Let our heads spin and turn
　　As the dance-floor we spurn—
　　There was never such pleasure as
　　　this!

[They all exit, dancing.]

IRMA. It's time for your afternoon nap.

COUNTESS. But suppose they come, Irma!

IRMA. I'll watch out for them.

COUNTESS. Thank you, Irma. I am tired. [She smiles.] Did you ever see a trial end more happily in your life?

IRMA. Lie down and close your eyes a moment.

[The COUNTESS stretches out on the chaiselongue and shuts her eyes. IRMA tiptoes out. In a moment, PIERRE comes down softly, the feather boa in his hands. He stands over the *chaise-longue, looking tenderly down at the sleeping woman, then kneels beside her and takes her hand.*]

COUNTESS [*without opening her eyes*]. Is it you, Adolphe Bertaut?

PIERRE. It's only Pierre.

COUNTESS. Don't lie to me, Adolphe Bertaut. These are your hands. Why do you complicate things always? Say that it's you.

PIERRE. Yes. It is I.

COUNTESS. Would it cost you so much to call me Aurelia?

PIERRE. It's I, Aurelia.

COUNTESS. Why did you leave me, Adolphe Bertaut? Was she so very lovely, this Georgette of yours?

PIERRE. No. You are a thousand times lovelier.

COUNTESS. But she was clever.

PIERRE. She was stupid.

COUNTESS. It was her soul, then, that drew you? When you looked into her eyes, you saw a vision of heaven, perhaps?

PIERRE. I saw nothing.

COUNTESS. That's how it is with men. They love you because you are beautiful and clever and soulful—and at the first opportunity they leave you for someone who is plain and dull and soulless. But why does it have to be like that, Adolphe Bertaut? Why?

PIERRE. Why, Aurelia?

COUNTESS. I know very well she wasn't rich. Because when I saw you that time at the grocer's, and you snatched the only good melon from right under my nose, your cuffs, my poor friend, were badly frayed. . . .

PIERRE. Yes. She was poor.

COUNTESS. "Was" poor? Is she dead then? If it's because she's dead that you've come back to me—then no. Go away. I will not take their leavings from the dead. I refuse to inherit you. . . .

PIERRE. She's quite well.

COUNTESS. Your hands are still the same, Adolphe Bertaut. Your touch is young and firm. Because it's the only part of you that has stayed with me. The rest of you is pretty far gone, I'm afraid. I can see why you'd rather not come near me when my eyes are open. It's thoughtful of you.

PIERRE. Yes. I've aged.

COUNTESS. Not I. I am young because I haven't had to live down my youth, like you. I have it with me still, as fresh and beautiful as ever. But when you walk now in the park at Colombes with Georgette, I'm sure . . .

PIERRE. There is no longer a park at Colombes.

COUNTESS. Is there a park still at St. Cloud? Is there a park at Versailles? I've never gone back to see. But I think, if they could move, those trees would have walked away in disgust the day you went there with Georgette. . . .

PIERRE. They did. Not many are left.

COUNTESS. You take her also, I suppose, to hear *Denise?*

PIERRE. No one hears *Denise* any more.

COUNTESS. It was on the way home from *Denise,* Adolphe Bertaut, that I first took your arm. Because it was windy and it was late. I have never set foot in that street again. I go the other way round. It's not easy, in the winter, when there's ice. One is quite apt to fall. I often do.

PIERRE. Oh, my darling—forgive me.

COUNTESS. No, never. I will never forgive you. It was very bad taste to take her to the very places where we'd been together.

PIERRE. All the same, I swear, Aurelia . . .

COUNTESS. Don't swear. I know what you did. You gave her the same flowers. You bought her the same chocolates. But has she any left? No. I have all your flowers still. I have twelve chocolates. No, I will never forgive you as long as I live.

PIERRE. I always loved you, Aurelia.

COUNTESS. You "loved" me? Then you too are dead, Adolphe Bertaut?

PIERRE. No. I love you. I shall always love you, Aurelia.

COUNTESS. Yes. I know. That much I've always known. I knew it the moment you went away, Adolphe, and I knew that nothing could ever change it. Georgette is in his arms now—yes. But he loves me. Tonight he's taken Georgette to hear *Denise*—yes. But he loves me. . . . I know it. You never loved her. Do you think I believed for one moment that absurd story about her running off with the osteopath? Of course not. Since you didn't love her, obviously she stayed with you. And, after that, when she came back, and I heard about her going off with the surveyor—I knew that couldn't be true, either. You'll never get rid of her, Adolphe Bertaut—never. Because you don't love her.

PIERRE. I need your pity, Aurelia. I need your love. Don't forget me. . . .

COUNTESS. Farewell, Adolphe Bertaut. Farewell. Let go my hand, and give it to little Pierre. [PIERRE *lets go her hand, and after a moment takes it again. The* COUNTESS *opens her eyes.*] Pierre? Ah, it's you. Has he gone?

PIERRE. Yes, Countess.

COUNTESS. I didn't hear him go. Oh, he knows how to make a quick exit, that one. [*She sees the boa.*] Good heavens! Wherever did you find it?

PIERRE. In the wardrobe, Countess. When I took off the mirror.

COUNTESS. Was there a purple felt shopping bag with it?

PIERRE. Yes, Countess.

COUNTESS. And a little child's sewing box?

PIERRE. No, Countess.

COUNTESS. Oh, they're frightened now. They're trembling for their lives. You see what they're up to? They're quietly putting back all the things they have stolen. I never open that wardrobe, of course, on account of the old woman in the mirror. But I have sharp eyes. I don't need to open it to see what's in it. Up to this morning, that wardrobe was empty. And now—you see? But, dear me, how stupid they are! The one thing I really miss is my little sewing box. It's something they stole from me when I was a child. They haven't put it back? You're quite sure?

PIERRE. What was it like?

COUNTESS. Green cardboard with paper lace and gold stamping. I got it for Christmas when I was seven. They stole it the very next day. I cried my eyes out every time I thought of it—until I was eight.

PIERRE. It's not there, Countess.

COUNTESS. The thimble was gilt. I swore I'd never use any other. Look at my poor fingers. . . .

PIERRE. They've kept the thimble too.

COUNTESS. Splendid! Then I'm under no obligation to be merciful. Put the boa around my neck, Pierre. I want them to see me wearing it. They'll think it's a real boa.

[IRMA *runs in excitedly.*]

IRMA. Here they come, Countess! You were right—it's a procession. The street is full of limousines and taxis!

COUNTESS. I will receive them. [*As* PIERRE *hesitates to leave her.*] Don't worry. There's nothing to be frightened of. [PIERRE *goes out.*] Irma, did you remember to stir the kerosene into the water?

IRMA. Yes, Countess. Here it is.

COUNTESS [*looking critically at the bottle*]. You might as well pour in what's left of the tea. [IRMA *shakes up the liquid.*]Don't forget, I'm supposed to be deaf. I want to hear what they're thinking.

IRMA. Yes, Countess.

COUNTESS [*putting the finishing touches to her make-up*]. I don't have to be merciful—but, after all, I do want to be just. . . .

[IRMA *goes up to the landing and exits. As soon as she is done, the* COUNTESS *presses the brick, and the trap door opens. There is a confused sound of auto horns in the street above, and the noise of an approaching crowd.*]

IRMA [*offstage*]. Yes, Mr. President. Come in, Mr. President. You're expected, Mr. President. This way, Mr. President. [*The* PRESIDENTS *come down, led by the* PRESIDENT. *They all look alike, are dressed alike, and all have long cigars.*] The Countess is quite deaf, gentlemen. You'll have to shout. [*She announces.*] The presidents of the boards of directors!

THE PRESIDENT. I had a premonition, Madame, when I saw you this morning, that we should meet again. [*The* COUNTESS *smiles vaguely. He continues, a tone louder.*] I want to thank you for your trust. You may place yourself in our hands with complete confidence.

SECOND PRESIDENT. Louder. The old trot can't hear you.

THE PRESIDENT. I have a letter here, Madame, in which . . .

SECOND PRESIDENT. Louder. Louder.

THIRD PRESIDENT [*shouting*]. Is it true that you've located . . . ? [*The* COUNTESS *stares at him blankly. He shouts at the top of his voice.*] Oil? [*The* COUNTESS *nods with a smile, and points down. The* PRESIDENT *produces a legal paper and a fountain pen.*] Sign here.

COUNTESS. What is it? I haven't my glasses.

THE PRESIDENT. Your contract.

[*He offers the pen.*]

COUNTESS. Thank you.

SECOND PRESIDENT [*normal voice*]. What is it?

THIRD PRESIDENT. Waiver of all rights. [*He takes it back signed.*] Thank you. [*He hands it to the* SECOND PRESIDENT.] Witness. [*The* SECOND PRESIDENT *witnesses it. The* PRESIDENT *passes it on to the* THIRD PRESIDENT.] Notarize. [*The paper is notarized. The* PRESIDENT *turns to the* COUNTESS *and shouts.*] My congratulations. And now, Madame—[*He produces a gold brick wrapped in tissue paper.*] If you'll show us the well, this package is yours.

COUNTESS. What is it?

THE PRESIDENT. Pure gold. Twenty-four karat. For you.

COUNTESS. Thank you very much. [*She takes it.*] It's heavy.

SECOND PRESIDENT. Are you going to give her that?

THE PRESIDENT. Don't worry. We'll pick it up again on the way out. [*He shouts at the* COUNTESS, *pointing at the trap door.*] Is this the way?

COUNTESS. That's the way.

[*The* SECOND PRESIDENT *tries to slip in first. The* PRESIDENT *pulls him back.*]

THE PRESIDENT. Just a minute, Mr. President. After me, if you don't mind. And watch those cigars. It's oil, you know.

[*But as he is about to descend, the* COUNTESS *steps forward.*]

COUNTESS. Just one moment . . .

THE PRESIDENT. Yes?

COUNTESS. Did any of you happen to bring along a little sewing box?

THE PRESIDENT. Sewing box? [*He pulls back another impatient* PRESIDENT.] Take it easy.

COUNTESS. Or a little gold thimble?

THE PRESIDENT. Not me.

THE PRESIDENTS. Not us.

COUNTESS. What a pity!

THE PRESIDENT. Can we go down now?

COUNTESS. Yes. You may go down now. Watch your step!

[*They hurry down eagerly. When they have quite disappeared,* IRMA *appears on the landing and announces the next echelon.*]

IRMA. Countess, the Prospectors.

COUNTESS. Heavens! Are there more than one?

IRMA. There's a whole delegation.

COUNTESS. Send them down.

[*The* PROSPECTOR *comes in, following his nose.*]

IRMA. Come in, please.

THE PROSPECTOR [*sniffing the air like a bloodhound*]. I smell something. . . . Who's that?

IRMA. The Countess. She is very deaf.

THE PROSPECTOR. Good.

[*The* PROSPECTORS *also look alike. Sharp clothes, Western hats and long noses. They crowd down the stairs after the* PROSPECTOR, *sniffing in unison. The* PROSPECTOR *is especially talented. He casts about on the scent until it leads him to the decanter on the table. He pours himself a glass, drinks it off, and belches with much satisfaction. The others join him at once, and follow his example. They all belch in unison.*]

THE PROSPECTORS. Oil?

THE PROSPECTOR. Oil!

COUNTESS. Oil.

THE PROSPECTOR. Traces? Puddles?

COUNTESS. Pools. Gushers.

SECOND PROSPECTOR. Characteristic odor? [*He sniffs.*]

THE PROSPECTOR. Chanel Number 5. Nectar! Undoubtedly—the finest—rarest! [*He drinks.*] Sixty gravity crude: straight gasoline! [*To the* COUNTESS.] How found? By blast? Drill?

COUNTESS. By finger.

THE PROSPECTOR [*whipping out a document*]. Sign here, please.

COUNTESS. What is it?

THE PROSPECTOR. Agreement for dividing the profits . . .

[*The* COUNTESS *signs.*]

SECOND PROSPECTOR [*To* FIRST PROSPECTOR]. What is it?

THE PROSPECTOR [*pocketing the paper*]. Application to enter a lunatic asylum. Down there?

COUNTESS. Down there.

[*The* PROSPECTORS *go down, sniffing.*]

[IRMA *enters.*]

IRMA. The gentlemen of the press are here.

COUNTESS. The rest of the machine! Show them in.

IRMA. The Public Relations Counsellors! [*They enter, all shapes and sizes, all in blue*

pin-striped suits and black homburg hats.]
The Countess is very deaf, gentlemen. You'll
have to shout!

FIRST PRESS AGENT. You don't say—Delighted to make the acquaintance of so charming and beautiful a lady . . .

SECOND PRESS AGENT. Louder. She can't
hear you.

FIRST PRESS AGENT. What a face! [*Shouts.*]
Madame, we are the press. You know our
power. We fix all values. We set all standards.
Your entire future depends on us.

COUNTESS. How do you do?

FIRST PRESS AGENT. What will we charge
the old trull? The usual thirty?

SECOND PRESS AGENT. Forty.

THIRD PRESS AGENT. Sixty.

FIRST PRESS AGENT. All right—seventy-five.
[*He fills in a form and offers it to the* COUNTESS.] Sign here, Countess. This contract
really gives you a break.

COUNTESS. That is the entrance.

FIRST PRESS AGENT. Entrance to what?

COUNTESS. The oil well.

FIRST PRESS AGENT. Oh, we don't need to
see that, Madame.

COUNTESS. Don't need to see it?

FIRST PRESS AGENT. No, no—we don't have
to see it to write about it. We can imagine it.
An oil well is an oil well. "That's oil we
know on earth, and oil we need to know."

[*He bows.*]

COUNTESS. But if you don't see it, how can
you be sure the oil is there?

FIRST PRESS AGENT. If it's there, well and
good. If it's not, by the time we get through,
it will be. You underestimate the creative
aspect of our profession, Madame. [*The*
COUNTESS *shakes her head, handing back the*
papers.] I warn you, if you insist on rubbing
our noses in this oil, it will cost you 10 percent extra.

COUNTESS. It's worth it.

[*She signs. They cross toward the trap door.*]

SECOND PRESS AGENT [*descending*]. You
see, Madame, we of the press can refuse a lady
nothing.

THIRD PRESS AGENT. Especially, such a lady.

[THIRD PRESS AGENT *starts going down.*]

SECOND PRESS AGENT [*going down. Gallantly*].
It's plain to see, Madame, that even fountains

of oil have their nymphs. . . . I can use that
somewhere. That's copy!

[*The* PRESS AGENTS *go down. As he disappears, the* FIRST PRESS AGENT *steals the gold*
brick and blows a kiss gallantly to the COUNTESS, *who blows one back.*]

[*There is a high-pitched chatter offstage,*
and IRMA *comes in, trying hard to hold back*
THREE WOMEN *who pay no attention to her*
whatever. These WOMEN *are tall, slender, and*
as soulless as if they were molded of wax. They
march down the steps, erect and abstracted
like animated window models, but chattering
incessantly.]

IRMA. But, ladies, please—you have no
business here—you are not expected. [*To the*
COUNTESS.] There are some strange ladies
coming. . . .

COUNTESS. Show them in, Irma. [*The*
WOMEN *come down without taking the slight-*
est interest in their surroundings.] Who are
you?

FIRST WOMAN. Madame, we are the most
powerful pressure group in the world.

SECOND WOMAN. We are the ultimate
dynamic.

THIRD WOMAN. The mainspring of all
combinations.

FIRST WOMAN. Nothing succeeds without
our assistance. Is that the well, Madame?

COUNTESS. That is the well.

FIRST WOMAN. Put out your cigarettes,
girls. We don't want any explosions. Not with
my brand-new eyelashes.

[*They go down, still chattering. The* COUNTESS *crosses to the wall to close the trap. As*
she does so, there is a commotion on the
landing.]

IRMA. Countess . . .

[*A* MAN *rushes in breathlessly.*]

MAN. Just a minute! Just a minute!

[*He rushes for the trap door.*]

COUNTESS. Wait! Who are you?

MAN. I'm in a hurry. Excuse me. It's my
only chance!

[*He rushes down.*]

COUNTESS. But . . . [*But he is gone. She*
shrugs her shoulders, and presses the brick.
The trap closes. She rings the bell for IRMA.]
My gold brick! Why, they've stolen my gold
brick! [*She moves toward the trap. It is now*

closed.] Well, let them take their god with them.

[IRMA *enters and sees with astonishment that the stage is empty of all but the* COUNTESS. *Little by little, the scene is suffused with light, faint at first, but increasing as if the very walls were glowing with the quiet radiance of universal joy. Only around the closed trap a shadow lingers.*]

IRMA.   But what's happened? They've gone! They've vanished!

COUNTESS.   They've evaporated, Irma. They were wicked. Wickedness evaporates.

[PIERRE *enters. He is followed by the* VAGABONDS, *all of them. The new radiance of the world is now very perceptible. It glows from their faces.*]

PIERRE.   Oh, Countess . . . !

WAITER.   Countess, everything's changed. Now you can breathe again. Now you can see.

PIERRE.   The air is pure. The sky is clear!

IRMA.   Life is beautiful again.

THE RAGPICKER [*rushes in*].   Countess—the pigeons! The pigeons are flying!

FLOWER GIRL.   They don't have to walk any more.

THE RAGPICKER.   They're flying. . . . The air is like crystal. And young grass is sprouting on the pavements.

COUNTESS.   Is it possible?

IRMA [*interpreting for the* DEAF-MUTE]. Now, Juggler, you can throw your fireballs up as high as you please—they won't go out.

SERGEANT.   On the street, utter strangers are shaking hands, they don't know why, and offering each other almond bars!

COUNTESS.   Oh, my friends . . .

WAITER.   Countess, we thank you. . . .

[*They go on talking with happy and animated gestures, but we no longer hear them, for their words blend into a strain of unearthly music which seems to thrill from the uttermost confines of the universe. And out of this music comes a voice.*]

FIRST VOICE.   Countess . . .

[*Only the* COUNTESS *hears it. She turns from the group of* VAGABONDS *in wonder.*]

SECOND VOICE.   Countess . . .

THIRD VOICE.   Countess . . .

[*As she looks up in rapture, the* FIRST VOICE *speaks again.*]

FIRST VOICE.   Countess, we thank you. We are the friends of animals.

SECOND VOICE.   We are the friends of people.

THIRD VOICE.   We are the friends of friendship.

FIRST VOICE.   You have freed us!

SECOND VOICE.   From now on, there will be no hungry cats. . . .

THIRD VOICE.   And we shall tell the Duchess her dog's right name!

[*The* VOICES *fade off. And now another group of voices is heard.*]

FIRST VOICE.   Countess, we thank you. We are the friends of flowers.

SECOND VOICE.   From now on, every plant in Paris will be watered. . . .

THIRD VOICE.   And the sewers will be fragrant with jasmine!

[*These voices, too, are silent. For an instant, the stage is vibrant with music. Then the* DEAF-MUTE *speaks, and his voice is the most beautiful of all.*]

DEAF-MUTE.   Sadness flies on the wings of morning, and out of the heart of darkness comes the light.

[*Suddenly a group of figures detaches itself from the shadows. These are exactly similar in face and figure and in dress. They are shabby in the fashion of 1900 and their cuffs are badly frayed. Each bears in his hand a ripe melon.*]

FIRST ADOLPHE BERTAUT.   Countess, we thank you. We, too, are freed at last. We are the Adolphe Bertauts of the world.

SECOND ADOLPHE BERTAUT.   We are no longer timid.

THIRD ADOLPHE BERTAUT.   We are no longer weak.

FIRST ADOLPHE BERTAUT.   From this day on, we shall hold fast to what we love. For your sake, henceforth, we shall be handsome, and our cuffs forever immaculate and new. Countess, we bring you this melon and with it our hearts . . . ! [*They all kneel.*] Will you do us the honor to be our wife?

COUNTESS [*sadly*].   Too late! Too late! [*She waves them aside. They take up their melons sadly and vanish. The voices of the* VAGABONDS *are heard again, and the music dies.*] Too late! Too late!

PIERRE.   Too late, Countess?

IRMA. Too late for what?

COUNTESS. I say that it's too late for them. On the twenty-fourth of May, 1881, the most beautiful Easter in the memory of man, it was not too late. And on the fifth of September, 1887, the day they caught the trout and broiled it on the open fire by the brook at Villeneuve, it was not too late. And it was even not too late for them on the twenty-first of August, 1897, the day the Czar visited Paris with his guard. But they did nothing and they said nothing, and now—kiss each other, you two, this very instant!

IRMA. You mean . . . ?

PIERRE. You mean . . . ?

IRMA. But, Countess . . .

COUNTESS. It's three hours since you've met and known and loved each other. Kiss each other quickly. [PIERRE hesitates.] Look at him. He hesitates. He trembles. Happiness frightens him. . . . How like a man! Oh, Irma, kiss him, kiss him! If two people who love each other let a single instant wedge itself between them, it grows—it becomes a month, a year, a century; it becomes too late. Kiss him, Irma, kiss him while there is time, or in a moment his hair will be white and there will be another madwoman in Paris!

Oh, make her kiss him, all of you! [*They kiss.*] Bravo! Oh, if only you'd had the courage to do that thirty years ago, how different I would be today! Dear Deaf-Mute, be still—your words dazzle our eyes! And Irma is too busy to translate for you. [*They kiss once more.*] Well, there we are. The world is saved. And you see how simple it all was? Nothing is ever so wrong in this world that a sensible woman can't set it right in the course of an afternoon. Only, the next time, don't wait until things begin to look black. The minute you notice anything, tell me at once.

THE RAGPICKER. We will, Countess. We will.

COUNTESS [*puts on her hat. Her tone becomes businesslike*]. Irma. My bones. My gizzard.

IRMA. I have them ready, Countess.

COUNTESS. Good. [*She puts the bones into her basket and starts for the stairs.*] Well, let's get on to more important things. Four o'clock. My poor cats must be starved. What a bore for them if humanity had to be saved every afternoon. They don't think much of it, as it is.

CURTAIN

Questions

1. Giraudoux's basic method of attack here is caricature, taking some real quality and exaggerating it until it appears grotesque. Cite several examples of this technique and discuss its effectiveness as an instrument of satire. (For example, what values do the President and his friends represent?)

2. Discuss the four madwomen and the significance of their hallucinations.

3. Is greed for money the only moral flaw in the President and his partners?

4. Consider carefully the trial scene in Act II. What is the significance of the roles assumed by the various characters? Does the defense make any valid points? How is the verdict arrived at?

5. Giraudoux once defined his art as provoking "not study in libraries, but personal relationships with the seasons and small animals, an excessive pantheism, and politeness toward creation." Does this description fit the Countess?

6. What function does the subplot dealing with Pierre have?

7. Is the conclusion of the play in any way ironic, or are we to understand it as a clearcut triumph of virtue over evil?

Animal Farm

In a late essay describing his education in an English school, George Orwell (1903-50)—who was born Eric Blair—tells the story of how he fought and beat an insufferable bully named Hall who was older, stronger, and more favored: "I would get back on him by hitting him when he did not expect it. . . . I walked up to Hall with the most harmless air I could assume, and then, getting the weight of my body behind it, smashed my fist into his face. He was flung backwards by the blow and some blood ran out of his mouth. His always sanguine face turned almost black with rage. Then he turned away to rinse his mouth at the washing-basins." This is a good description of Orwell's satiric activities throughout his life. Whenever he found power and gifts misused he smashed out with all his weight. After a period in the imperial police in Burma he wrote the savage exposé of British imperialism titled *Burmese Days* (1934). Then in a series of books he went on to deal honestly and devastatingly with the condition of the poor in an industrial society in *Down and Out in Paris and London* (written in 1933) and in *The Road to Wigan Pier* (1937); the problems of the lower middle class in *Keep the Aspidistra Flying* (1936); and the question of the Spanish Civil War in *Homage to Catalonia* (1938). (He fought for the Loyalists in this war and was seriously wounded.) During these years Orwell had little recognition, and it was only after *Animal Farm* was published in 1946 that he became widely known. His reputation was secured by the publication in 1949 of his terrifying vision of the future, *1984*.

For some years now a controversy has been raging over Orwell. When he died V. S. Pritchett called him "the conscience of his generation," but an early friend has recently characterized Orwell as the most naïve person he ever knew, and another critic has argued that Orwell's apocalyptic vision of the world in *Animal Farm* and in *1984* was no more than a projection of the terrible fears and repressions he knew as a child. Both views are, I believe, correct. His conscience was of the stern, old-fashioned, nineteenth-century liberal variety which never quite adjusted to the "realities" of the world. The unforgettable terrors of a childhood in which, because he was socially unimportant and physically unattractive, the adults in a snobbish school made no effort to disguise from him the fact that money and position are what count in this world, no doubt settled his way of sizing up experience for the remainder of his life. But it is these two qualities which made him a great satirist. His fear of power made him sensitive to the misuse of it in a historical period whose major problem has been too much power in the wrong hands; his moral naïveté gave him an uncompromising ethical code by which to judge the tyrants great and small, and it also gave him the courage to speak out when others remained silent.

Orwell's attractiveness for most readers is his unwillingness ever to follow blindly the line of any party. In an age when most people believe that values can be preserved only by absolute commitment to some absolute position, the honest man who believes that truth never resides in extremes achieves a kind of tragic stature. Orwell refused to give himself over entirely to either the political left or the right. He went to Spain to fight the fascists, but when he discovered that the communists were using the war to destroy all noncommunist liberal parties, he wrote a penetrating report of the entire mess. When he perceived the totalitarian dangers in English socialism he wrote in *1984* as savage an attack on this political theory as he earlier had written on imperialism in *Burmese Days* and on capitalism in *Down and Out*. Orwell's fundamental belief was that men must be given a chance to earn a decent living and to preserve their individual dignity. In his lifetime he found no political philosophy or party which *in practice* provided these opportunities, and, though he never ceased trying, he may well have come to the belief that there is something inherent in human nature and society which prevents the achievement of what seem such modest goals. It is with problems such as these that *Animal Farm* ultimately deals.

Until he wrote *Animal Farm,* Orwell's characteristic satiric form had been the report. His materials were chosen and arranged in such a way as to condemn some particular social arrangement or political philosophy, but he maintained, even in his novels, the manner of a strict, factual reporter of conditions and events. This was equivalent in satire to the assumption of the harmless air which he had used to get within range of the bully at school. In *Animal Farm,* however, he chose for the first time an unrealistic, expressionistic device, the beast fable, as his satiric vehicle. The beast fable—a very ancient satiric technique—is basically the dramatic realization of metaphor; in a realistic work a man might be called a pig, but in the beast fable he is presented as an actual pig. Satirists have always found this translation of metaphor to dramatic fact an extremely effective way of portraying the true nature of vice and folly.

By concluding our selection of satires with a beast fable we have run the full range from realism to expressionism in satire. The first item, Philip Wylie's attack on American education, is pure realism. The author speaks in his own person and denounces actual conditions. *Animal Farm,* at the other end of the range, is pure expressionism. The author has disappeared altogether and the "persons" and events of the story have no literal equivalents in real life. When we consider this range of satiric technique, it would, I believe, be a mistake to seek for one satiric method which is superior to all others. Instead we must try to understand what the special value of each method is, why it is suitable for its particular subject, what it permits the author to do and what it denies him.

CHAPTER I

Mr. Jones, of the Manor Farm, had locked the hen-houses for the night, but was too drunk to remember to shut the popholes. With the ring of light from his lantern dancing from side to side, he lurched across the yard, kicked off his boots at the back door, drew himself a last glass of beer from the barrel in the scullery, and made his way up to bed, where Mrs. Jones was already snoring.

As soon as the light in the bedroom went out there was a stirring and a fluttering all through the farm buildings. Word had gone round during the day that old Major, the prize Middle White boar, had had a strange dream on the previous night and wished to communicate it to the other animals. It had been agreed that they should all meet in the big barn as soon as Mr. Jones was safely out of the way. Old Major (so he was always called, though the name under which he had been exhibited was Willingdon Beauty) was so highly regarded on the farm that everyone was quite ready to lose an hour's sleep in order to hear what he had to say.

At one end of the big barn, on a sort of raised platform, Major was already ensconced on his bed of straw, under a lantern which hung from a beam. He was twelve years old and had lately grown rather stout, but he was still a majestic-looking pig, with a wise and benevolent appearance in spite of the fact that his tushes had never been cut. Before long the other animals began to arrive and make themselves comfortable after their different fashions. First came the three dogs, Bluebell, Jessie, and Pincher, and then the pigs, who settled down in the straw immediately in front of the platform. The hens perched themselves on the window-sills, the pigeons fluttered up to the rafters, the sheep and cows lay down behind the pigs and began to chew the cud. The two cart-horses, Boxer and Clover, came in together, walking very slowly and setting down their vast hairy hoofs with great care lest there should be some small animal concealed in the straw. Clover was a stout motherly mare approaching middle life, who had never quite

Animal Farm by George Orwell, copyright, 1946, by Harcourt, Brace & World, Inc. and Martin Secker & Warburg Limited.

got her figure back after her fourth foal. Boxer was an enormous beast, nearly eighteen hands high, and as strong as any two ordinary horses put together. A white stripe down his nose gave him a somewhat stupid appearance, and in fact he was not of first-rate intelligence, but he was universally respected for his steadiness of character and tremendous powers of work. After the horses came Muriel, the white goat, and Benjamin, the donkey. Benjamin was the oldest animal on the farm, and the worst tempered. He seldom talked, and when he did, it was usually to make some cynical remark—for instance, he would say that God had given him a tail to keep the flies off, but that he would sooner have had no tail and no flies. Alone among the animals on the farm he never laughed. If asked why, he would say that he saw nothing to laugh at. Nevertheless, without openly admitting it, he was devoted to Boxer; the two of them usually spent their Sundays together in the small paddock beyond the orchard, grazing side by side and never speaking.

The two horses had just lain down when a brood of ducklings, which had lost their mother, filed into the barn, cheeping feebly and wandering from side to side to find some place where they would not be trodden on. Clover made a sort of wall round them with her great foreleg, and the ducklings nestled down inside it and promptly fell asleep. At the last moment Mollie, the foolish, pretty white mare who drew Mr. Jones's trap, came mincing daintily in, chewing at a lump of sugar. She took a place near the front and began flirting her white mane, hoping to draw attention to the red ribbons it was plaited with. Last of all came the cat, who looked round, as usual, for the warmest place, and finally squeezed herself in between Boxer and Clover; there she purred contentedly throughout Major's speech without listening to a word of what he was saying.

All the animals were now present except Moses, the tame raven, who slept on a perch behind the back door. When Major saw that they had all made themselves comfortable and were waiting attentively, he cleared his throat and began:

"Comrades, you have heard already about the strange dream that I had last night. But

I will come to the dream later. I have something else to say first. I do not think, comrades, that I shall be with you for many months longer, and before I die, I feel it my duty to pass on to you such wisdom as I have acquired. I have had a long life, I have had much time for thought as I lay alone in my stall, and I think I may say that I understand the nature of life on this earth as well as any animal now living. It is about this that I wish to speak to you.

"Now, comrades, what is the nature of this life of ours? Let us face it: our lives are miserable, laborious, and short. We are born, we are given just so much food as will keep the breath in our bodies, and those of us who are capable of it are forced to work to the last atom of our strength; and the very instant that our usefulness has come to an end we are slaughtered with hideous cruelty. No animal in England knows the meaning of happiness or leisure after he is a year old. No animal in England is free. The life of an animal is misery and slavery: that is the plain truth.

"But is this simply part of the order of nature? Is it because this land of ours is so poor that it cannot afford a decent life to those who dwell upon it? No, comrades, a thousand times no! The soil of England is fertile, its climate is good, it is capable of affording food in abundance to an enormously greater number of animals than now inhabit it. This single farm of ours would support a dozen horses, twenty cows, hundreds of sheep—and all of them living in a comfort and a dignity that are now almost beyond our imagining. Why then do we continue in this miserable condition? Because nearly the whole of the produce of our labour is stolen from us by human beings. There, comrades, is the answer to all our problems. It is summed up in a single word—Man. Man is the only real enemy we have. Remove Man from the scene, and the root cause of hunger and overwork is abolished for ever.

"Man is the only creature that consumes without producing. He does not give milk, he does not lay eggs, he is too weak to pull the plough, he cannot run fast enough to catch rabbits. Yet he is lord of all the animals. He sets them to work, he gives back to them the bare minimum that will prevent them from starving, and the rest he keeps for himself.

Our labour tills the soil, our dung fertilises it, and yet there is not one of us that owns more than his bare skin. You cows that I see before me, how many thousands of gallons of milk have you given during this last year? And what has happened to that milk which should have been breeding up sturdy calves? Every drop of it has gone down the throats of our enemies. And you hens, how many eggs have you laid in this last year, and how many of those eggs ever hatched into chickens? The rest have all gone to market to bring in money for Jones and his men. And you, Clover, where are those four foals you bore, who should have been the support and pleasure of your old age? Each was sold at a year old—you will never see one of them again. In return for your four confinements and all your labour in the fields, what have you ever had except your bare rations and a stall?

"And even the miserable lives we lead are not allowed to reach their natural span. For myself I do not grumble, for I am one of the lucky ones. I am twelve years old and have had over four hundred children. Such is the natural life of a pig. But no animal escapes the cruel knife in the end. You young porkers who are sitting in front of me, every one of you will scream your lives out at the block within a year. To that horror we all must come—cows, pigs, hens, sheep, everyone. Even the horses and the dogs have no better fate. You, Boxer, the very day that those great muscles of yours lose their power, Jones will sell you to the knacker, who will cut your throat and boil you down for the foxhounds. As for the dogs, when they grow old and toothless, Jones ties a brick round their necks and drowns them in the nearest pond.

"Is it not crystal clear, then, comrades, that all the evils of this life of ours spring from the tyranny of human beings? Only get rid of Man, and the produce of our labour would be our own. Almost overnight we could become rich and free. What then must we do? Why, work night and day, body and soul, for the overthrow of the human race! That is my message to you, comrades: Rebellion! I do not know when that Rebellion will come, it might be in a week or in a hundred years, but I know, as surely as I see this straw beneath my feet, that sooner or later justice will be done.

Fix your eyes on that, comrades, throughout the short remainder of your lives! And above all, pass on this message of mine to those who come after you, so that future generations shall carry on the struggle until it is victorious.

"And remember, comrades, your resolution must never falter. No argument must lead you astray. Never listen when they tell you that Man and the animals have a common interest, that the prosperity of the one is the prosperity of the others. It is all lies. Man serves the interests of no creature except himself. And among us animals let there be perfect unity, perfect comradeship in the struggle. All men are enemies. All animals are comrades."

At this moment there was a tremendous uproar. While Major was speaking four large rats had crept out of their holes and were sitting on their hindquarters, listening to him. The dogs had suddenly caught sight of them, and it was only by a swift dash for their holes that the rats saved their lives. Major raised his trotter for silence.

"Comrades," he said, "here is a point that must be settled. The wild creatures, such as rats and rabbits—are they our friends or our enemies? Let us put it to the vote. I propose this question to the meeting: Are rats comrades?"

The vote was taken at once, and it was agreed by an overwhelming majority that rats were comrades. There were only four dissentients, the three dogs and the cat, who was afterwards discovered to have voted on both sides. Major continued:

"I have little more to say. I merely repeat, remember always your duty of enmity towards Man and all his ways. Whatever goes upon two legs is an enemy. Whatever goes upon four legs, or has wings, is a friend. And remember also that in fighting against Man, we must not come to resemble him. Even when you have conquered him, do not adopt his vices. No animal must ever live in a house, or sleep in a bed, or wear clothes, or drink alcohol, or smoke tobacco, or touch money, or engage in trade. All the habits of Man are evil. And, above all, no animal must ever tyrannise over his own kind. Weak or strong, clever or simple, we are all brothers. No animal must ever kill any other animal. All animals are equal.

"And now, comrades, I will tell you about my dream of last night. I cannot describe that dream to you. It was a dream of the earth as it will be when Man has vanished. But it reminded me of something that I had long forgotten. Many years ago, when I was a little pig, my mother and the other sows used to sing an old song of which they knew only the tune and the first three words. I had known that tune in my infancy, but it had long since passed out of my mind. Last night, however, it came back to me in my dream. And what is more, the words of the song also came back— words, I am certain, which were sung by the animals of long ago and have been lost to memory for generations. I will sing you that song now, comrades. I am old and my voice is hoarse, but when I have taught you the tune, you can sing it better for yourselves. It is called *Beasts of England*."

Old Major cleared his throat and began to sing. As he had said, his voice was hoarse, but he sang well enough, and it was a stirring tune, something between *Clementine* and *La Cucaracha*. The words ran:

Beasts of England, beasts of Ireland,
Beasts of every land and clime,
Hearken to my joyful tidings
Of the golden future time.

Soon or late the day is coming,
Tyrant Man shall be o'erthrown,
And the fruitful fields of England
Shall be trod by beasts alone.

Rings shall vanish from our noses,
And the harness from our back,
Bit and spur shall rust forever,
Cruel whips no more shall crack.

Riches more than mind can picture,
Wheat and barley, oats and hay,
Clover, beans, and mangel-wurzels
Shall be ours upon that day.

Bright will shine the fields of England,
Purer shall its waters be,
Sweeter yet shall blow its breezes
On the day that sets us free.

For that day we all must labour,
Though we die before it break;
Cows and horses, geese and turkeys,
All must toil for freedom's sake.

Beasts of England, beasts of Ireland,
Beasts of every land and clime,
Hearken well and spread my tidings
Of the golden future time.

The singing of this song threw the animals into the wildest excitement. Almost before Major had reached the end, they had begun singing it for themselves. Even the stupidest of them had already picked up the tune and a few of the words, and as for the clever ones, such as the pigs and dogs, they had the entire song by heart within a few minutes. And then, after a few preliminary tries, the whole farm burst out into *Beasts of England* in tremendous unison. The cows lowed it, the dogs whined it, the sheep bleated it, the horses whinnied it, the ducks quacked it. They were so delighted with the song that they sang it right through five times in succession, and might have continued singing it all night if they had not been interrupted.

Unfortunately, the uproar awoke Mr. Jones, who sprang out of bed, making sure that there was a fox in the yard. He seized the gun which always stood in a corner of his bedroom, and let fly a charge of number 6 shot into the darkness. The pellets buried themselves in the wall of the barn and the meeting broke up hurriedly. Everyone fled to his own sleeping-place. The birds jumped on to their perches, the animals settled down in the straw, and the whole farm was asleep in a moment.

CHAPTER II

Three nights later old Major died peacefully in his sleep. His body was buried at the foot of the orchard.

This was early in March. During the next three months there was much secret activity. Major's speech had given to the more intelligent animals on the farm a completely new outlook on life. They did not know when the Rebellion predicted by Major would take place, they had no reason for thinking that it would be within their own lifetime, but they saw clearly that it was their duty to prepare for it. The work of teaching and organising the others fell naturally upon the pigs, who were generally recognised as being the cleverest of the animals. Pre-eminent among the

pigs were two young boars named Snowball and Napoleon, whom Mr. Jones was breeding up for sale. Napoleon was a large, rather fierce-looking Berkshire boar, the only Berkshire on the farm, not much of a talker, but with a reputation for getting his own way. Snowball was a more vivacious pig than Napoleon, quicker in speech and more inventive, but was not considered to have the same depth of character. All the other male pigs on the farm were porkers. The best known among them was a small fat pig named Squealer, with very round cheeks, twinkling eyes, nimble movements, and a shrill voice. He was a brilliant talker, and when he was arguing some difficult point he had a way of skipping from side to side and whisking his tail which was somehow very persuasive. The others said of Squealer that he could turn black into white.

These three had elaborated old Major's teachings into a complete system of thought, to which they gave the name of Animalism. Several nights a week, after Mr. Jones was asleep, they held secret meetings in the barn and expounded the principles of Animalism to the others. At the beginning they met with much stupidity and apathy. Some of the animals talked of the duty of loyalty to Mr. Jones, whom they referred to as "Master," or made elementary remarks such as "Mr. Jones feeds us. If he were gone, we should starve to death." Others asked such questions as "Why should we care what happens after we are dead?" or "If this Rebellion is to happen anyway, what difference does it make whether we work for it or not?", and the pigs had great difficulty in making them see that this was contrary to the spirit of Animalism. The stupidest questions of all were asked by Mollie, the white mare. The very first question she asked Snowball was: "Will there still be sugar after the Rebellion?"

"No," said Snowball firmly. "We have no means of making sugar on this farm. Besides, you do not need sugar. You will have all the oats and hay you want."

"And shall I still be allowed to wear ribbons in my mane?" asked Mollie.

"Comrade," said Snowball, "those ribbons that you are so devoted to are the badge of slavery. Can you not understand that liberty is worth more than ribbons?"

Mollie agreed, but she did not sound very convinced.

The pigs had an even harder struggle to counteract the lies put about by Moses, the tame raven. Moses, who was Mr. Jones's especial pet, was a spy and a tale-bearer, but he was also a clever talker. He claimed to know of the existence of a mysterious country called Sugarcandy Mountain, to which all animals went when they died. It was situated somewhere up in the sky, a little distance beyond the clouds, Moses said. In Sugarcandy Mountain it was Sunday seven days a week, clover was in season all the year round, and lump sugar and linseed cake grew on the hedges. The animals hated Moses because he told tales and did no work, but some of them believed in Sugarcandy Mountain, and the pigs had to argue very hard to persuade them that there was no such place.

Their most faithful disciples were the two carthorses, Boxer and Clover. These two had great difficulty in thinking anything out for themselves, but having once accepted the pigs as their teachers, they absorbed everything that they were told, and passed it on to the other animals by simple arguments. They were unfailing in their attendance at the secret meetings in the barn, and led the singing of *Beasts of England,* with which the meetings always ended.

Now, as it turned out, the Rebellion was achieved much earlier and more easily than anyone had expected. In past years Mr. Jones, although a hard master, had been a capable farmer, but of late he had fallen on evil days. He had become much disheartened after losing money in a lawsuit, and had taken to drinking more than was good for him. For whole days at a time he would lounge in his Windsor chair in the kitchen, reading the newspapers, drinking, and occasionally feeding Moses on crusts of bread soaked in beer. His men were idle and dishonest, the fields were full of weeds, the buildings wanted roofing, the hedges were neglected, and the animals were underfed.

June came and the hay was almost ready for cutting. On Midsummer's Eve, which was a Saturday, Mr. Jones went into Willingdon and got so drunk at the Red Lion that he did not come back till midday on Sunday. The men had milked the cows in the early morning and then had gone out rabbiting, without bothering to feed the animals. When Mr. Jones got back he immediately went to sleep on the drawing-room sofa with the *News of the World* over his face, so that when evening came, the animals were still unfed. At last they could stand it no longer. One of the cows broke in the door of the store-shed with her horn and all the animals began to help themselves from the bins. It was just then that Mr. Jones woke up. The next moment he and his four men were in the store-shed with whips in their hands, lashing out in all directions. This was more than the hungry animals could bear. With one accord, though nothing of the kind had been planned beforehand, they flung themselves upon their tormentors. Jones and his men suddenly found themselves being butted and kicked from all sides. The situation was quite out of their control. They had never seen animals behave like this before, and this sudden uprising of creatures whom they were used to thrashing and maltreating just as they chose, frightened them almost out of their wits. After only a moment or two they gave up trying to defend themselves and took to their heels. A minute later all five of them were in full flight down the cart-track that led to the main road, with the animals pursuing them in triumph.

Mrs. Jones looked out of the bedroom window, saw what was happening, hurriedly flung a few possessions into a carpet bag, and slipped out of the farm by another way. Moses sprang off his perch and flapped after her, croaking loudly. Meanwhile the animals had chased Jones and his men out on to the road and slammed the five-barred gate behind them. And so, almost before they knew what was happening, the Rebellion had been successfully carried through: Jones was expelled, and the Manor Farm was theirs.

For the first few minutes the animals could hardly believe in their good fortune. Their first act was to gallop in a body right round the boundaries of the farm, as though to make quite sure that no human being was hiding anywhere upon it; then they raced back to the farm buildings to wipe out the last traces of Jones's hated reign. The harness-room at the end of the stables was broken open; the bits, the nose-rings, the dog-chains, the cruel knives with which Mr. Jones had been used to castrate the pigs and lambs, were all flung down the well. The reins, the halters, the blinkers, the degrading nosebags, were thrown on to the rubbish fire which was burning in the yard. So were the whips. All the animals capered with joy when they saw the whips going up in flames. Snowball also threw on to the fire the ribbons with which the horses' manes and tails had usually been decorated on market days.

"Ribbons," he said, "should be considered as clothes, which are the mark of a human being. All animals should go naked."

When Boxer heard this he fetched the small straw hat which he wore in summer to keep the flies out of his ears, and flung it on to the fire with the rest.

In a very little while the animals had destroyed everything that reminded them of Mr. Jones. Napoleon then led them back to the store-shed and served out a double ration of corn to everybody, with two biscuits for each dog. Then they sang *Beasts of England* from end to end seven times running, and after that they settled down for the night and slept as they had never slept before.

But they woke at dawn as usual, and suddenly remembering the glorious thing that had happened, they all raced out into the pasture together. A little way down the pasture there was a knoll that commanded a view of most of the farm. The animals rushed to the top of it and gazed round them in the clear morning light. Yes, it was theirs—everything that they could see was theirs! In the ecstasy of that thought they gambolled round and round, they hurled themselves into the air in great leaps of excitement. They rolled in the dew, they cropped mouthfuls of the sweet summer grass, they kicked up clods of the black earth and snuffed its rich scent. Then they made a tour of inspection of the whole farm and surveyed with speechless admiration the ploughland, the hayfield, the orchard, the pool, the spinney. It was as though they had never seen these things before, and even now they could hardly believe that it was all their own.

Then they filed back to the farm buildings and halted in silence outside the door of the farmhouse. That was theirs too, but they were frightened to go inside. After a moment, however, Snowball and Napoleon butted the door open with their shoulders and the animals entered in single file, walking with the utmost care for fear of disturbing anything. They tiptoed from room to room, afraid to speak above a whisper and gazing with a kind of awe at the unbelievable luxury, at the beds with their feather mattresses, the looking-glasses, the horsehair sofa, the Brussels carpet, the lithograph of Queen Victoria over the drawing-room mantelpiece. They were just coming down the stairs when Mollie was discovered to be missing. Going back, the others found that she had remained behind in the best bedroom. She had taken a piece of blue ribbon from Mrs. Jones's dressing-table, and was holding it against her shoulder and admiring herself in the glass in a very foolish manner. The others reproached her sharply, and they went outside. Some hams hanging in the kitchen were taken out for burial, and the barrel of beer in the scullery was stove in with a kick from Boxer's hoof, otherwise nothing in the house was touched. A unanimous resolution was passed on the spot that the farmhouse should be preserved as a museum. All were agreed that no animal must ever live there.

The animals had their breakfast, and then Snowball and Napoleon called them together again.

"Comrades," said Snowball, "it is half-past six and we have a long day before us. Today we begin the hay harvest. But there is another matter that must be attended to first."

The pigs now revealed that during the past three months they had taught themselves to read and write from an old spelling book which had belonged to Mr. Jones's children and which had been thrown on the rubbish heap. Napoleon sent for pots of black and white paint and led the way down to the five-barred gate that gave on to the main road. Then Snowball (for it was Snowball who was best at writing) took a brush between the two knuckles of his trotter, painted out MANOR FARM from the top bar of the gate and in its place painted ANIMAL FARM. This was to be the name of the farm from now onwards. After this they went back to the farm buildings, where Snowball and Napoleon sent for a ladder which they caused to be set against the end wall of the big barn. They explained that by their studies of the past three months the pigs had succeeded in reducing the principles of Animalism to Seven Commandments. These Seven Commandments would now be inscribed on the wall; they would form an unalterable law by which all the animals on Animal Farm must live for ever after. With some difficulty (for it is not easy for a pig to balance himself on a ladder) Snowball climbed up and set to work, with Squealer a few rungs below him holding the paint-pot. The Commandments were written on the tarred wall in great white letters that could be read thirty yards away. They ran thus:

The Seven Commandments

1. Whatever goes upon two legs is an enemy.
2. Whatever goes upon four legs, or has wings, is a friend.
3. No animal shall wear clothes.
4. No animal shall sleep in a bed.
5. No animal shall drink alcohol.
6. No animal shall kill any other animal.
7. All animals are equal.

It was very neatly written, and except that "friend" was written "freind" and one of the "S's" was the wrong way round, the spelling was correct all the way through. Snowball read it aloud for the benefit of the others. All the animals nodded in complete agreement, and the cleverer ones at once began to learn the Commandments by heart.

"Now, comrades," cried Snowball, throwing down the paint-brush, "to the hayfield! Let us make it a point of honour to get in the harvest more quickly than Jones and his men could do."

But at this moment the three cows, who had seemed uneasy for some time past, set up a loud lowing. They had not been milked for twenty-four hours, and their udders were almost bursting. After a little thought, the pigs sent for buckets and milked the cows fairly successfully, their trotters being well adapted to this task. Soon there were five buckets of frothing creamy milk at which many of the animals looked with considerable interest.

"What is going to happen to all that milk?" said someone.

"Jones used sometimes to mix some of it in our mash," said one of the hens.

"Never mind the milk, comrades!" cried Napoleon, placing himself in front of the buckets. "That will be attended to. The harvest is more important. Comrade Snowball will lead the way. I shall follow in a few minutes. Forward, comrades! The hay is waiting."

So the animals trooped down to the hayfield to begin the harvest, and when they came back in the evening it was noticed that the milk had disappeared.

CHAPTER III

How they toiled and sweated to get the hay in! But their efforts were rewarded, for the harvest was an even bigger success than they had hoped.

Sometimes the work was hard; the implements had been designed for human beings and not for animals, and it was a great drawback that no animal was able to use any tool that involved standing on his hind legs. But the pigs were so clever that they could think of a way round every difficulty. As for the horses, they knew every inch of the field, and in fact understood the business of mowing and raking far better than Jones and his men had ever done. The pigs did not actually work, but directed and supervised the others. With their superior knowledge it was natural that they should assume the leadership. Boxer and Clover would harness themselves to the cutter or the horse-rake (no bits or reins were needed in these days, of course) and tramp steadily round and round the field with a pig walking behind and calling out "Gee up, comrade!" or "Whoa back, comrade!" as the case might be. And every animal down to the humblest worked at turning the hay and gathering it. Even the ducks and hens toiled to and fro all day in the sun, carrying tiny wisps of hay in their beaks. In the end they finished the harvest in two days' less time than it had usually taken Jones and his men. Moreover, it was the biggest harvest that the farm had ever seen. There was no wastage whatever; the hens and ducks with their sharp eyes had gathered up the very last stalk. And not an animal on the farm had stolen so much as a mouthful.

All through that summer the work of the farm went like clockwork. The animals were happy as they had never conceived it possible to be. Every mouthful of food was an acute positive pleasure, now that it was truly their own food, produced by themselves and for themselves, not doled out to them by a grudging master. With the worthless parasitical human beings gone, there was more for everyone to eat. There was more leisure too, inexperienced though the animals were. They met with many difficulties—for instance, later in the year, when they harvested the corn, they had to tread it out in the ancient style and blow away the chaff with their breath, since the farm possessed no threshing machine—but the pigs with their cleverness and Boxer with his tremendous muscles always pulled them through. Boxer was the admiration of everybody. He had been a hard worker even in Jones's time, but now he seemed more like three horses than one; there were days when the entire work of the farm seemed to rest on his mighty shoulders. From morning to night he was pushing and pulling, always at the spot where the work was hardest. He had made an arrangement with one of the cockerels to call him in the mornings half an hour earlier than anyone else, and would put in some volunteer labour at whatever seemed to be most needed, before the regular day's work began. His answer to every problem, every setback, was "I will work harder!"—which he had adopted as his personal motto.

But everyone worked according to his capacity. The hens and ducks, for instance, saved five bushels of corn at the harvest by gathering up the stray grains. Nobody stole, nobody grumbled over his rations, the quarrelling and biting and jealousy which had been normal features of life in the old days had almost disappeared. Nobody shirked—or almost nobody. Mollie, it was true, was not good at getting up in the mornings, and had a way of leaving work early on the ground that there was a stone in her hoof. And the behaviour of the cat was somewhat peculiar. It was soon noticed that when there was work to be done the cat could never be found. She would vanish for hours on end, and then reappear at mealtimes, or in the evening after work was over, as though nothing had happened. But she always made such excellent excuses, and purred so affectionately, that it was impossible not to believe in her good intentions. Old Benjamin, the donkey, seemed quite unchanged since the Rebellion. He did his work in the same slow obstinate way as he had done it in Jones's time, never shirking and never volunteering for extra work either. About the Rebellion and its results he would express no opinion. When asked whether he was not happier now that Jones was gone, he would say only "Donkeys live a long time. None of you has ever seen a dead donkey," and the others had to be content with this cryptic answer.

On Sundays there was no work. Breakfast was an hour later than usual, and after breakfast there was a ceremony which was observed every week without fail. First came the hoisting of the flag. Snowball had found in the harness-room an old green tablecloth of Mrs. Jones's and had painted on it a hoof and a horn in white. This was run up the flagstaff in the farmhouse garden every Sunday morning. The flag was green, Snowball explained, to represent the green fields of England, while the hoof and horn signified the future Republic of the Animals which would arise when the human race had been finally overthrown. After the hoisting of the flag all the animals trooped into the big barn for a general assembly which was known as the Meeting. Here the work of the coming week was planned out and resolutions were put forward and debated. It was always the pigs who put forward the resolutions. The other animals understood how to vote, but could never think of any resolutions of their own. Snowball and Napoleon were by far the most active in the debates. But it was noticed that these two were never in agreement: whatever suggestion either of them made, the other could be counted on to oppose it. Even when it was resolved—a thing no one could object to in itself—to set aside the small paddock behind the orchard as a home of rest for animals who were past work, there was a stormy debate over the correct retiring age for each class of animal. The Meeting always ended with the singing of *Beasts of England,* and the afternoon was given up to recreation.

The pigs had set aside the harness-room as a headquarters for themselves. Here, in the evenings, they studied blacksmithing, carpentering, and other necessary arts from books which they had brought out of the farmhouse. Snowball also busied himself with organising the other animals into what he called Animal Committees. He was indefatigable at this. He formed the Egg Production Committee for the hens, the Clean Tails League for the cows, the Wild Comrades' Re-education Committee (the object of this was to tame the rats and rabbits), the Whiter Wool Movement for the sheep, and various others, besides instituting classes in reading and writing. On the whole, these projects were a failure. The attempt to tame the wild creatures, for instance, broke down almost immediately. They continued to behave very much as before, and when treated with generosity, simply took advantage of it. The cat joined the Re-education Committee and was very active in it for some days. She was seen one day sitting on a roof and talking to some sparrows who were just out of her reach. She was telling them that all animals were now comrades and that any sparrow who chose could come and perch on her paw; but the sparrows kept their distance.

The reading and writing classes, however, were a great success. By the autumn almost every animal on the farm was literate in some degree.

As for the pigs, they could already read and write perfectly. The dogs learned to read fairly well, but were not interested in reading anything except the Seven Commandments. Muriel, the goat, could read somewhat better than the dogs, and sometimes used to read to the others in the evenings from scraps of newspaper which she found on the rubbish heap. Benjamin could read as well as any pig, but never exercised his faculty. So far as he knew, he said, there was nothing worth reading. Clover learnt the whole alphabet, but could not put words together. Boxer could not get beyond the letter D. He would trace out A, B, C, D, in the dust with his great hoof, and then would stand staring at the letters with his ears back, sometimes shaking his forelock, trying with all his might to remember what came next and never succeeding. On several occasions, indeed, he did learn E, F, G, H, but by the time he knew them, it was always discovered that he had forgotten A, B, C, and D. Finally he decided to be content with the first four letters, and used to write them out once or twice every day to refresh his memory. Mollie refused to learn any but the six letters which spelt her own name. She would form these very neatly out of pieces of twig, and would then decorate them with a flower or two and walk round them admiring them.

None of the other animals on the farm could get further than the letter A. It was also found that the stupider animals, such as the sheep, hens, and ducks, were unable to learn the Seven Commandments by heart. After much thought Snowball declared that the Seven Commandments could in effect be reduced to a single maxim, namely: "Four legs good, two legs bad." This, he said, contained the essential principle of Animalism. Whoever had thoroughly grasped it would be safe from human influences. The birds at first objected, since it seemed to them that they also had two legs, but Snowball proved to them that this was not so.

"A bird's wing, comrades," he said, "is an organ of propulsion and not of manipulation. It should therefore be regarded as a leg. The distinguishing mark of man is the *hand,* the instrument with which he does all his mischief."

The birds did not understand Snowball's long words, but they accepted his explanation, and all the humbler animals set to work to learn the new maxim by heart. FOUR LEGS GOOD, TWO LEGS BAD, was inscribed on the end wall of the barn, above the Seven Commandments and in bigger letters. When they had once got it by heart, the sheep developed a great liking for this maxim, and often as they lay in the field they would all start bleating "Four legs good, two legs bad! Four legs good, two legs bad!" and keep it up for hours on end, never growing tired of it.

Napoleon took no interest in Snowball's committees. He said that the education of the young was more important than anything that could be done for those who were already grown up. It happened that Jessie and Bluebell had both whelped soon after the hay harvest, giving birth between them to nine sturdy puppies. As soon as they were weaned, Napoleon took them away from their mothers, saying that he would make himself responsible for their education. He took them up into a loft which could only be reached by a ladder from the harness-room, and there kept them in such seclusion that the rest of the farm soon forgot their existence.

The mystery of where the milk went to was soon cleared up. It was mixed every day into the pigs' mash. The early apples were now ripening, and the grass of the orchard was littered with windfalls. The animals had assumed as a matter of course that these would be shared out equally; one day, however, the order went forth that all the windfalls were to be collected and brought to the harness-room for the use of the pigs. At this some of the other animals murmured, but it was no use. All the pigs were in full agreement on this point, even Snowball and Napoleon. Squealer was sent to make the necessary explanations to the others.

"Comrades!" he cried. "You do not imagine, I hope, that we pigs are doing this in a spirit of selfishness and privilege? Many of us actually dislike milk and apples. I dislike them myself. Our sole object in taking these things is to preserve our health. Milk and apples (this has been proved by Science, comrades) contain substances absolutely necessary to the well-being of a pig. We pigs are brainworkers. The whole management and organisation of this farm depend on us. Day and night we are watching over your welfare. It is for *your* sake that we drink that milk and eat those apples. Do you know what would happen if we pigs failed in our duty? Jones would come back! Yes, Jones would come back! Surely, comrades," cried Squealer almost pleadingly, skipping from side to side and whisking his tail, "surely there is no one among you who wants to see Jones come back?"

Now if there was one thing that the animals were completely certain of, it was that they did not want Jones back. When it was put to them in this light, they had no more to say. The importance of keeping the pigs in good health was all too obvious. So it was agreed without further argument that the milk and the windfall apples (and also the main crop of apples when they ripened) should be reserved for the pigs alone.

CHAPTER IV

By the late summer the news of what had happened on Animal Farm had spread across half the county. Every day Snowball and Napoleon sent out flights of pigeons whose instructions were to mingle with the animals on neighbouring farms, tell them the story of the Rebellion, and teach them the tune of *Beasts of England*.

Most of this time Mr. Jones had spent sitting in the taproom of the Red Lion at Willingdon, complaining to anyone who would listen of the monstrous injustice he had suffered in being turned out of his property by a pack of good-for-nothing animals. The other farmers sympathised in principle, but they did not at first give him much help. At heart, each of them was secretly wondering whether he could not somehow turn Jones's misfortune to his own advantage. It was lucky that the owners of the two farms which adjoined Animal Farm were on permanently bad terms. One of them, which was named Foxwood, was a large, neglected, old-fashioned farm, much overgrown by woodland, with all its pastures worn out and its hedges in a disgraceful condition. Its owner, Mr. Pilkington, was an easy-going gentleman farmer who spent most of his time in fishing or hunting according to the season. The other farm, which was called Pinchfield, was smaller and better kept. Its owner was a Mr. Frederick, a tough, shrewd man, perpetually involved in lawsuits and with a name for driving hard bargains. These two disliked each other so much that it was difficult for them to come to any agreement, even in defence of their own interests.

Nevertheless, they were both thoroughly frightened by the rebellion on Animal Farm, and very anxious to prevent their own animals from learning too much about it. At first they pretended to laugh to scorn the idea of animals managing a farm for themselves. The whole thing would be over in a fortnight, they said. They put it about that the animals on the Manor Farm (they insisted on calling it the Manor Farm; they would not tolerate the name "Animal Farm") were perpetually fighting among themselves and were also rapidly starving to death. When time passed and the animals had evidently not starved to death, Frederick and Pilkington changed their tune and began to talk of the terrible wickedness that now flourished on Animal Farm. It was given out that the animals there practised cannibalism, tortured one another with red-hot horseshoes, and had their females in common. This was what came of rebelling against the laws of Nature, Frederick and Pilkington said.

However, these stories were never fully believed. Rumours of a wonderful farm, where the human beings had been turned out and the animals managed their own affairs, continued to circulate in vague and distorted forms, and throughout that year a wave of rebelliousness ran through the countryside. Bulls which had always been tractable suddenly turned savage, sheep broke down hedges and devoured the clover, cows kicked the pail over, hunters refused their fences and shot their riders on to the other side. Above all, the tune and even the words of *Beasts of England* were known everywhere. It had spread with astonishing speed. The human beings could not contain their rage when they heard this song, though they pretended to think it merely ridiculous. They could not understand, they said, how even animals could bring themselves to sing such contemptible rubbish. Any animal caught singing it was given a flogging on the spot. And yet the song was irrepressible. The blackbirds whistled it in the hedges, the pigeons cooed it in the elms, it got into the din of the smithies and the tune of the church bells. And when the human beings listened to it, they secretly trembled, hearing in it a prophecy of their future doom.

Early in October, when the corn was cut and stacked and some of it was already threshed, a flight of pigeons came whirling through the air and alighted in the yard of Animal Farm in the wildest excitement. Jones and all his men, with half a dozen others from Foxwood and Pinchfield, had entered the five-barred gate and were coming up the cart-track that led to the farm. They were all carrying sticks, except Jones, who was marching ahead with a gun in his hands. Obviously they were going to attempt the recapture of the farm.

This had long been expected, and all preparations had been made. Snowball, who had studied an old book of Julius Caesar's campaigns which he had found in the farmhouse, was in charge of the defensive operations. He gave his orders quickly, and in a couple of minutes every animal was at his post.

As the human beings approached the farm buildings, Snowball launched his first attack. All the pigeons, to the number of thirty-five, flew to and fro over the men's heads and muted upon them from mid-air; and while the men were dealing with this, the geese, who had been hiding behind the hedge, rushed out and pecked viciously at the calves of their legs. However, this was only a light skirmishing manoeuvre, intended to create a little disorder, and the men easily drove the geese off with their sticks. Snowball now launched his second line of attack. Muriel, Benjamin, and all the sheep, with Snowball at the head of them, rushed forward and prodded and butted the men from every side, while Benjamin turned around and lashed at them with his small hoofs. But once again the men, with their sticks and their hobnailed boots, were too strong for them; and suddenly, at a squeal from Snowball, which was the signal for retreat, all the animals turned and fled through the gateway into the yard.

The men gave a shout of triumph. They saw, as they imagined, their enemies in flight, and they rushed after them in disorder. This was just what Snowball had intended. As soon as they were well inside the yard, the three horses, the three cows, and the rest of the pigs, who had been lying in ambush in the cowshed, suddenly emerged in their rear, cutting them off. Snowball now gave the signal for the charge. He himself dashed straight for Jones. Jones saw him coming, raised his gun and fired. The pellets scored bloody streaks along Snowball's back, and a sheep dropped dead. Without halting for an instant, Snowball flung his fifteen stone against Jones's legs. Jones was hurled into a pile of dung and his gun flew out of his hands. But the most terrifying spectacle of all was Boxer, rearing up on his hind legs and striking out with his great iron-shod hoofs like a stallion. His very first blow took a stable-lad from Foxwood on the skull and stretched him lifeless in the mud. At the sight, several men dropped their sticks and tried to run. Panic overtook them, and the next moment all the animals together were chasing them round and round the yard. They were gored, kicked, bitten, trampled on. There was not an animal on the farm that did not take vengeance on them after his own fashion.

Even the cat suddenly leapt off a roof onto a cowman's shoulders and sank her claws in his neck, at which he yelled horribly. At a moment when the opening was clear, the men were glad enough to rush out of the yard and make a bolt for the main road. And so within five minutes of their invasion they were in ignominious retreat by the same way as they had come, with a flock of geese hissing after them and pecking at their calves all the way.

All the men were gone except one. Back in the yard Boxer was pawing with his hoof at the stable-lad who lay face down in the mud, trying to turn him over. The boy did not stir.

"He is dead," said Boxer sorrowfully. "I had no intention of doing that. I forgot that I was wearing iron shoes. Who will believe that I did not do this on purpose?"

"No sentimentality, comrade!" cried Snowball, from whose wounds the blood was still dripping. "War is war. The only good human being is a dead one."

"I have no wish to take life, not even human life," repeated Boxer, and his eyes were full of tears.

"Where is Mollie?" exclaimed somebody.

Mollie in fact was missing. For a moment there was great alarm; it was feared that the men might have harmed her in some way, or even carried her off with them. In the end, however, she was found hiding in her stall with her head buried among the hay in the manger. She had taken to flight as soon as the gun went off. And when the others came back from looking for her, it was to find that the stable-lad, who in fact was only stunned, had already recovered and made off.

The animals had now reassembled in the wildest excitement, each recounting his own exploits in the battle at the top of his voice. An impromptu celebration of the victory was held immediately. The flag was run up and *Beasts of England* was sung a number of times, then the sheep who had been killed was given a solemn funeral, a hawthorn bush being planted on her grave. At the graveside Snowball made a little speech, emphasising the need for all animals to be ready to die for Animal Farm if need be.

The animals decided unanimously to create a military decoration, "Animal Hero, First Class," which was conferred there and then on Snowball and Boxer. It consisted of a brass medal (they were really some old horse-brasses which had been found in the harness-room), to be worn on Sundays and holidays. There was also "Animal Hero, Second Class," which was conferred posthumously on the dead sheep.

There was much discussion as to what the battle should be called. In the end, it was named the Battle of the Cowshed, since that was where the ambush had been sprung. Mr. Jones's gun had been found lying in the mud, and it was known that there was a supply of cartridges in the farmhouse. It was decided to set the gun up at the foot of the flagstaff, like a piece of artillery, and to fire it twice a year—once on October the twelfth, the anniversary of the Battle of the Cowshed, and once on Midsummer Day, the anniversary of the Rebellion.

CHAPTER V

As winter drew on, Mollie became more and more troublesome. She was late for work every morning and excused herself by saying that she had overslept, and she complained of mysterious pains, although her appetite was excellent. On every kind of pretext she would run away from work and go to the drinking pool, where she would stand foolishly gazing at her own reflection in the water. But there were also rumours of something more serious. One day as Mollie strolled blithely into the yard, flirting her long tail and chewing at a stalk of hay, Clover took her aside.

"Mollie," she said, "I have something very serious to say to you. This morning I saw you looking over the hedge that divides Animal Farm from Foxwood. One of Mr Pilkington's men was standing on the other side of the hedge. And—I was a long way away, but I am almost certain I saw this—he was talking to you and you were allowing him to stroke your nose. What does that mean, Mollie?"

"He didn't! I wasn't! It isn't true!" cried Mollie, beginning to prance about and paw the ground.

"Mollie! Look me in the face. Do you give me your word of honour that that man was not stroking your nose?"

"It isn't true!" repeated Mollie, but she could not look Clover in the face, and the next moment she took to her heels and galloped away into the field.

A thought struck Clover. Without saying anything to the others, she went to Mollie's stall and turned over the straw with her hoof. Hidden under the straw was a little pile of lump sugar and several bunches of ribbon of different colours.

Three days later Mollie disappeared. For some weeks nothing was known of her whereabouts, then the pigeons reported that they had seen her on the other side of Willingdon. She was between the shafts of a smart dogcart painted red and black, which was standing outside a public-house. A fat red-faced man in check breeches and gaiters, who looked like a publican, was stroking her nose and feeding her with sugar. Her coat was newly clipped and she wore a scarlet ribbon round her forelock. She appeared to be enjoying herself, so the pigeons said. None of the animals ever mentioned Mollie again.

In January there came bitterly hard weather. The earth was like iron, and nothing could be done in the fields. Many meetings were held in the big barn, and the pigs occupied themselves with planning out the work of the coming season. It had come to be accepted that the pigs, who were manifestly cleverer than the other animals, should decide all questions of farm policy, though their decisions had to be ratified by a majority vote. This arrangement would have worked well enough if it had not been for the disputes between Snowball and Napoleon. These two disagreed at every point where disagreement was possible. If one of them suggested sowing a bigger acreage with barley, the other was certain to demand a bigger acreage of oats, and if one of them said that such and such a field was just right for cabbages, the other would declare that it was useless for anything except roots. Each had his own following, and there were some violent debates. At the Meetings Snowball often won over the majority by his brilliant speeches, but Napoleon was better at canvassing support for himself in between times. He was especially successful with the sheep. Of late the sheep had taken to bleating "Four legs good, two legs bad" both in and out of season, and they often interrupted the Meeting with this. It was noticed that they were especially liable to break into "Four legs good, two legs bad" at crucial moments in Snowball's speeches. Snowball had made a close study of some back numbers of the *Farmer and Stockbreeder* which he had found in the farmhouse, and was full of plans for innovations and improvements. He talked learnedly about field-drains, silage, and basic slag, and had worked out a complicated scheme for all the animals to drop their dung directly in the fields, at a different spot every day, to save the labour of cartage. Napoleon produced no schemes of his own, but said quietly that Snowball's would come to nothing, and seemed to be biding his time. But of all their controversies, none was so bitter as the one that took place over the windmill.

In the long pasture, not far from the farm buildings, there was a small knoll which was the highest point on the farm. After surveying the ground, Snowball declared that this was just the place for a windmill, which could be made to operate a dynamo and supply the farm with electrical power. This would light the stalls and warm them in winter, and would also run a circular saw, a chaff-cutter, a mangel-slicer, and an electric milking machine. The animals had never heard of anything of this kind before (for the farm was an old-fashioned one and had only the most primitive machinery), and they listened in astonishment while Snowball conjured up pictures of fantastic machines which would do their work for them while they grazed at their ease in the fields or improved their minds with reading and conversation.

Within a few weeks Snowball's plans for the windmill were fully worked out. The mechanical details came mostly from three books which had belonged to Mr. Jones—*One Thousand Useful Things to Do About the House, Every Man His Own Bricklayer,* and *Electricity for Beginners.* Snowball used as his study a shed which had once been used for incubators and had a smooth wooden floor, suitable for drawing on. He was closeted there for hours at a time. With his books held open by a stone, and with a piece of chalk gripped between the knuckles of his trotter, he would move rapidly to and fro, drawing in line after line and uttering little whimpers of excitement. Gradually the plans grew into a complicated mass of cranks and cog-wheels, covering more than half the floor, which the other animals found completely unintelligible but very impressive. All of them came to look at Snowball's drawings at least once a day. Even the hens and ducks came, and were at pains not to tread on the chalk marks. Only Napoleon held aloof. He had declared himself against the windmill from the start. One day, however, he arrived unexpectedly to examine the plans. He walked heavily round the shed, looked closely at every detail of the plans and snuffed at them once or twice, then stood for a little while contemplating them out of the corner of his eye; then suddenly he lifted his leg, urinated over the plans, and walked out without uttering a word.

The whole farm was deeply divided on the subject of the windmill. Snowball did not deny that to build it would be a difficult business. Stone would have to be carried and built up into walls, then the sails would have to be made and after that there would be need for dynamos and cables. (How these were to be procured, Snowball did not say.) But he maintained that it could all be done in a year. And thereafter, he declared, so much labour would be saved that the animals would only need to work three days a week. Napoleon, on the other hand, argued that the great need of the moment was to increase food production, and that if they wasted time on the windmill they would all starve to death. The animals formed themselves into two factions under the slogan, "Vote for Snowball and the three-day week" and "Vote for Napoleon and the full manger." Benjamin was the only animal who did not side with either faction. He refused to believe either that food would become more plentiful or that the windmill would save work. Windmill or no windmill, he said, life would go on as it had always gone on—that is, badly.

Apart from the disputes over the windmill, there was the question of the defence of the farm. It was fully realised that though the human beings had been defeated in the Battle of the Cowshed they might make another and more determined attempt to recapture the farm and reinstate Mr. Jones. They had all the more reason for doing so because the news of their defeat had spread across the countryside and made the animals on the neighbouring farms more restive than ever. As usual, Snowball and Napoleon were in disagreement. According to Napoleon, what the animals must do was to procure firearms and train themselves in the use of them. According to Snowball, they must send out more and more pigeons and stir up rebellion among the animals on the other farms. The one argued that if they could not defend themselves they were bound to be conquered, the other argued that if rebellions happened everywhere they would have no need to defend themselves. The animals listened first to Napoleon, then to Snowball, and could not make up their minds which was right; indeed, they always found themselves in agreement with the one who was speaking at the moment.

At last the day came when Snowball's plans were completed. At the Meeting on the following Sunday the question of whether or not to begin work on the windmill was to be put to the vote. When the animals had assembled in the big barn, Snowball stood up and, though occasionally interrupted by bleating from the sheep, set forth his reasons for advocating the building of the windmill. Then Napoleon stood up to reply. He said very quietly that the windmill was nonsense and that he advised nobody to vote for it, and promptly sat down again; he had spoken for barely thirty seconds, and seemed almost indifferent as to the effect he produced. At this Snowball sprang to his feet, and shouting down the sheep, who had begun bleating again, broke into a passionate appeal in favour of the windmill. Until now the animals had been about equally divided in their sympathies, but in a moment Snowball's eloquence had carried them away. In glowing sentences he painted a picture of Animal Farm as it might be when sordid labour was lifted from the animals' backs. His imagination had now run far beyond chaff-cutters and turnip-slicers. Electricity, he said, could operate threshing machines, ploughs, harrows, rollers, and reapers and binders, besides supplying every stall with its own electric light, hot and cold water, and an electric heater. By the time he had finished speaking, there was no doubt as to which way the vote would go. But just at this moment Napoleon stood up and, casting a peculiar sidelong look at Snowball, uttered a high-pitched whimper of a kind no one had ever heard him utter before.

At this there was a terrible baying sound outside, and nine enormous dogs wearing brass-studded collars came bounding into the barn. They dashed straight for Snowball, who only sprang from his place just in time to escape their snapping jaws. In a moment he was out of the door and they were after him. Too amazed and frightened to speak, all the animals crowded through the door to watch the chase. Snowball was racing across the long pasture that led to the road. He was running as only a pig can run, but the dogs were close on his heels. Suddenly he slipped and it seemed certain that they had him. Then he was up again, running faster than ever, then the dogs were gaining on him again. One of them all but closed his jaws on Snowball's tail, but Snowball whisked it free just in time. Then he put on an extra spurt and, with a few inches to spare, slipped through a hole in the hedge and was seen no more.

Silent and terrified, the animals crept back into the barn. In a moment the dogs came bounding back. At first no one had been able to imagine where these creatures came from, but the problem was soon solved: they were the puppies whom Napoleon had taken away from their mothers and reared privately. Though not yet full-grown, they were huge dogs, and as fierce-looking as wolves. They kept close to Napoleon. It was noticed that they wagged their tails to him in the same way as the other dogs had been used to do to Mr. Jones.

Napoleon, with the dogs following him, now mounted on to the raised portion of the floor where Major had previously stood to deliver his speech. He announced that from now on the Sunday-morning Meetings would come to an end. They were unnecessary, he said, and wasted time. In future all questions relating to the working of the farm would be settled by a special committee of pigs, presided over by himself. These would meet in private and afterwards communicate their decisions to the others. The animals would still assemble on Sunday mornings to salute the flag, sing *Beasts of England,* and receive their orders for the week; but there would be no more debates.

In spite of the shock that Snowball's expulsion had given them, the animals were dismayed by this announcement. Several of them would have protested if they could have found the right arguments. Even Boxer was vaguely troubled. He set his ears back, shook his forelock several times, and tried hard to marshal his thoughts; but in the end he could not think of anything to say. Some of the pigs themselves, however, were more articulate. Four young porkers in the front row uttered shrill squeals of disapproval, and all four of them sprang to their feet and began speaking at once. But suddenly the dogs sitting round Napoleon let out deep, menacing growls, and the pigs fell silent and sat down again. Then the sheep broke out into a tremendous bleating of "Four legs good, two legs bad!" which went on for nearly a quarter of an hour and put an end to any chance of discussion.

Afterwards Squealer was sent round the farm to explain the new arrangement to the others.

"Comrades," he said, "I trust that every animal here appreciates the sacrifice that Comrade Napoleon has made in taking this extra labour upon himself. Do not imagine, comrades, that leadership is a pleasure! On the contrary, it is a deep and heavy responsibility. No one believes more firmly than Comrade Napoleon that all animals are equal. He would be only too happy to let you make your decisions for yourselves. But sometimes you might make the wrong decisions, comrades, and then where should we be? Suppose you had decided to follow Snowball, with his moonshine of windmills—Snowball, who, as we now know, was no better than a criminal?"

"He fought bravely at the Battle of the Cowshed," said somebody.

"Bravery is not enough," said Squealer. "Loyalty and obedience are more important. And as to the Battle of the Cowshed, I believe the time will come when we shall find that Snowball's part in it was much exaggerated. Discipline, comrades, iron discipline! That is the watchword for today. One false step, and our enemies would be upon us. Surely, comrades, you do not want Jones back?"

Once again this argument was unanswerable. Certainly the animals did not want Jones back; if the holding of debates on Sunday mornings was liable to bring him back, then the debates must stop. Boxer, who had now had time to think things over, voiced the general feeling by saying: "If Comrade Napoleon says it, it must be right." And from then on he adopted the maxim, "Napoleon is always right," in addition to his private motto of "I will work harder."

By this time the weather had broken and the spring ploughing had begun. The shed where Snowball had drawn his plans of the windmill had been shut up and it was assumed that the plans had been rubbed off the floor. Every Sunday morning at ten o'clock the animals assembled in the big barn to receive their orders for the week. The skull of old Major, now clean of flesh, had been disinterred from the orchard and set upon a stump at the foot of the flagstaff, beside the gun. After the hoisting of the flag, the animals were required to file past the skull in a reverent manner before entering the barn. Nowadays they did not sit all together as they had done in the past. Napoleon, with Squealer and another pig named Minimus, who had a remarkable gift for composing songs and poems, sat on the front of the raised platform, with the nine young dogs forming a semicircle round them, and the other pigs sitting behind. The rest of the animals sat facing them in the main body of the barn. Napoleon read out the orders for the week in a gruff soldierly style, and after a single singing of *Beasts of England,* all the animals dispersed.

On the third Sunday after Snowball's expulsion, the animals were somewhat surprised to hear Napoleon announce that the windmill was to be built after all. He did not give any reason for having changed his mind, but merely warned the animals that this extra task would mean very hard work; it might even be necessary to reduce their rations. The plans, however, had all been prepared, down to the last detail. A special committee of pigs had been at work upon them for the past three weeks. The building of the windmill, with various other improvements, was expected to take two years.

That evening Squealer explained privately to the other animals that Napoleon had never in reality been opposed to the windmill. On the contrary, it was he who had advocated it in the beginning, and the plan which Snowball had drawn on the floor of the incubator shed had actually been stolen from among Napoleon's papers. The windmill was, in fact, Napoleon's own creation. Why, then, asked somebody, had he spoken so strongly against it? Here Squealer looked very sly. That, he said, was Comrade Napoleon's cunning. He had *seemed* to oppose the windmill, simply as a manoeuvre to get rid of Snowball, who was a dangerous character and a bad influence. Now that Snowball was out of the way, the plan could go forward without his interference. This, said Squealer, was something called tactics. He repeated a number of times, "Tactics, comrades, tactics!" skipping round and whisking his tail with a merry laugh. The animals were not certain what the word meant, but Squealer spoke so persuasively, and the three dogs who happened to be with him growled so threateningly, that they accepted his explanation without further questions.

CHAPTER VI

All that year the animals worked like slaves. But they were happy in their work; they grudged no effort or sacrifice, well aware that everything that they did was for the benefit of themselves and those of their kind who would come after them, and not for a pack of idle, thieving human beings.

Throughout the spring and summer they worked a sixty-hour week, and in August Napoleon announced that there would be work on Sunday afternoons as well. This work was strictly voluntary, but any animal who absented himself from it would have his rations reduced by half. Even so, it was found necessary to leave certain tasks undone. The harvest was a little less successful than in the previous year, and two fields which should have been sown with roots in the early summer were not sown because the ploughing had not been completed early enough. It was possible to foresee that the coming winter would be a hard one.

The windmill presented unexpected difficulties. There was a good quarry of limestone on the farm, and plenty of sand and cement had been found in one of the outhouses, so that all the materials for building were at hand. But the problem the animals could not at first solve was how to break up the stone into pieces of suitable size. There seemed no way of doing this except with picks and crowbars, which no animal could use, because no animal could stand on his hind legs. Only after weeks of vain effort did the right idea occur to somebody—namely, to utilise the force of gravity. Huge boulders, far too big to be used as they were, were lying all over the bed of the quarry. The animals lashed ropes round these, and then all together, cows, horses, sheep, any animal that could lay hold of the rope—even the pigs sometimes joined in at critical moments—they dragged them with desperate slowness up the slope to the top of the quarry, where they were toppled over the edge, to shatter to pieces below. Transporting the stone when it was once broken was comparatively simple. The horses carried it off in cart-loads, the sheep dragged single blocks, even Muriel and Benjamin yoked themselves into an old governess-cart and did their share. By late summer a sufficient store of stone had accumulated, and then the building began, under the superintendence of the pigs.

But it was a slow, laborious process. Frequently it took a whole day of exhausting effort to drag a single boulder to the top of the quarry, and sometimes when it was pushed over the edge it failed to break. Nothing could have been achieved without Boxer, whose strength seemed equal to that of all the rest of the animals put together. When the boulder began to slip and the animals cried out in despair at finding themselves dragged down the hill, it was always Boxer who strained himself against the rope and brought the boulder to a stop. To see him toiling up the slope inch by inch, his breath coming fast, the tips of his hoofs clawing at the ground, and his great sides matted with sweat, filled everyone with admiration. Clover warned him sometimes to be careful not to overstrain himself, but Boxer would never listen to her. His two slogans, "I will work harder" and "Napoleon is always right," seemed to him a sufficient answer to all problems. He had made arrangements with the cockerel to call him three-quarters of an hour earlier in the mornings instead of half an hour. And in his spare moments, of which there were not many nowadays, he would go alone to the quarry, collect a load of broken stone, and drag it down to the site of the windmill unassisted.

The animals were not badly off throughout that summer, in spite of the hardness of their work. If they had no more food than they had had in Jones's day, at least they did not have less. The advantage of only having to feed themselves, and not having to support five extravagant human beings as well, was so great that it would have taken a lot of failures to outweigh it. And in many ways the animal method of doing things was more efficient and saved labour. Such jobs as weeding, for instance, could be done with a thoroughness impossible to human beings. And again, since no animal now stole, it was unnecessary to fence off pasture from arable land, which saved a lot of labour on the upkeep of hedges and gates. Nevertheless, as the summer wore on, various unforeseen shortages began to make themselves felt. There was need of paraffin oil, nails, string, dog biscuits, and iron for the horses' shoes, none of which could be produced on the farm. Later there would also be need for seeds and artificial manures, besides various tools and, finally the machinery for the windmill. How these were to be procured, no one was able to imagine.

One Sunday morning, when the animals assembled to receive their orders, Napoleon announced that he had decided upon a new policy. From now onwards Animal Farm would engage in trade with the neighbouring farms: not, of course, for any commercial purpose, but simply in order to obtain certain materials which were urgently necessary. The needs of the windmill must override everything else, he said. He was therefore making arrangements to sell a stack of hay and part of the current year's wheat crop, and later on, if more money were needed, it would have to be made up by the sale of eggs, for which there was always a market in Willingdon. The hens, said Napoleon, should welcome this sacrifice as their own special contribution towards the building of the windmill.

Once again the animals were conscious of a vague uneasiness. Never to have any dealings with human beings, never to engage in trade, never to make use of money—had not these been among the earliest resolutions passed at that first triumphant Meeting after

Jones was expelled? All the animals remembered passing such resolutions: or at least they thought that they remembered it. The four young pigs who had protested when Napoleon abolished the Meetings raised their voices timidly, but they were promptly silenced by a tremendous growling from the dogs. Then, as usual, the sheep broke into "Four legs good, two legs bad!" and the momentary awkwardness was smoothed over. Finally Napoleon raised his trotter for silence and announced that he had already made all the arrangements. There would be no need for any of the animals to come in contact with human beings, which would clearly be most undesirable. He intended to take the whole burden upon his own shoulders. A Mr. Whymper, a solicitor living in Willingdon, had agreed to act as intermediary between Animal Farm and the outside world, and would visit the farm every Monday morning to receive his instructions. Napoleon ended his speech with his usual cry of "Long live Animal Farm!" and after the singing of *Beasts of England* the animals were dismissed.

Afterwards Squealer made a round of the farm and set the animals' minds at rest. He assured them that the resolution against engaging in trade and using money had never been passed, or even suggested. It was pure imagination, probably traceable in the beginning to lies circulated by Snowball. A few animals still felt faintly doubtful, but Squealer asked them shrewdly, "Are you certain that this is not something that you have dreamed, comrades? Have you any record of such a resolution? Is it written down anywhere?" And since it was certainly true that nothing of the kind existed in writing, the animals were satisfied that they had been mistaken.

Every Monday Mr. Whymper visited the farm as had been arranged. He was a sly-looking little man with side whiskers, a solicitor in a very small way of business, but sharp enough to have realised earlier than anyone else that Animal Farm would need a broker and that the commissions would be worth having. The animals watched his coming and going with a kind of dread, and avoided him as much as possible. Nevertheless, the sight of Napoleon, on all fours, delivering orders to Whymper, who stood on two legs, roused their pride and partly reconciled them to the new arrangement. Their relations with the human race were now not quite the same as they had been before. The human beings did not hate Animal Farm any less now that it was prospering; indeed, they hated it more than ever. Every human being held it as an article of faith that the farm would go bankrupt sooner or later, and, above all, that the windmill would be a failure. They would meet in the public-houses and prove to one another by means of diagrams that the windmill was bound to fall down, or that if it did stand up, then that it would never work. And yet, against their will, they had developed a certain respect for the efficiency with which the animals were managing their own affairs. One symptom of this was that they had begun to call Animal Farm by its proper name and ceased to pretend that it was called the Manor Farm. They had also dropped their championship of Jones, who had given up hope of getting his farm back and gone to live in another part of the county. Except through Wymper, there was as yet no contact between Animal Farm and the outside world, but there were constant rumours that Napoleon was about to enter into a definite business agreement either with Mr. Pilkington of Foxwood or with Mr. Frederick of Pinchfield—but never, it was noticed, with both simultaneously.

It was about this time that the pigs suddenly moved into the farmhouse and took up their residence there. Again the animals seemed to remember that a resolution against this had been passed in the early days, and again Squealer was able to convince them that this was not the case. It was absolutely necessary, he said, that the pigs, who were the brains of the farm, should have a quiet place to work in. It was also more suited to the dignity of the Leader (for of late he had taken to speaking of Napoleon under the title of "Leader") to live in a house than in a mere sty. Nevertheless, some of the animals were disturbed when they heard that the pigs not only took their meals in the kitchen and used the drawing-room as a recreation room, but also slept in the beds. Boxer passed it off as usual with "Napoleon is always right!", but Clover, who thought she remembered a definite ruling against beds, went to the end of the barn and tried to puzzle out the Seven Commandments which were inscribed there. Finding herself unable to read more than individual letters, she fetched Muriel.

"Muriel," she said, "read me the Fourth Commandment. Does it not say something about never sleeping in a bed?"

With some difficulty Muriel spelt it out.

"It says, 'No animal shall sleep in a bed *with sheets,*'" she announced finally.

Curiously enough, Clover had not remembered that the Fourth Commandment mentioned sheets; but as it was there on the wall, it must have done so. And Squealer, who happened to be passing at this moment, attended by two or three dogs, was able to put the whole matter in its proper perspective.

"You have heard then, comrades," he said, "that we pigs now sleep in the beds of the farmhouse? And why not? You did not suppose, surely, that there was ever a ruling against *beds*? A bed merely means a place to sleep in. A pile of straw in a stall is a bed, properly regarded. The rule was against *sheets*, which are a human invention. We have removed the sheets from the farmhouse beds, and sleep between blankets. And very comfortable beds they are too! But not more comfortable than we need, I can tell you, comrades, with all the brainwork we have to do nowadays. You would not rob us of our repose, would you, comrades? You would not have us too tired to carry out our duties? Surely none of you wishes to see Jones back?"

The animals reassured him on this point immediately, and no more was said about the pigs sleeping in the farmhouse beds. And when, some days afterwards, it was announced that from now on the pigs would get up an hour later in the mornings than the other animals, no complaint was made about that either.

By the autumn the animals were tired but happy. They had had a hard year, and after the sale of part of the hay and corn, the stores of food for the winter were none too plentiful, but the windmill compensated for everything. It was almost half built now. After the harvest there was a stretch of clear dry weather, and the animals toiled harder than ever, thinking it well worth while to plod to and fro all day with blocks of stone if by doing so they could raise the walls another foot. Boxer would even come out at nights and work for an hour or two on his own by the light of the harvest moon. In their spare moments the animals would walk round and round the half-finished mill, admiring the strength and perpendicularity of its walls and marvelling that they should ever have been able to build anything so imposing. Only old Benjamin refused to grow enthusiastic about the windmill, though, as usual, he would utter nothing beyond the cryptic remark that donkeys live a long time.

November came, with raging south-west winds. Building had to stop because it was now too wet to mix the cement. Finally there came a night when the gale was so violent that the farm buildings rocked on their foundations and several tiles were blown off the roof of the barn. The hens woke up squawking with terror because they had all dreamed simultaneously of hearing a gun go off in the distance. In the morning the animals came out of their stalls to find that the flagstaff had been blown down and an elm tree at the foot of the orchard had been plucked up like a radish. They had just noticed this when a cry of despair broke from every animal's throat. A terrible sight had met their eyes. The windmill was in ruins.

With one accord they dashed down to the spot. Napoleon, who seldom moved out of a walk, raced ahead of them all. Yes, there it lay, the fruit of all their struggles, levelled to its foundations, the stones they had broken and carried so laboriously scattered all around. Unable at first to speak, they stood gazing mournfully at the litter of fallen stone. Napoleon paced to and fro in silence, occasionally snuffing at the ground. His tail had grown rigid and twitched sharply from side to side, a sign in him of intense mental activity. Suddenly he halted as though his mind were made up.

"Comrades," he said quietly, "do you know who is responsible for this? Do you know the enemy who has come in the night and overthrown our windmill? SNOWBALL!" he suddenly roared in a voice of thunder. "Snowball has done this thing! In sheer malignity, thinking to set back our plans and avenge himself for his ignominious expulsion, this traitor has crept here under cover of night and destroyed our work of nearly a year. Comrades, here and now I pronounce the death sentence upon Snowball. 'Animal Hero, Second Class,' and half a bushel of apples to any animal who brings him to justice. A full bushel to anyone who captures him alive!"

The animals were shocked beyond measure to learn that even Snowball could be guilty of such an action. There was a cry of indignation, and everyone began thinking out ways of catching Snowball if he should ever come back. Almost immediately the footprints of a pig were discovered in the grass at a little distance from the knoll. They could only be traced for a few yards, but appeared to lead to a hole in the hedge. Napoleon snuffed deeply at them and pronounced them to be Snowball's. He gave it as his opinion that Snowball had probably come from the direction of Foxwood Farm.

"No more delays, comrades!" cried Napoleon when the footprints had been examined. "There is work to be done. This very morning we begin rebuilding the windmill, and we will build all through the winter, rain or shine. We will teach this miserable traitor that he cannot undo our work so easily. Remember, comrades, there must be no alteration in our plans: they shall be carried out to the day. Forward, comrades! Long live the windmill! Long live Animal Farm!"

CHAPTER VII

It was a bitter winter. The stormy weather was followed by sleet and snow, and then by a hard frost which did not break till well into February. The animals carried on as best they could with the rebuilding of the windmill, well knowing that the outside world was watching them and that the envious human beings would rejoice and triumph if the mill were not finished on time.

Out of spite, the human beings pretended not to believe that it was Snowball who had destroyed the windmill: they said that it had fallen down because the walls were too thin. The animals knew that this was not the case. Still, it had been decided to build the walls three feet thick this time instead of eighteen inches as before, which meant collecting much larger quantities of stone. For a long time the quarry was full of snowdrifts and nothing

could be done. Some progress was made in the dry frosty weather that followed, but it was cruel work, and the animals could not feel so hopeful about it as they had felt before. They were always cold, and usually hungry as well. But Boxer and Clover never lost heart. Squealer made excellent speeches on the joy of service and the dignity of labour, but the other animals found more inspiration in Boxer's strength and his never-failing cry of "I will work harder!"

In January food fell short. The corn ration was drastically reduced, and it was announced that an extra potato ration would be issued to make up for it. Then it was discovered that the greater part of the potato crop had been frosted in the clamps, which had not been covered thickly enough. The potatoes had become soft and discoloured, and only a few were edible. For days at a time the animals had nothing to eat but chaff and mangels. Starvation seemed to stare them in the face.

It was vitally necessary to conceal this fact from the outside world. Emboldened by the collapse of the windmill, the human beings were inventing fresh lies about Animal Farm. Once again it was being put about that all the animals were dying of famine and disease, and that they were continually fighting among themselves and had resorted to cannibalism and infanticide. Napoleon was well aware of the bad results that might follow if the real facts of the food situation were known, and he decided to make use of Mr. Whymper to spread a contrary impression. Hitherto the animals had had little or no contact with Whymper on his weekly visits: now, however, a few selected animals, mostly sheep, were instructed to remark casually in his hearing that rations had been increased. In addition, Napoleon ordered the almost empty bins in the store-shed to be filled nearly to the brim with sand, which was then covered up with what remained of the grain and meal. On some suitable pretext Whymper was led through the store-shed and allowed to catch a glimpse of the bins. He was deceived, and continued to report to the outside world that there was no food shortage on Animal Farm.

Nevertheless, towards the end of January it became obvious that it would be necessary to procure some more grain from somewhere. In these days Napoleon rarely appeared in public, but spent all his time in the farmhouse, which was guarded at each door by fierce-looking dogs. When he did emerge, it was in a ceremonial manner, with an escort of six dogs who closely surrounded him and growled if anyone came too near. Frequently he did not even appear on Sunday mornings, but issued his orders through one of the other pigs, usually Squealer.

One Sunday morning Squealer announced that the hens, who had just come in to lay again, must surrender their eggs. Napoleon had accepted, through Whymper, a contract for four hundred eggs a week. The price of these would pay for enough grain and meal to keep the farm going till summer came on and conditions were easier.

When the hens heard this, they raised a terrible outcry. They had been warned earlier that this sacrifice might be necessary, but had not believed that it would really happen. They were just getting their clutches ready for the spring sitting, and they protested that to take the eggs away now was murder. For the first time since the expulsion of Jones, there was something resembling a rebellion. Led by three young Black Minorca pullets, the hens made a determined effort to thwart Napoleon's wishes. Their method was to fly up to the rafters and there lay their eggs, which smashed to pieces on the floor. Napoleon acted swiftly and ruthlessly. He ordered the hens' rations to be stopped, and decreed that any animal giving so much as a grain of corn to a hen should be punished by death. The dogs saw to it that these orders were carried out. For five days the hens held out, then they capitulated and went back to their nesting boxes. Nine hens had died in the meantime. Their bodies were buried in the orchard, and it was given out that they had died of coccidiosis. Whymper heard nothing of this affair, and the eggs were duly delivered, a grocer's van driving up to the farm once a week to take them away.

All this while no more had been seen of Snowball. He was rumoured to be hiding on one of the neighbouring farms, either Foxwood or Pinchfield. Napoleon was by this time on slightly better terms with the other farmers than before. It happened that there was in the yard a pile of timber which had been stacked there ten years earlier when a beech spinney was cleared. It was well seasoned, and Whymper had advised Napoleon to sell it; both Mr. Pilkington and Mr. Frederick were anxious to buy it. Napoleon was hesitating between the two, unable to make up his mind. It was noticed that whenever he seemed on the point of coming to an agreement with Frederick, Snowball was declared to be in hiding at Foxwood, while, when he inclined toward Pilkington, Snowball was said to be at Pinchfield.

Suddenly, early in the spring, an alarming thing was discovered. Snowball was secretly frequenting the farm by night! The animals were so disturbed that they could hardly sleep in their stalls. Every night, it was said, he came creeping in under cover of darkness and performed all kinds of mischief. He stole the corn, he upset the milk-pails, he broke the eggs, he trampled the seedbeds, he gnawed the bark off the fruit trees. Whenever anything went wrong it became usual to attribute it to Snowball. If a window was broken or a drain was blocked up, someone was certain to say that Snowball had come in the night and done it, and when the key of the store-shed was lost, the whole farm was convinced that Snowball had thrown it down the well. Curiously enough, they went on believing this even after the mislaid key was found under a sack of meal. The cows declared unanimously that Snowball crept into their stalls and milked them in their sleep. The rats, which had been troublesome that winter, were also said to be in league with Snowball.

Napoleon decreed that there should be a full investigation into Snowball's activities. With his dogs in attendance he set out and made a careful tour of inspection of the farm buildings, the other animals following at a respectful distance. At every few steps Napoleon stopped and snuffed the ground for traces of Snowball's footsteps, which, he said, he could detect by the smell. He snuffed in every corner, in the barn, in the cow-shed, in the hen-houses, in the vegetable garden, and found traces of Snowball almost everywhere. He would put his snout to the ground, give several deep sniffs, and exclaim in a terrible voice, "Snowball! He has been here! I can smell him distinctly!" and at the word "Snowball" all the dogs let out blood-curdling growls and showed their side teeth.

The animals were thoroughly frightened. It seemed to them as though Snowball were some kind of invisible influence pervading the air about them and menacing them with all kinds of dangers. In the evening Squealer called them together, and with an alarmed expression on his face told them that he had some serious news to report.

"Comrades!" cried Squealer, making little nervous skips, "a most terrible thing has been discovered. Snowball has sold himself to Frederick of Pinchfield Farm, who is even now plotting to attack us and take our farm away from us! Snowball is to act as his guide when the attack begins. But there is worse than that. We had thought that Snowball's rebellion was caused simply by his vanity and ambition. But we were wrong, comrades. Do you know what the real reason was? Snowball was in league with Jones from the very start! He was Jones's secret agent all the time. It has all been proved by documents which he left behind him and which we have only just discovered. To my mind this explains a great deal, comrades. Did we not see for ourselves how he attempted—fortunately without success—to get us defeated and destroyed at the Battle of the Cowshed?"

The animals were stupefied. This was a wickedness far outdoing Snowball's destruction of the windmill. But it was some minutes before they could fully take it in. They all remembered, or thought they remembered, how they had seen Snowball charging ahead of them at the Battle of the Cowshed, how he had rallied and encouraged them at every turn, and how he had not paused for an instant even when the pellets from Jones's gun had wounded his back. At first it was a little difficult to see how this fitted in with his being on Jones's side. Even Boxer, who seldom asked questions, was puzzled. He lay down, tucked his fore hoofs beneath him, shut his eyes, and with a hard effort managed to formulate his thoughts.

"I do not believe that," he said. "Snowball fought bravely at the Battle of the Cowshed. I saw him myself. Did we not give him 'Animal Hero, First Class,' immediately afterwards?"

"That was our mistake, comrade. For we know now—it is all written down in the secret documents that we have found—that in reality he was trying to lure us to our doom."

"But he was wounded," said Boxer. "We all saw him running with blood."

"That was part of the arrangement!" cried Squealer. "Jones's shot only grazed him. I could show you this in his own writing, if you were able to read it. The plot was for Snowball, at the critical moment, to give the signal for flight and leave the field to the enemy. And he very nearly succeeded—I will even say, comrades, he *would* have succeeded if it had not been for our heroic Leader, Comrade Napoleon. Do you not remember how, just at the moment when Jones and his men had got inside the yard, Snowball suddenly turned and fled, and many animals followed him? And do you not remember, too, that it was just at that moment, when panic was spreading and all seemed lost, that Comrade Napoleon sprang forward with a cry of 'Death to Humanity!' and sank his teeth in Jones's leg? Surely you remember *that*, comrades?" exclaimed Squealer, frisking from side to side.

Now when Squealer described the scene so graphically, it seemed to the animals that they did remember it. At any rate, they remembered that at the critical moment of the battle Snowball had turned to flee. But Boxer was still a little uneasy.

"I do not believe that Snowball was a traitor at the beginning," he said finally. "What he has done since is different. But I believe that at the Battle of the Cowshed he was a good comrade."

"Our Leader, Comrade Napoleon," announced Squealer, speaking very slowly and firmly, "has stated categorically—categorically, comrade—that Snowball was Jones's agent from the very beginning—yes, and from long before the Rebellion was ever thought of."

"Ah, that is different!" said Boxer. "If Comrade Napoleon says it, it must be right."

"That is the true spirit, comrade!" cried Squealer, but it was noticed he cast a very ugly look at Boxer with his little twinkling eyes. He turned to go, then paused and added impressively: "I warn every animal on this farm to keep his eyes very wide open. For we have reason to think that some of Snowball's secret agents are lurking among us at this moment!"

Four days later, in the late afternoon, Napoleon ordered all the animals to assemble in the yard. When they were all gathered together, Napoleon emerged from the farmhouse, wearing both his medals (for he had recently awarded himself "Animal Hero, First Class," and "Animal Hero, Second Class"), with his nine huge dogs frisking round him and uttering growls that sent shivers down all the animals' spines. They all cowered silently in their places, seeming to know in advance that some terrible thing was about to happen.

Napoleon stood sternly surveying his audience; then he uttered a high-pitched whimper. Immediately the dogs bounded forward, seized four of the pigs by the ear and dragged them, squealing with pain and terror, to Napoleon's feet. The pigs' ears were bleeding, the dogs had tasted blood, and for a few moments they appeared to go quite mad. To the amazement of everybody, three of them flung themselves upon Boxer. Boxer saw them coming and put out his great hoof, caught a dog in mid-air, and pinned him to the ground. The dog shrieked for mercy and the other two fled with their tails between their legs. Boxer looked at Napoleon to know whether he should crush the dog to death or let it go. Napoleon appeared to change countenance, and sharply ordered Boxer to let the dog go, whereat Boxer lifted his hoof, and the dog slunk away, bruised and howling.

Presently the tumult died down. The four pigs waited, trembling, with guilt written on every line of their countenances. Napoleon now called upon them to confess their crimes. They were the same four pigs as had protested when Napoleon abolished the Sunday Meetings. Without any further prompting they confessed that they had been secretly in touch with Snowball ever since his expulsion, that they had collaborated with him in destroying the windmill, and that they had entered into an agreement with him to hand over Animal Farm to Mr. Frederick. They added that Snowball had privately admitted to them that he had been Jones's secret agent

for years past. When they had finished their confession, the dogs promptly tore their throats out, and in a terrible voice Napoleon demanded whether any other animal had anything to confess.

The three hens who had been the ringleaders in the attempted rebellion over the eggs now came forward and stated that Snowball had appeared to them in a dream and incited them to disobey Napoleon's orders. They, too, were slaughtered. Then a goose came forward and confessed to having secreted six ears of corn during the last year's harvest and eaten them in the night. Then a sheep confessed to having urinated in the drinking pool—urged to do this, so she said, by Snowball—and two other sheep confessed to having murdered an old ram, an especially devoted follower of Napoleon, by chasing him round and round a bonfire when he was suffering from a cough. They were all slain on the spot. And so the tale of confessions and executions went on, until there was a pile of corpses lying before Napoleon's feet and the air was heavy with the smell of blood, which had been unknown there since the expulsion of Jones.

When it was all over, the remaining animals, except for the pigs and dogs, crept away in a body. They were shaken and miserable. They did not know which was more shocking—the treachery of the animals who had leagued themselves with Snowball, or the cruel retribution they had just witnessed. In the old days there had often been scenes of bloodshed equally terrible, but it seemed to all of them that it was far worse now that it was happening among themselves. Since Jones had left the farm, until today, no animal had killed another animal. Not even a rat had been killed. They had made their way on to the little knoll where the half-finished windmill stood, and with one accord they all lay down as though huddling together for warmth—Clover, Muriel, Benjamin, the cows, the sheep, and a whole flock of geese and hens—everyone, indeed, except the cat, who had suddenly disappeared just before Napoleon ordered the animals to assemble. For some time nobody spoke. Only Boxer remained on his feet. He fidgeted to and fro, swishing his long black tail against his sides and occasionally uttering a little whinny of surprise. Finally he said:

"I do not understand it. I would not have believed that such things could happen on our farm. It must be due to some fault in ourselves. The solution, as I see it, is to work harder. From now onwards I shall get up a full hour earlier in the mornings."

And he moved off at his lumbering trot and made for the quarry. Having got there, he collected two successive loads of stone and dragged them down to the windmill before retiring for the night.

The animals huddled about Clover, not speaking. The knoll where they were lying gave them a wide prospect across the countryside. Most of Animal Farm was within their view—the long pasture stretching down to the main road, the hayfield, the spinney, the drinking pool, the ploughed fields where the young wheat was thick and green, and the red roofs of the farm buildings with the smoke curling from the chimneys. It was a clear spring evening. The grass and the bursting hedges were gilded by the level rays of the sun. Never had the farm—and with a kind of surprise they remembered that it was their own farm, every inch of it their own property—appeared to the animals so desirable a place. As Clover looked down the hillside her eyes filled with tears. If she could have spoken her thoughts, it would have been to say that this was not what they had aimed at when they had set themselves years ago to work for the overthrow of the human race. These scenes of terror and slaughter were not what they had looked forward to on that night when old Major first stirred them to rebellion. If she herself had had any picture of the future, it had been of a society of animals set free from hunger and the whip, all equal, each working according to his capacity, the strong protecting the weak, as she had protected the lost brood of ducklings with her foreleg on the night of Major's speech. Instead—she did not know why—they had come to a time when no one dared speak his mind, when fierce, growling dogs roamed everywhere, and when you had to watch your comrades torn to pieces after confessing to shocking crimes. There was no thought of rebellion or disobedience in her mind. She knew that, even as things were, they were far better off than they had been in the days of Jones, and that before all else it was needful to prevent the return of the human beings. Whatever happened she would remain faithful, work hard, carry out the orders that were given to her, and accept the leadership of Napoleon. But still, it was not for this that she and all the other animals had hoped and toiled. It was not for this that they had built the windmill and faced the bullets of Jones's gun. Such were her thoughts, though she lacked the words to express them.

At last, feeling this to be in some way a substitute for the words she was unable to find, she began to sing *Beasts of England*. The other animals sitting round her took it up, and they sang it three times over—very tunefully, but slowly and mournfully, in a way they had never sung it before.

They had just finished singing it for the third time when Squealer, attended by two dogs, approached them with the air of having something important to say. He announced that, by a special decree of Comrade Napoleon, *Beasts of England* had been abolished. From now onwards it was forbidden to sing it.

The animals were taken aback.

"Why?" cried Muriel.

"It's no longer needed, comrade," said Squealer stiffly. "*Beasts of England* was the song of the Rebellion. But the Rebellion is now completed. The execution of the traitors this afternoon was the final act. The enemy both external and internal has been defeated. In *Beasts of England* we expressed our longing for a better society in days to come. But that society has now been established. Clearly this song has no longer any purpose."

Frightened though they were, some of the animals might possibly have protested, but at this moment the sheep set up their usual bleating of "Four legs good, two legs bad," which went on for several minutes and put an end to the discussion.

So *Beasts of England* was heard no more. In its place Minimus, the poet, had composed another song which began:

Animal Farm, Animal Farm,
Never through me shalt thou come to harm!

and this was sung every Sunday morning after the hoisting of the flag. But somehow neither the words nor the tune ever seemed to the animals to come up to *Beasts of England*.

CHAPTER VIII

A few days later, when the terror caused by the executions had died down, some of the animals remembered—or thought they remembered—that the Sixth Commandment decreed "No animal shall kill any other animal." And though no one cared to mention it in the hearing of the pigs or the dogs, it was felt that the killings which had taken place did not square with this. Clover asked Benjamin to read her the Sixth Commandment, and when Benjamin, as usual, said that he refused to meddle in such matters, she fetched Muriel. Muriel read the Commandment for her. It ran: "No animal shall kill any other animal *without cause.*" Somehow or other, the last two words had slipped out of the animals' memory. But they saw now that the Commandment had not been violated; for clearly there was good reason for killing the traitors who had leagued themselves with Snowball.

Throughout the year the animals worked even harder than they had worked in the previous year. To rebuild the windmill, with walls twice as thick as before, and to finish it by the appointed date, together with the regular work of the farm, was a tremendous labour. There were times when it seemed to the animals that they worked longer hours and fed no better than they had done in Jones's day. On Sunday mornings Squealer, holding down a long strip of paper with his trotter, would read out to them lists of figures proving that the production of every class of foodstuff had increased by two hundred per cent, three hundred per cent, or five hundred per cent, as the case might be. The animals saw no reason to disbelieve him, especially as they could no longer remember very clearly what conditions had been like before the Rebellion. All the same, there were days when they felt that they would sooner have had less figures and more food.

All orders were now issued through Squealer or one of the other pigs. Napoleon himself was not seen in public as often as once in a fortnight. When he did appear, he was attended not only by his retinue of dogs but by a black cockerel who marched in front of him and acted as a kind of trumpeter, letting out a loud "cock-a-doodle-doo" before Napoleon spoke. Even in the farmhouse, it was said, Napoleon inhabited separate apartments from the others. He took his meals alone, with two dogs to wait upon him, and always ate from the Crown Derby dinner service which had been in the glass cupboard in the drawing-room. It was also announced that the gun would be fired every year on Napoleon's birthday, as well as on the other two anniversaries.

Napoleon was now never spoken of simply as "Napoleon." He was always referred to in formal style as "our Leader, Comrade Napoleon," and the pigs liked to invent for him such titles as Father of All Animals, Terror of Mankind, Protector of the Sheep-fold, Ducklings' Friend, and the like. In his speeches, Squealer would talk with the tears rolling down his cheeks of Napoleon's wisdom, the goodness of his heart, and the deep love he bore to all animals everywhere, even and especially the unhappy animals who still lived in ignorance and slavery on other farms. It had become usual to give Napoleon the credit for every successful achievement and every stroke of good fortune. You would often hear one hen remark to another, "Under the guidance of our Leader, Comrade Napoleon, I have laid five eggs in six days"; or two cows, enjoying a drink at the pool, would exclaim, "Thanks to the leadership of Comrade Napoleon, how excellent this water tastes!" The general feeling on the farm was well expressed in a poem entitled *Comrade Napoleon,* which was composed by Minimus and which ran as follows:

Friend of fatherless!
Fountain of happiness!
Lord of the swill-bucket! Oh, how my soul is on
Fire when I gaze at thy
Calm and commanding eye,
Like the sun in the sky,
Comrade Napoleon!

Thou are the giver of
All that thy creatures love,
Full belly twice a day, clean straw to roll upon;
Every beast great or small
Sleeps at peace in his stall,
Thou watchest over all,
Comrade Napoleon!

Had I a sucking-pig,
Ere he had grown as big
Even as a pint bottle or as a rolling-pin,

He should have learned to be
Faithful and true to thee,
Yes, his first squeak should be
"Comrade Napoleon!"

Napoleon approved of this poem and caused
it to be inscribed on the wall of the big barn,
at the opposite end from the Seven Commandments. It was surmounted by a portrait of
Napoleon, in profile, executed by Squealer in
white paint.

Meanwhile, through the agency of Whymper, Napoleon was engaged in complicated
negotiations with Frederick and Pilkington.
The pile of timber was still unsold. Of the
two, Frederick was the more anxious to get
hold of it, but he would not offer a reasonable price. At the same time there were renewed rumours that Frederick and his men
were plotting to attack Animal Farm and to
destroy the windmill, the building of which
had aroused furious jealousy in him. Snowball was known to be still skulking on Pinchfield Farm. In the middle of the summer the
animals were alarmed to hear that three hens
had come forward and confessed that, inspired
by Snowball, they had entered into a plot to
murder Napoleon. They were executed immediately, and fresh precautions for Napoleon's safety were taken. Four dogs guarded
his bed at night, one at each corner, and a
young pig named Pinkeye was given the task
of tasting all his food before he ate it, lest
it should be poisoned.

At about the same time it was given out that
Napoleon had arranged to sell the pile of
timber to Mr. Pilkington; he was also going
to enter into a regular agreement for the exchange of certain products between Animal
Farm and Foxwood. The relations between
Napoleon and Pilkington, though they were
only conducted through Whymper, were now
almost friendly. The animals distrusted Pilkington, as a human being, but greatly preferred him to Frederick, whom they both
feared and hated. As the summer wore on,
and the windmill neared completion, the
rumours of an impending treacherous attack
grew stronger and stronger. Frederick, it was
said, intended to bring against them twenty
men all armed with guns, and he had already
bribed the magistrates and police, so that if
he could once get hold of the title-deeds of
Animal Farm they would ask no questions.
Moreover, terrible stories were leaking out
from Pinchfield about the cruelties that Frederick practised upon his animals. He had
flogged an old horse to death, he starved his
cows, he had killed a dog by throwing it into
the furnace, he amused himself in the evenings by making cocks fight with splinters of
razor-blade tied to their spurs. The animals'
blood boiled with rage when they heard of
these things being done to their comrades,
and sometimes they clamoured to be allowed
to go out in a body and attack Pinchfield
Farm, drive out the humans, and set the animals free. But Squealer counselled them to
avoid rash actions and trust in Comrade
Napoleon's strategy.

Nevertheless, feeling against Frederick continued to run high. One Sunday morning Napoleon appeared in the barn and explained
that he had never at any time contemplated
selling the pile of timber to Frederick; he
considered it beneath his dignity, he said, to
have dealings with scoundrels of that description. The pigeons who were still sent out to
spread tidings of the Rebellion were forbidden
to set foot anywhere on Foxwood, and were
also ordered to drop their former slogan of
"Death to Humanity" in favour of "Death to
Frederick." In the late summer yet another of
Snowball's machinations was laid bare. The
wheat crop was full of weeds, and it was discovered that on one of his nocturnal visits
Snowball had mixed weed seeds with the seed
corn. A gander who had been privy to the
plot had confessed his guilt to Squealer and
immediately committed suicide by swallowing
deadly nightshade berries. The animals now
also learned that Snowball had never—as many
of them had believed hitherto—received the
order of "Animal Hero, First Class." This was
merely a legend which had been spread some
time after the Battle of the Cowshed by Snowball himself. So far from being decorated, he
had been censured for showing cowardice in
the battle. Once again some of the animals
heard this with a certain bewilderment, but
Squealer was soon able to convince them that
their memories had been at fault.

In the autumn, by a tremendous, exhausting
effort—for the harvest had to be gathered at

almost the same time—the windmill was finished. The machinery had still to be installed, and Whymper was negotiating the purchase of it, but the structure was completed. In the teeth of every difficulty, in spite of inexperience, of primitive implements, of bad luck and of Snowball's treachery, the work had been finished punctually to the very day! Tired out but proud, the animals walked round and round their masterpiece, which appeared even more beautiful in their eyes than when it had been built the first time. Moreover, the walls were twice as thick as before. Nothing short of explosives would lay them low this time! And when they thought of how they had laboured, what discouragements they had overcome, and the enormous difference that would be made in their lives when the sails were turning and the dynamos running—when they thought of all this, their tiredness forsook them and they gambolled round and round the windmill, uttering cries of triumph. Napoleon himself, attended by his dogs and his cockerel, came down to inspect the completed work; he personally congratulated the animals on their achievement, and announced that the mill would be named Napoleon Mill.

Two days later the animals were called together for a special meeting in the barn. They were struck dumb with surprise when Napoleon announced that he had sold the pile of timber to Frederick. Tomorrow Frederick's wagons would arrive and begin carting it away. Throughout the whole period of his seeming friendship with Pilkington, Napoleon had really been in secret agreement with Frederick.

All relations with Foxwood had been broken off; insulting messages had been sent to Pilkington. The pigeons had been told to avoid Pinchfield Farm and to alter their slogan from "Death to Frederick" to "Death to Pilkington." At the same time Napoleon assured the animals that the stories of an impending attack on Animal Farm were completely untrue, and that the tales about Frederick's cruelty to his own animals had been greatly exaggerated. All these rumours had probably originated with Snowball and his agents. It now appeared that Snowball was not, after all, hiding on Pinchfield Farm, and in fact had never been there in his life: he was living—in

considerable luxury, so it was said—at Foxwood, and had in reality been a pensioner of Pilkington for years past.

The pigs were in ecstasies over Napoleon's cunning. By seeming to be friendly with Pilkington he had forced Frederick to raise his price by twelve pounds. But the superior quality of Napoleon's mind, said Squealer, was shown in the fact that he trusted nobody, not even Frederick. Frederick had wanted to pay for the timber with something called a cheque, which, it seemed, was a piece of paper with a promise to pay written upon it. But Napoleon was too clever for him. He had demanded payment in real five-pound notes, which were to be handed over before the timber was removed. Already Frederick had paid up; and the sum he had paid was just enough to buy the machinery for the windmill.

Meanwhile the timber was being carted away at high speed. When it was all gone, another special meeting was held in the barn for the animals to inspect Frederick's banknotes. Smiling beatifically, and wearing both his decorations, Napoleon reposed on a bed of straw on the platform, with the money at his side, neatly piled on a china dish from the farmhouse kitchen. The animals filed slowly past, and each gazed his fill. And Boxer put out his nose to sniff at the bank-notes, and the flimsy white things stirred and rustled in his breath.

Three days later there was a terrible hullabaloo. Whymper, his face deadly pale, came racing up the path on his bicycle, flung it down in the yard and rushed straight into the farmhouse. The next moment a choking roar of rage sounded from Napoleon's apartments. The news of what had happened sped round the farm like wildfire. The bank-notes were forgeries! Frederick had got the timber for nothing!

Napoleon called the animals together immediately and in a terrible voice pronounced the death sentence upon Frederick. When captured, he said, Frederick should be boiled alive. At the same time he warnd them that after this treacherous deed the worst was to be expected. Frederick and his men might make their long-expected attack at any moment. Sentinels were placed at all the approaches to the farm. In addition, four pigeons were sent to Foxwood with a conciliatory message, which it was hoped might re-establish good relations with Pilkington.

The very next morning the attack came. The animals were at breakfast when the lookouts came racing in with the news that Frederick and his followers had already come through the five-barred gate. Boldly enough the animals sallied forth to meet them, but this time they did not have the easy victory that they had had in the Battle of the Cowshed. There were fifteen men, with half a dozen guns between them, and they opened fire as soon as they got within fifty yards. The animals could not face the terrible explosions and the stinging pellets, and in spite of the efforts of Napoleon and Boxer to rally them, they were soon driven back. A number of them were already wounded. They took refuge in the farm buildings and peeped cautiously out from chinks and knot-holes. The whole of the big pasture, including the windmill, was in the hands of the enemy. For the moment even Napoleon seemed at a loss. He paced up and down without a word, his tail rigid and twitching. Wistful glances were sent in the direction of Foxwood. If Pilkington and his men would help them, the day might yet be won. But at this moment the four pigeons, who had been sent out on the day before, returned, one of them bearing a scrap of paper from Pilkington. On it was pencilled the words: "Serves you right."

Meanwhile Frederick and his men had halted about the windmill. The animals watched them, and a murmur of dismay went round. Two of the men had produced a crowbar and a sledge hammer. They were going to knock the windmill down.

"Impossible!" cried Napoleon. "We have built the walls far too thick for that. They could not knock it down in a week. Courage, comrades!"

But Benjamin was watching the movements of the men intently. The two with the hammer and the crowbar were drilling a hole near the base of the windmill. Slowly, and with an air almost of amusement, Benjamin nodded his long muzzle.

"I thought so," he said. "Do you not see what they are doing? In another moment they are going to pack blasting powder into that hole."

Terrified, the animals waited. It was impossible now to venture out of the shelter of the buildings. After a few minutes the men were seen to be running in all directions. Then there was a deafening roar. The pigeons swirled into the air, and all the animals, except Napoleon, flung themselves flat on their bellies and hid their faces. When they got up again, a huge cloud of black smoke was hanging where the windmill had been. Slowly the breeze drifted it away. The windmill had ceased to exist!

At this sight the animals' courage returned to them. The fear and despair they had felt a moment earlier were drowned in their rage against this vile, contemptible act. A mighty cry for vengeance went up, and without waiting for further orders they charged forth in a body and made straight for the enemy. This time they did not heed the cruel pellets that swept over them like hail. It was a savage, bitter battle. The men fired again and again, and, when the animals got to close quarters, lashed out with their sticks and their heavy boots. A cow, three sheep, and two geese were killed, and nearly everyone was wounded. Even Napoleon, who was directing operations from the rear, had the tip of his tail chipped by a pellet. But the men did not go unscathed either. Three of them had their heads broken by blows from Boxer's hoofs; another was gored in the belly by a cow's horn; another had his trousers nearly torn off by Jessie and Bluebell. And when the nine dogs of Napoleon's own bodyguard, whom he had instructed to make a detour under cover of the hedge, suddenly appeared on the men's flank, baying ferociously, panic overtook them. They saw that they were in danger of being surrounded. Frederick shouted to his men to get out while the going was good, and the next moment the cowardly enemy was running for dear life. The animals chased them right down to the bottom of the field, and got in some last kicks at them as they forced their way through the thorn hedge.

They had won, but they were weary and bleeding. Slowly they began to limp back towards the farm. The sight of their dead comrades stretched upon the grass moved some of them to tears. And for a little while they halted in sorrowful silence at the place where the windmill had once stood. Yes, it was gone; almost the last trace of their labour was gone! Even the foundations were partially destroyed. And in rebuilding it they could not this time, as before, make use of the fallen stones. This time the stones had vanished too. The force of the explosion had flung them to distances of hundreds of yards. It was as though the windmill had never been.

As they approached the farm Squealer, who had unaccountably been absent during the fighting, came skipping towards them, whisking his tail and beaming with satisfaction. And the animals heard, from the direction of the farm buildings, the solemn booming of a gun.

"What is that gun firing for?" said Boxer.

"To celebrate our victory!" cried Squealer.

"What victory?" said Boxer. His knees were bleeding, he had lost a shoe and split his hoof, and a dozen pellets had lodged themselves in his hind leg.

"What victory, comrade? Have we not driven the enemy off our soil—the sacred soil of Animal Farm?"

"But they have destroyed the windmill. And we had worked on it for two years!"

"What matter? We will build another windmill. We will build six windmills if we feel like it. You do not appreciate, comrade, the mighty thing that we have done. The enemy was in occupation of this very ground that we stand upon. And now—thanks to the leadership of Comrade Napoleon—we have won every inch of it back again!"

"Then we have won back what we had before," said Boxer.

"That is our victory," said Squealer.

They limped into the yard. The pellets under the skin of Boxer's leg smarted painfully. He saw ahead of him the heavy labour of rebuilding the windmill from the foundations, and already in imagination he braced himself for the task. But for the first time it occurred to him that he was eleven years old and that perhaps his great muscles were not quite what they had once been.

But when the animals saw the green flag flying, and heard the gun firing again—seven times it was fired in all—and heard the speech that Napoleon made, congratulating them on their conduct, it did seem to them after all that they had won a great victory. The animals slain in the battle were given a solemn funeral. Boxer and Clover pulled the wagon which served as a hearse, and Napoleon himself walked at the head of the procession. Two whole days were given over to celebrations. There were songs, speeches, and more firing of the gun, and a special gift of an apple was bestowed on every animal, with two ounces of corn for each bird and three biscuits for each dog. It was announced that the battle would be called the Battle of the Windmill, and that Napoleon had created a new decoration, the Order of the Green Banner, which he had conferred upon himself. In the general rejoicings the unfortunate affair of the bank-notes was forgotten.

It was a few days later than this that the pigs came upon a case of whisky in the cellars of the farmhouse. It had been overlooked at the time when the house was first occupied. That night there came from the farmhouse the sound of loud singing, in which, to everyone's surprise, the strains of *Beasts of England* were mixed up. At about half-past nine Napoleon, wearing an old bowler hat of Mr. Jones's, was distinctly seen to emerge from the back door, gallop rapidly round the yard, and disappear indoors again. But in the morning a deep silence hung over the farmhouse. Not a pig appeared to be stirring. It was nearly nine o'clock when Squealer made his appearance, walking slowly and dejectedly, his eyes dull, his tail hanging limply behind him, and with every appearance of being seriously ill. He called the animals together and told them that he had a terrible piece of news to impart. Comrade Napoleon was dying!

A cry of lamentation went up. Straw was laid down outside the doors of the farmhouse, and the animals walked on tiptoe. With tears in their eyes they asked one another what they should do if their Leader were taken away from them. A rumour went round that Snowball had after all contrived to introduce poison into Napoleon's food. At eleven o'clock Squealer came out to make another announcement. As his last act upon earth, Comrade Napoleon had pronounced a solemn decree:

the drinking of alcohol was to be punished by death.

By the evening, however, Napoleon appeared to be somewhat better, and the following morning Squealer was able to tell them that he was well on the way to recovery. By the evening of that day Napoleon was back at work, and on the next day it was learned that he had instructed Whymper to purchase in Willingdon some booklets on brewing and distilling. A week later Napoleon gave orders that the small paddock beyond the orchard, which it had previously been intended to set aside as a grazing-ground for animals who were past work, was to be ploughed up. It was given out that the pasture was exhausted and needed re-seeding; but it soon became known that Napoleon intended to sow it with barley.

About this time there occurred a strange incident which hardly anyone was able to understand. One night at about twelve o'clock there was a loud crash in the yard, and the animals rushed out of their stalls. It was a moonlit night. At the foot of the end wall of the big barn, where the Seven Commandments were written, there lay a ladder broken in two pieces. Squealer, temporarily stunned, was sprawling beside it, and near at hand there lay a lantern, a paint-brush, and an overturned pot of white paint. The dogs immediately made a ring round Squealer, and escorted him back to the farmhouse as soon as he was able to walk. None of the animals could form any idea as to what this meant, except old Benjamin, who nodded his muzzle with a knowing air, and seemed to understand, but would say nothing.

But a few days later Muriel, reading over the Seven Commandments to herself, noticed that there was yet another of them which the animals had remembered wrong. They had thought the Fifth Commandment was "No animal shall drink alcohol," but there were two words that they had forgotten. Actually the Commandment read: "No animal shall drink alcohol *to excess*."

CHAPTER IX

Boxer's split hoof was a long time in healing. They had started the rebuilding of the windmill the day after the victory celebrations were ended. Boxer refused to take even a day off work, and made it a point of honour not to let it be seen that he was in pain. In the evenings he would admit privately to Clover that the hoof troubled him a great deal. Clover treated the hoof with poultices of herbs which she prepared by chewing them, and both she and Benjamin urged Boxer to work less hard. "A horse's lungs do not last for ever," she said to him. But Boxer would not listen. He had, he said, only one real ambition left—to see the windmill well under way before he reached the age for retirement.

At the beginning, when the laws of Animal Farm were first formulated, the retiring age had been fixed for horses and pigs at twelve, for cows at fourteen, for dogs at nine, for sheep at seven, and for hens and geese at five. Liberal old-age pensions had been agreed upon. As yet no animal had actually retired on pension, but of late the subject had been discussed more and more. Now that the small field beyond the orchard had been set aside for barley, it was rumoured that a corner of the large pasture was to be fenced off and turned into a grazing-ground for superannuated animals. For a horse, it was said, the pension would be five pounds of corn a day and, in winter, fifteen pounds of hay, with a carrot or possibly an apple on public holidays. Boxer's twelfth birthday was due in the late summer of the following year.

Meanwhile life was hard. The winter was as cold as the last one had been, and food was even shorter. Once again all rations were reduced, except those of the pigs and the dogs. A too rigid equality in rations, Squealer explained, would have been contrary to the principles of Animalism. In any case he had no difficulty in proving to the other animals that they were *not* in reality short of food, whatever the appearances might be. For the time being, certainly, it had been found necessary to make a readjustment of rations (Squealer always spoke of it as a "readjustment," never as a "reduction"), but in comparison with the days of Jones, the improvement was enormous. Reading out the figures in a shrill, rapid voice, he proved to them in detail that they had more oats, more hay, more turnips than they had had in Jones's day, that they worked shorter hours, that their drinking water was of better quality, that they lived longer, that a larger proportion of their young ones survived infancy, and that they had more straw in their stalls and suffered less from fleas. The animals believed every word of it. Truth to tell, Jones and all he stood for had almost faded out of their memories. They knew that life nowadays was harsh and bare, that they were often hungry and often cold, and that they were usually working when they were not asleep. But doubtless it had been worse in the old days. They were glad to believe so. Besides, in those days they had been slaves and now they were free, and that made all the difference, as Squealer did not fail to point out.

There were many more mouths to feed now. In the autumn the four sows had all littered about simultaneously, producing thirty-one young pigs between them. The young pigs were piebald, and as Napoleon was the only boar on the farm, it was possible to guess at their parentage. It was announced that later, when bricks and timber had been purchased, a schoolroom would be built in the farmhouse garden. For the time being, the young pigs were given their instruction by Napoleon himself in the farmhouse kitchen. They took their exercise in the garden, and were discouraged from playing with the other young animals. About this time, too, it was laid down as a rule that when a pig and any other animal met on the path, the other animal must stand aside: and also that all pigs, of whatever degree, were to have the privilege of wearing green ribbons on their tails on Sundays.

The farm had had a fairly successful year, but was still short of money. There were the bricks, sand, and lime for the schoolroom to be purchased, and it would also be necessary to begin saving up again for the machinery for the windmill. Then there were lamp oil and candles for the house, sugar for Napoleon's own table (he forbade this to the other pigs, on the ground that it made them fat), and all the usual replacements such as tools, nails, string, coal, wire, scrap-iron, and dog biscuits. A stump of hay and part of the potato crop were sold off, and the contract for eggs was increased to six hundred a week, so that that year the hens barely hatched enough chicks to keep their numbers at the same level. Rations, reduced in December, were reduced again in February, and lanterns in the stalls were forbidden to save oil. But the pigs seemed comfortable enough, and in fact were putting on weight if anything. One afternoon in late February a warm, rich, appetising scent, such as the animals had never smelt before, wafted itself across the yard from the little brewhouse, which had been disused in Jones's time, and which stood beyond the kitchen. Someone said it was the smell of cooking barley. The animals sniffed the air hungrily and wondered whether a warm mash was being prepared for their supper. But no warm mash appeared, and on the following Sunday it was announced that from now onwards all barley would be reserved for the pigs. The field beyond the orchard had already been sown with barley. And the news soon leaked out that every pig was now receiving a ration of a pint of beer daily, with half a gallon for Napoleon himself, which was always served to him in the Crown Derby soup tureen.

But if there were hardships to be borne, they were partly offset by the fact that life nowadays had a greater dignity than it had had before. There were more songs, more speeches, more processions. Napoleon had commanded that once a week there should be held something called a Spontaneous Demonstration, the object of which was to celebrate the struggles and triumphs of Animal Farm. At the appointed time the animals would leave their work and march round the precincts of the farm in military formation, with the pigs leading, then the horses, then the cows, then the sheep, and then the poultry. The dogs flanked the procession and at the head of all marched Napoleon's black cockerel. Boxer and Clover always carried between them a green banner marked with the hoof and the horn and the caption, "Long live Comrade Napoleon!" Afterwards there were recitations of poems composed in Napoleon's honour, and a speech by Squealer giving particulars of the latest increases in the production of foodstuffs, and on occasion a shot was fired from the gun. The sheep were the greatest devotees of the Spontaneous Demonstration, and if anyone complained (as a few animals sometimes did, when no pigs or dogs were near) that they wasted time and meant a lot of standing about in the cold, the sheep were sure to silence him with a tremendous bleating of "Four legs good, two legs bad!" But by and large the animals enjoyed these celebrations. They found it comforting to be reminded that, after all, they were truly their own masters and that the work they did was for their own benefit. So that, what with the songs, the processions, Squealer's lists of figures, the thunder of the gun, the crowing of the cockerel, and the fluttering of the flag, they were able to forget that their bellies were empty, at least part of the time.

In April, Animal Farm was proclaimed a Republic, and it became necessary to elect a President. There was only one candidate, Napoleon, who was elected unanimously. On the same day it was given out that fresh documents had been discovered which revealed further details about Snowball's complicity with Jones. It now appeared that Snowball had not, as the animals had previously imagined, merely attempted to lose the Battle of the Cowshed by means of a stratagem, but had been openly fighting on Jones's side. In fact, it was he who had actually been the leader of the human forces, and had charged into battle with the words "Long live Humanity!" on his lips. The wounds on Snowball's back, which a few of the animals still remembered to have seen, had been inflicted by Napoleon's teeth.

In the middle of the summer Moses the raven suddenly reappeared on the farm, after an absence of several years. He was quite unchanged, still did no work, and talked in the same strain as ever about Sugarcandy Mountain. He would perch on a stump, flap his black wings, and talk by the hour to anyone who would listen. "Up there, comrades," he would say solemnly, pointing to the sky with his large beak—"up there, just on the other side of that dark cloud that you can see—there it lies, Sugarcandy Mountain, that happy country where we poor animals shall rest for ever from our labours!" He even claimed to have been there on one of his higher flights, and to have seen the everlasting fields of clover and the linseed cake and lump sugar growing on the hedges. Many of the animals believed him. Their lives now, they reasoned, were hungry and laborious; was it not right and just that a better world should exist somewhere else? A thing that was difficult to de-termine was the attitude of the pigs towards Moses. They all declared contemptuously that his stories about Sugarcandy Mountain were lies, and yet they allowed him to remain on the farm, not working, with an allowance of a gill of beer a day.

After his hoof had healed up, Boxer worked harder than ever. Indeed, all the animals worked like slaves that year. Apart from the regular work of the farm, and the rebuilding of the windmill, there was the schoolhouse for the young pigs, which was started in March. Sometimes the long hours on insufficient food were hard to bear, but Boxer never faltered. In nothing that he said or did was there any sign that his strength was not what it had been. It was only his appearance that was a little altered; his hide was less shiny than it had used to be, and his great haunches seemed to have shrunken. The others said, "Boxer will pick up when the spring grass comes on"; but the spring came and Boxer grew no fatter. Sometimes on the slope leading to the top of the quarry, when he braced his muscles against the weight of some vast boulder, it seemed that nothing kept him on his feet except the will to continue. At such times his lips were seen to form the words, "I will work harder"; he had no voice left. Once again Clover and Benjamin warned him to take care of his health, but Boxer paid no attention. His twelfth birthday was approaching. He did not care what happened so long as a good store of stone was accumulated before he went on pension.

Late one evening in the summer, a sudden rumour ran round the farm that something had happened to Boxer. He had gone out alone to drag a load of stone down to the windmill. And sure enough, the rumour was true. A few minutes later two pigeons came racing in with the news: "Boxer has fallen! He is lying on his side and can't get up!"

About half the animals on the farm rushed out to the knoll where the windmill stood. There lay Boxer, between the shafts of the cart, his neck stretched out, unable even to raise his head. His eyes were glazed, his sides matted with sweat. A thin stream of blood had trickled out of his mouth. Clover dropped to her knees at his side.

"Boxer!" she cried, "how are you?"

"It is my lung," said Boxer in a weak voice. "It does not matter. I think you will be able to finish the windmill without me. There is a pretty good store of stone accumulated. I had only another month to go in any case. To tell you the truth, I had been looking forward to my retirement. And perhaps, as Benjamin is growing old too, they will let him retire at the same time and be a companion to me."

"We must get help at once," said Clover. "Run, somebody, and tell Squealer what has happened."

All the other animals immediately raced back to the farmhouse to give Squealer the news. Only Clover remained, and Benjamin, who lay down at Boxer's side, and, without speaking, kept the flies off him with his long tail. After about a quarter of an hour Squealer appeared, full of sympathy and concern. He said that Comrade Napoleon had learned with the very deepest distress of this misfortune to one of the most loyal workers on the farm, and was already making arrangements to send Boxer to be treated in the hospital at Willingdon. The animals felt a little uneasy at this. Except for Mollie and Snowball, no other animal had ever left the farm, and they did not like to think of their sick comrade in the hands of human beings. However, Squealer easily convinced them that the veterinary surgeon in Willingdon could treat Boxer's case more satisfactorily than could be done on the farm. And about half an hour later, when Boxer had somewhat recovered, he was with difficulty got on to his feet, and managed to limp back to his stall, where Clover and Benjamin had prepared a good bed of straw for him.

For the next two days Boxer remained in his stall. The pigs had sent out a large bottle of pink medicine which they had found in the medicine chest in the bathroom, and Clover administered it to Boxer twice a day after meals. In the evenings she lay in his stall and talked to him, while Benjamin kept the flies off him. Boxer professed not to be sorry for what had happened. If he made a good recovery, he might expect to live another three years, and he looked forward to the peaceful days that he would spend in the corner of the big pasture. It would be the first time that he had had leisure to study and improve his mind. He intended, he said, to devote the rest of his life to learning the remaining twenty-two letters of the alphabet.

However, Benjamin and Clover could only be with Boxer after working hours, and it was in the middle of the day when the van came to take him away. The animals were all at work weeding turnips under the supervision of a pig, when they were astonished to see Benjamin come galloping from the direction of the farm buildings, braying at the top of his voice. It was the first time that they had ever seen Benjamin excited—indeed, it was the first time that anyone had ever seen him gallop. "Quick, quick!" he shouted. "Come at once! They're taking Boxer away!" Without waiting for orders from the pig, the animals broke off work and raced back to the farm buildings. Sure enough, there in the yard was a large closed van, drawn by two horses, with lettering on its side and a sly-looking man in a low-crowned bowler hat sitting on the driver's seat. And Boxer's stall was empty.

The animals crowded round the van. "Good-bye, Boxer!" they chorused, "good-bye!"

"Fools! Fools!" shouted Benjamin, prancing round them and stamping the earth with his small hoofs. "Fools! Do you not see what is written on the side of that van?"

That gave the animals pause, and there was a hush. Muriel began to spell out the words. But Benjamin pushed her aside and in the midst of a deadly silence he read:

" 'Alfred Simmonds, Horse Slaughterer and Glue Boiler, Willingdon. Dealer in Hides and Bone-Meal. Kennels Supplied.' Do you not understand what that means? They are taking Boxer to the knacker's!"

A cry of horror burst from all the animals. At this moment the man on the box whipped up his horses and the van moved out of the yard at a smart trot. All the animals followed, crying out at the tops of their voices. Clover forced her way to the front. The van began to gather speed. Clover tried to stir her stout limbs to a gallop, and achieved a canter. "Boxer!" she cried. "Boxer! Boxer! Boxer!" And just at this moment, as though he had heard the uproar outside, Boxer's face, with the white stripe down his nose, appeared at the small window at the back of the van.

"Boxer!" cried Clover in a terrible voice.

"Boxer! Get out! Get out quickly! They're taking you to your death!"

All the animals took up the cry of "Get out, Boxer, get out!" But the van was already gathering speed and drawing away from them. It was uncertain whether Boxer had understood what Clover had said. But a moment later his face disappeared from the window and there was the sound of a tremendous drumming of hoofs inside the van. He was trying to kick his way out. The time had been when a few kicks from Boxer's hoofs would have smashed the van to matchwood. But alas! his strength had left him; and in a few moments the sound of drumming hoofs grew fainter and died away. In desperation the animals began appealing to the two horses which drew the van to stop. "Comrades, comrades!" they shouted. "Don't take your own brother to his death!" But the stupid brutes, too ignorant to realise what was happening, merely set back their ears and quickened their pace. Boxer's face did not reappear at the window. Too late, someone thought of racing ahead and shutting the five-barred gate; but in another moment the van was through it and rapidly disappearing down the road. Boxer was never seen again.

Three days later it was announced that he had died in the hospital at Willingdon, in spite of receiving every attention a horse could have. Squealer came to announce the news to the others. He had, he said, been present during Boxer's last hours.

"It was the most affecting sight I have ever seen!" said Squealer, lifting his trotter and wiping away a tear. "I was at his bedside at the very last. And at the end, almost too weak to speak, he whispered in my ear that his sole sorrow was to have passed on before the windmill was finished. 'Forward, comrades!' he whispered. 'Forward in the name of the Rebellion. Long live Animal Farm! Long live Comrade Napoleon! Napoleon is always right.' Those were his very last words, comrades."

Here Squealer's demeanour suddenly changed. He fell silent for a moment, and his little eyes darted suspicious glances from side to side before he proceeded.

It had come to his knowledge, he said, that a foolish and wicked rumour had been circulated at the time of Boxer's removal. Some of the animals had noticed that the van which took Boxer away was marked "Horse Slaughterer," and had actually jumped to the conclusion that Boxer was being sent to the knacker's. It was almost unbelievable, said Squealer, that any animal could be so stupid. Surely, he cried indignantly, whisking his tail and skipping from side to side, surely they knew their beloved Leader, Comrade Napoleon, better than that? But the explanation was really very simple. The van had previously been the property of the knacker, and had been bought by the veterinary surgeon, who had not yet painted the old name out. That was how the mistake had arisen.

The animals were enormously relieved to hear this. And when Squealer went on to give further graphic details of Boxer's death-bed, the admirable care he had received, and the expensive medicines for which Napoleon had paid without a thought as to the cost, their last doubts disappeared and the sorrow that they felt for their comrade's death was tempered by the thought that at least he had died happy.

Napoleon himself appeared at the meeting on the following Sunday morning and pronounced a short oration in Boxer's honour. It had not been possible, he said, to bring back their lamented comrade's remains for interment on the farm, but he had ordered a large wreath to be made from the laurels in the farmhouse garden and sent down to be placed on Boxer's grave. And in a few days' time the pigs intended to hold a memorial banquet in Boxer's honour. Napoleon ended his speech with a reminder of Boxer's two favourite maxims, "I will work harder" and "Comrade Napoleon is always right"—maxims, he said, which every animal would do well to adopt as his own.

On the day appointed for the banquet, a grocer's van drove up from Willingdon and delivered a large wooden crate at the farmhouse. That night there was the sound of uproarious singing, which was followed by what sounded like a violent quarrel and ended at about eleven o'clock with a tremendous crash of glass. No one stirred in the farmhouse before noon on the following day, and the word went round that from somewhere or other the pigs had acquired the money to buy themselves another case of whisky.

CHAPTER X

Years passed. The seasons came and went, the short animal lives fled by. A time came when there was no one who remembered the old days before the Rebellion, except Clover, Benjamin, Moses the raven, and a number of the pigs.

Muriel was dead; Bluebell, Jessie, and Pincher were dead. Jones too was dead—he had died in an inebriates' home in another part of the country. Snowball was forgotten. Boxer was forgotten, except by the few who had known him. Clover was an old stout mare now, stiff in the joints and with a tendency to rheumy eyes. She was two years past the retiring age, but in fact no animal had ever actually retired. The talk of setting aside a corner of the pasture for superannuated animals had long since been dropped. Napoleon was now a mature boar of twenty-four stone. Squealer was so fat that he could with difficulty see out of his eyes. Only old Benjamin was much the same as ever, except for being a little greyer about the muzzle, and, since Boxer's death, more morose and taciturn than ever.

There were many more creatures on the farm now, though the increase was not so great as had been expected in earlier years. Many animals had been born to whom the Rebellion was only a dim tradition, passed on by word of mouth, and others had been bought who had never heard mention of such a thing before their arrival. The farm possessed three horses now besides Clover. They were fine upstanding beasts, willing workers and good comrades, but very stupid. None of them proved able to learn the alphabet beyond the letter B. They accepted everything that they were told about the Rebellion and the principles of Animalism, especially from Clover, for whom they had an almost filial respect; but it was doubtful whether they understood very much of it.

The farm was more prosperous now, and better organised: it had even been enlarged by two fields which had been bought from Mr. Pilkington. The windmill had been successfully completed at last, and the farm possessed a threshing machine and a hay elevator of its own, and various new buildings had been added to it. Whymper had bought himself a dogcart. The windmill, however, had not after all been used for generating electrical power. It was used for milling corn, and brought in a handsome money profit. The animals were hard at work building yet another windmill; when that one was finished, so it was said, the dynamos would be installed. But the luxuries of which Snowball had once taught the animals to dream, the stalls with electric light and hot and cold water, and the three-day week, were no longer talked about. Napoleon had denounced such ideas as contrary to the spirit of Animalism. The truest happiness, he said, lay in working hard and living frugally.

Somehow it seemed as though the farm had grown richer without making the animals themselves any richer—except, of course, for the pigs and the dogs. Perhaps this was partly because there were so many pigs and so many dogs. It was not that these creatures did not work, after their fashion. There was, as Squealer was never tired of explaining, endless work in the supervision and organisation of the farm. Much of this work was of a kind that the other animals were too ignorant to understand. For example, Squealer told them that the pigs had to expend enormous labours every day upon mysterious things called "files," "reports," "minutes," and "memoranda." These were large sheets of paper which had to be closely covered with writing, and as soon as they were so covered, they were burnt in the furnace. This was of the highest importance for the welfare of the farm, Squealer said. But still, neither pigs nor dogs produced any food by their own labour; and there were very many of them, and their appetites were always good.

As for the others, their life, so far as they knew, was as it had always been. They were generally hungry, they slept on straw, they drank from the pool, they laboured in the fields; in winter they were troubled by the cold, and in summer by the flies. Sometimes the older ones among them racked their dim memories and tried to determine whether in the early days of the Rebellion, when Jones's expulsion was still recent, things had been better or worse than now. They could not remember. There was nothing with which they could compare their present lives: they had nothing to go upon except Squealer's lists of figures, which invariably demonstrated that everything was getting better and better. The animals found the problem insoluble; in any case, they had little time for speculating on such things now. Only old Benjamin professed to remember every detail of his long life and to know that things never had been, nor ever could be much better or much worse —hunger, hardship, and disappointment being, so he said, the unalterable law of life.

And yet the animals never gave up hope. More, they never lost, even for an instant, their sense of honour and privilege in being members of Animal Farm. They were still the only farm in the whole county—in all England!—owned and operated by animals. Not one of them, not even the youngest, not even the newcomers who had been brought from farms ten or twenty miles away, ever ceased to marvel at that. And when they heard the gun booming and saw the green flag fluttering at the masthead, their hearts swelled with imperishable pride, and the talk turned always towards the old heroic days, the expulsion of Jones, the writing of the Seven Commandments, the great battles in which the human invaders had been defeated. None of the old dreams had been abandoned. The Republic of the Animals which Major had foretold, when the green fields of England should be untrodden by human feet, was still believed in. Some day it was coming: it might not be soon, it might not be within the lifetime of any animal now living, but still it was coming. Even the tune of *Beasts of England* was perhaps hummed secretly here and there: at any rate, it was a fact that every animal on the farm knew it, though no one would have dared to sing it aloud. It might be that their lives were hard and that not all of their hopes had been fulfilled; but they were conscious that they were not as other animals. If they went hungry, it was not from feeding tyrannical human beings; if they worked hard, at least they worked for themselves. No creature among them went upon two legs. No creature called any other creature "Master." All animals were equal.

One day in early summer Squealer ordered the sheep to follow him, and led them out to a piece of waste ground at the other end of the farm, which had become overgrown with birch saplings. The sheep spent the whole day there browsing at the leaves under Squealer's supervision. In the evening he returned to the farmhouse himself, but, as it was warm weather, told the sheep to stay where they were. It ended by their remaining there for a whole week, during which time the other animals saw nothing of them. Squealer was with them for the greater part of every day. He was, he said, teaching them to sing a new song, for which privacy was needed.

It was just after the sheep had returned, on a pleasant evening when the animals had finished work and were making their way back to the farm buildings, that the terrified neighing of a horse sounded from the yard. Startled, the animals stopped in their tracks. It was Clover's voice. She neighed again, and all the animals broke into a gallop and rushed into the yard. Then they saw what Clover had seen.

It was a pig walking on his hind legs.

Yes, it was Squealer. A little awkwardly, as though not quite used to supporting his considerable bulk in that position, but with perfect balance, he was strolling across the yard. And a moment later, out from the door of the farmhouse came a long file of pigs, all walking on their hind legs. Some did it better than others, one or two were even a trifle unsteady and looked as though they would have liked the support of a stick, but every one of them made his way right round the yard successfully. And finally there was a tremendous baying of dogs and a shrill crowing from the black cockerel, and out came Napoleon himself, majestically upright, casting haughty glances from side to side, and with his dogs gambolling round him.

He carried a whip in his trotter.

There was a deadly silence. Amazed, terrified, huddling together, the animals watched the long line of pigs march slowly round the yard. It was as though the world had turned upside-down. Then there came a moment when the first shock had worn off and when, in spite of everything—in spite of their terror of the dogs, and of the habit, developed through long years, of never complaining, never criticising, no matter what happened— they might have uttered some word of protest. But just at that moment, as though at a signal, all the sheep burst out into a tremendous bleating of—

"Four legs good, two legs *better!* Four legs good, two legs *better!* Four legs good, two legs *better!*"

It went on for five minutes without stopping. And by the time the sheep had quieted down, the chance to utter any protest had passed, for the pigs had marched back into the farmhouse.

Benjamin felt a nose nuzzling at his shoulder. He looked round. It was Clover. Her old eyes looked dimmer than ever. Without saying anything, she tugged gently at his mane and led him round to the end of the big barn, where the Seven Commandments were written. For a minute or two they stood gazing at the tarred wall with its white lettering.

"My sight is failing," she said finally. "Even when I was young I could not have read what was written there. But it appears to me that that wall looks different. Are the Seven Commandments the same as they used to be, Benjamin?"

For once Benjamin consented to break his rule, and he read out to her what was written on the wall. There was nothing there now except a single Commandment. It ran:

ALL ANIMALS ARE EQUAL.
BUT SOME ANIMALS ARE MORE EQUAL THAN OTHERS

After that it did not seem strange when next day the pigs who were supervising the work of the farm all carried whips in their trotters. It did not seem strange to learn that the pigs had bought themselves a wireless set, were arranging to install a telephone, and had taken out subscriptions to *John Bull, Tit-Bits,* and the *Daily Mirror.* It did not seem strange when Napoleon was seen strolling in the farmhouse garden with a pipe in his mouth—no, not even when the pigs took Mr. Jones's clothes out of the wardrobes and put them on, Napoleon himself appearing in a black coat, ratcatcher breeches, and leather leggings, while his favourite sow appeared in the watered silk dress which Mrs. Jones had been used to wear on Sundays.

A week later, in the afternoon, a number of dogcarts drove up to the farm. A deputation of neighbouring farmers had been invited to make a tour of inspection. They were shown all over the farm, and expressed great admiration for everything they saw, especially the windmill. The animals were weeding the turnip field. They worked diligently, hardly raising their faces from the ground, and not knowing whether to be more frightened of the pigs or of the human visitors.

That evening loud laughter and bursts of singing came from the farmhouse. And suddenly, at the sound of the mingled voices, the animals were stricken with curiosity. What could be happening in there, now that for the first time animals and human beings were meeting on terms of equality? With one accord they began to creep as quietly as possible into the farmhouse garden.

At the gate they paused, half frightened to go on, but Clover led the way in. They tiptoed up to the house, and such animals as were tall enough peered in at the dining-room window. There, round the long table, sat half a dozen farmers and half a dozen of the more eminent pigs, Napoleon himself occupying the seat of honour at the head of the table. The pigs appeared completely at ease in their chairs. The company had been enjoying a game of cards, but had broken off for the moment, evidently in order to drink a toast. A large jug was circulating, and the mugs were being refilled with beer. No one noticed the wondering faces of the animals that gazed in at the window.

Mr. Pilkington, of Foxwood, had stood up, his mug in his hand. In a moment, he said, he would ask the present company to drink a toast. But before doing so, there were a few words that he felt it incumbent upon him to say.

It was a source of great satisfaction to him, he said—and, he was sure, to all others present —to feel that a long period of mistrust and misunderstanding had now come to an end. There had been a time—not that he, or any of the present company, had shared such sentiments—but there had been a time when the respected proprietors of Animal Farm had been regarded, he would not say with hostility, but perhaps with a certain measure of misgiving, by their human neighbours. Unfortunate incidents had occurred, mistaken ideas had been current. It had been felt that the existence of a farm owned and operated by pigs was somehow abnormal and was liable to have an unsettling effect in the neighbourhood. Too many farmers had assumed, without due enquiry, that on such a farm a spirit of licence and indiscipline would prevail. They had been nervous about the effects upon their own animals, or even upon their human employees. But all such doubts were now dispelled. Today he and his friends had visited Animal Farm and inspected every inch of it with their own eyes, and what did they find? Not only the most up-to-date methods, but a discipline and an orderliness which should be an example to all farmers everywhere. He believed that he was right in saying that the lower animals on Animal Farm did more work and received less food than any animals in the county. Indeed, he and his fellow-visitors today had observed many features which they intended to introduce on their own farms immediately.

He would end his remarks, he said, by emphasising once again the friendly feelings that subsisted, and ought to subsist, between Animal Farm and its neighbours. Between pigs and human beings there was not, and there need not be, any clash of interests whatever. Their struggles and their difficulties were one. Was not the labour problem the same everywhere? Here it became apparent that Mr. Pilkington was about to spring some carefully prepared witticism on the company, but for a moment he was too overcome by amusement to be able to utter it. After much choking, during which his various chins turned purple, he managed to get it out: "If you have your lower animals to contend with," he said, "we have our lower classes!" This *bon mot* set the table in a roar; and Mr. Pilkington once again congratulated the pigs on the low rations, the long working hours, and the general absence of pampering which he had observed on Animal Farm.

And now, he said finally, he would ask the company to rise to their feet and make certain that their glasses were full. "Gentlemen," concluded Mr. Pilkington, "gentlemen, I give you a toast: To the prosperity of Animal Farm!"

There was enthusiastic cheering and stamping of feet. Napoleon was so gratified that he left his place and came round the table to clink his mug against Mr. Pilkington's before emptying it. When the cheering had died down, Napoleon, who had remained on his feet, intimated that he too had a few words to say.

Like all of Napoleon's speeches, it was short and to the point. He too, he said, was happy that the period of misunderstanding was at an end. For a long time there had been rumours—circulated, he had reason to think, by some malignant enemy—that there was something subversive and even revolutionary in the outlook of himself and his colleagues. They had been credited with attempting to stir up rebellion among the animals on neighbouring farms. Nothing could be further from the truth! Their sole wish, now and in the past, was to live at peace and in normal business relations with their neighbours. This farm which he had the honour to control, he added, was a co-operative enterprise. The title-deeds, which were in his own possession, were owned by the pigs jointly.

He did not believe, he said, that any of the old suspicions still lingered, but certain changes had been made recently in the routine of the farm which should have the effect of promoting confidence still further. Hitherto the animals on the farm had had a rather foolish custom of addressing one another as "Comrade." This was to be suppressed. There had also been a very strange custom, whose origin was unknown, of marching every Sunday morning past a boar's skull which was nailed to a post in the garden. This, too, would be suppressed, and the skull had already been buried. His visitors might have observed, too, the green flag which flew from the masthead. If so, they would perhaps have noted that the white hoof and horn with which it had previously been marked had now been removed. It would be a plain green flag from now onwards.

He had only one criticism, he said, to make of Mr. Pilkington's excellent and neighbourly speech. Mr. Pilkington had referred throughout to "Animal Farm." He could not of course know—for he, Napoleon, was only now for the first time announcing it—that the name "Animal Farm" had been abolished. Henceforward the farm was to be known as "The Manor

Farm"—which, he believed, was its correct and original name.

"Gentlemen," concluded Napoleon, "I will give you the same toast as before, but in a different form. Fill your glasses to the brim. Gentlemen, here is my toast: To the prosperity of The Manor Farm!"

There was the same hearty cheering as before, and the mugs were emptied to the dregs. But as the animals outside gazed at the scene, it seemed to them that some strange thing was happening. What was it that had altered in the faces of the pigs? Clover's old dim eyes flitted from one face to another. Some of them had five chins, some had four, some had three. But what was it that seemed to be melting and changing? Then, the applause having come to an end, the company took up their cards and continued the game that had been interrupted, and the animals crept silently away.

But they had not gone twenty yards when they stopped short. An uproar of voices was coming from the farmhouse. They rushed back and looked through the window again. Yes, a violent quarrel was in progress. There were shoutings, bangings on the table, sharp suspicious glances, furious denials. The source of the trouble appeared to be that Napoleon and Mr. Pilkington had each played an ace of spades simultaneously.

Twelve voices were shouting in anger, and they were all alike. No question, now, what had happened to the faces of the pigs. The creatures outside looked from pig to man, and from man to pig, and from pig to man again; but already it was impossible to say which was which.

Questions

1. What types of human beings are represented by the various animals who gather to hear Major's dream? Do they between them make up a cross section of society?

2. Consider Major's speech about the miserable life of animals. This is in part a satire on the way in which men are treated, but it is also a fair description of man's cruelty to the beasts. What part does this cruelty play in the novel? Is it part of a larger theme?

3. Make a list of the various kinds of exploitation shown in the novel. Is it possible that Orwell is not satirizing Russia and communism only?

4. What kind of life does Orwell obviously think of as ideal? How does he remind us of this ideal during the course of the novel?

5. Distinguish the characters of the three pigs, Snowball, Squealer, and Napoleon. Why are the pigs leaders?

6. Discuss the ways in which *Animal Farm* bears out Lord Acton's statement, "Power tends to corrupt; absolute power corrupts absolutely."

7. Trace the manner in which the meaning of the word "equal" is gradually shifted. What aspect of modern *Realpolitik* is Orwell satirizing?

8. A variety of forces, not a single one, pervert the revolution. Discuss.

9. Discuss the character of Benjamin and his philosophy.

10. In what ways do the pigs distort and rearrange truth and history?

11. What is the significance of the last sentence of the book?

II. Theories

As Robert C. Elliott notes in his essay "The Satirist and Society," satire has never enjoyed a very high reputation with literary critics, and even the satiric writers have felt it necessary to apologize for their unpleasant art. In recent years, however, as the genre has attracted more attention, critics have written about it with a good deal more sympathy than was usual in the past.

The first three essays reprinted here trace the course of satire from its origins in sympathetic magic to the present, and each defines the nature of this kind of writing by a different method. The three critics agree in rejecting certain traditional approaches to satire—for example, the approach which seeks to attribute the peculiarities of satire to the unpleasant character of the author—and all are in essential agreement on how satire is to be understood; but each of the essays focuses on a different aspect of satire, and among them they provide the reader with a broad range of critical techniques. Each is part of a longer critical book, and the reader who desires further information may consult these. Robert C. Elliott's "The Satirist and Society" appears in slightly altered form in his fascinating discussion of the history and nature of satire, *The Power of Satire: Magic, Ritual, Art* (1960). Northrop Frye's "The Mythos of Winter: Irony and Satire" forms a section of his *Anatomy of Criticism* (1957). "A Theory of Satire" is the first chapter of *The Cankered Muse: The Satire of the English Renaissance* (1959). The fourth selection provides a description of several satiric techniques. Those who wish to consult additional critical writings on satire will find the following the most useful works: Horace, the first satire of the second book; Alexander Pope, "Epilogue to the Satires," the conclusion to the *Imitations of Horace;* John Dryden, "An Essay on Satire"; Mary Claire Randolph, "The Structural Design of Formal Verse Satire," *Philological Quarterly*, 21 (1942); Maynard Mack, "The Muse of Satire," *Yale Review,* 41 (1951-52): and James Sutherland, *English Satire* (1958).

ROBERT C. ELLIOTT

The Satirist and Society

Two cripples, characters in Yeats' play *The King's Threshold* (1904), speak:

> SECOND CRIPPLE. If I were the King I wouldn't meddle with him [Seanchan, Chief Poet of Ireland in the seventh century]; there is something queer about a man that makes rhymes. I knew a man that would be making rhymes year in and year out under a thorn at the crossing of three roads, and he was no sooner dead than every thorn-tree from Inchy to Kiltartan withered, and he a ragged man like ourselves.
> FIRST CRIPPLE. Those that make rhymes have a power from beyond the world.

The central notion here is clearly that of the artist as magician—as one set apart by reason of his gift, one to be regarded with awe, with reverence and with fear. The notion is not uncommon and in some respects survives today: "People speak with justice," says Freud, "of the 'magic of art' and compare artists with magicians. . . ." But Yeats' lines have a special application; in the play Seanchan is presented as a symbolic figure: he is The Artist, heroically prepared to die in defense of the ancient right of the poets. The Middle Irish tale from which Yeats took the episode, however, presents Seanchan as a particular kind of artist: he is a satirist, well known for his magical powers, best known, in fact, as a fore-

runner of The Pied Piper of Hamlin.[1] In a fit of pique Seanchan satirized certain mice who had stolen his food; his riddling verses end:

> You mice, which are in the roof of the house,
> Arise all of you, and fall down.

Ten mice plopped down dead at his feet. There is no mistaking the magic; and in view of the tradition behind Seanchan (comic as it is) the remarks of the Cripples in Yeats' play open up richly ambiguous areas of meaning.

The poet-satirists of Old Ireland were all magicians; they all had, at least potentially, "a power from beyond the world"; and so did other, non-Irish satirists. The historical fact has implications for the forms satire takes, for the language it uses, and, I believe, for the relation of satirist (ancient and modern) to society.

I

In the *Poetics* Aristotle declares that the earliest division of poetry occurred when the "graver spirits imitated noble actions, and the

FROM *ELH: A Journal of English Literary History* (Vol. 21, No. 3, September 1954). Reprinted by permission of The Johns Hopkins Press.

[1] The original tale is the *Immtheacht na Tromdáihme* [*Proceedings of the Great Bardic Institute*]; Owen Connellan's translation appears in Vol. V of *Transactions of the Ossianic Society* (1860). It is a remarkable tale—a satire on the Irish satirists, full of wild burlesque and very amusing. Of the episode from the tale which he utilized, Yeats says that he "twisted it about and revised its moral that the poet might have the best of it."

actions of good men" while the "more trivial sort imitated the actions of meaner persons, at first composing satires, as the former did hymns to the gods and the praises of famous men." The lampooners became writers of Comedy, and the Epic poets writers of Tragedy. "Tragedy—as also Comedy—[he says] was at first mere improvisation. The one originated with the leaders of the dithyramb, the other with those of the phallic songs, which are still in use in many of our cities." Old Comedy then developed, according to Aristotle, out of "satire," specifically out of satiric improvisations uttered by the Leaders of the Phallic Songs. Modern scholars, particularly the classical anthropologists Jane Harrison and F. M. Cornford, have shown in detail how that development must have taken place. The Phallic Songs were, of course, ritual performances devoted to increasing the fertility of the land, the herds, and the people. The ritual seems to have had two general parts: the invocation of good through the magic influence of the phallus, and the expulsion of evil by means of the magic power of satire, invective, lampoon—this last improvised by the Leaders of the Songs. In the apotropaic part of the ritual the satire might be hurled at wicked individuals by name or at evil influences generally; but for our purposes the important consideration is that the satire was thought to be magically efficacious. It was a coercion of certain natural forces through the magical potency of the word.

Here, in this much simplified account of a primitive ritual, is the first indication that in the beginning "satire" is inextricably involved with magic. There is much supporting evidence.

For example, Archilochus, the almost legendary "inventor" of the iambic measure—he flourished in the seventh century B.C.—was thought to have wielded more than natural power in his invectives against his enemies. Archilochus was betrothed to the daughter of Lycambes. For some reason Lycambes broke "the great oath made by salt and table" (as Archilochus says in one of the surviving fragments) and refused to allow the marriage. Archilochus composed iambics of such terrible virulence, or of such uncanny power, that Lycambes and his daughter hanged them-selves. A similar story is told of the sixth-century Hipponax, whose iambics, it is said, drove the sculptors Bupalis and Athenis to suicide. We can account for these stories only by recognizing the wide-spread belief from which they spring—the belief, as the classical scholar G. L. Hendrickson puts it, in "the destructive, supernatural power of words of ill-omened invective or imprecation. . . ."

Similar beliefs existed in other cultures. The ancient Arabic satirist, for example, was the seer, the oracle of his tribe. His enormous prestige derived from his role as magician, for his primary function was to compose magical satires, thought always to be fatal, against the tribal enemy. The Arabs thought of their satires concretely as weapons, and as the satirist led his people into battle—his hair anointed on one side only, his mantle hanging loose, shod with only one sandal—he would hurl his magical verses at the foe just as he would hurl a spear; and indeed the satires might be dodged, just as a spear could be dodged, by ducking and bobbing and skipping off.

The most impressive mass of evidence for the early connection of satire and magic, however, exists in the sagas and tales of pre-Christian and early Christian Ireland. Over forty years ago F. N. Robinson brilliantly demonstrated that, in Old Irish society, poetic invective, mockery, and magical malediction were inseparably bound together. The ancient Celtic poet, like his Arabic counterpart, was a seer, his almost unlimited privilege and power deriving unmistakably from his command over preternatural forces. Irish poet-satirists were called upon to levy taxes in areas where, presumably, the sword had proved ineffective as a means of collection—where, as the old laws put it, "points of satire" were regarded, but "points of weapons" were not. The most solemn treaties invoked the satirist's power as a threat to those who might think of violation. And in warfare the satirist had a proudly, even crucially, significant role; witness this brief dialogue from the saga of *The Second Battle of Moytura:*

"And thou, O Carpre, son of Etain," saith [King] Lugh to his poet, "what power can *you* wield in battle?"

"Not hard to say," quoth Carpre. "I will

make a *glam dicinn*[2] on them. And I will satirize them and shame them, so that through the spell of my art they will not resist warriors."

For these and other public services the Celtic poets were extravagantly rewarded.

Important as the satirist may have been, however, in defending and supporting and holding together the social order, his public role was overshadowed, in ancient legend, at any rate, by his individualistic, almost anarchic practices. Possessed of dreadful power, he exercised it ruthlessly. For example, the poet Nede, prompted by the basest motives, pronounced a satire against his uncle the King; the satire raised three blisters (marks of dreadful shame) on the King's cheek. He fled into hiding, and when a year later Nede found him, the King fell dead of shame at his feet. Certainly the worst of many predatory satirists was Aithirne the Importunate who roamed Ireland from kingdom to kingdom, exacting fantastic levies wherever he went. The one-eyed King Eochaid offered Aithirne whatever his people had of jewels and treasures to buy off the threatened satires. " 'There is, forsooth,' said Aithirne, 'the single eye there in thy head, to be given to me into my fist. . . .' So then the King put his finger under his eye, and tore it out of his head and gave it into Aithirne's fist." Of the King of Munster Aithirne demanded permission to sleep with his wife on the night that she was to give birth to a child. The Queen acceded "for the sake of her husband's honour, that his honour might not be taken away." The people of Leinster came out to meet Aithirne, offering him enormous gifts of jewels and treasures so that he would not leave invectives in their land. Aithirne departed from Leinster with a magic jewel and thrice fifty wives of the princes and nobles. It is something of a satisfaction to record that Aithirne finally came to a bad end. A satire that he had directed at Luaine, beloved of Conchobar, raised the familiar three blisters on her face and caused the girl to die of shame. Conchobar and the Ulstermen walled Aithirne the Importunate up in a fortress and burned the place about his ears.

2 Translated variously as a "metrical malediction," "extempore satire," "Satire from the Hill-tops," and, most recently, "an endless, biting attack."

Some of the great Celtic satirists of legend were able through the magic of their malefic verse to blight the fertility of the land itself— a curious reversal here of the function of satire in the fertility rituals of ancient Greece. For a whole year, it is said, Laidcenn, chief poet of Niall of the Nine Hostages, "kept satirizing and lampooning the men of Leinster . . . so that neither grass nor corn grew with them, nor a leaf, to the end of a year." That satirists could rhyme rats to death, following on Seanchan's lead, was a commonplace belief, well known later to Elizabethan writers; Shakespeare and Sydney refer to it, and Ben Jonson, with specific reference to the legendary powers of satire, writes:

> I could doe worse,
> Arm'd with Archilochus' fury, write Iambicks,
> Should make the desperate lashers hang themselves,
> Rime 'hem to death, as they doe Irish rats
> In drumming tunes. . . .

Still later Sir William Temple, Swift, and Pope are familiar with the tradition, which seems, indeed, to have flourished among the Irish folk well into the nineteenth century. Yeats exploits the mythic associations of the belief in these magnificently bitter lines from "Parnell's Funeral" (1934):

> Come, fix upon me that accusing eye.
> I thirst for accusation. All that was sung,
> All that was said in Ireland is a lie
> Bred out of the contagion of the throng,
> Saving the rhyme rats hear before they die.

One is tempted to tell more tales; but at this point a crucial problem must be faced: is there justification for adopting the translators' usage and calling the kind of magical imprecation discussed above "satire?" I am convinced that a genetic relation exists between magical invective and literary satire, but it would be impossible to explore that relation fully here. There are these facts, however, which Professor Robinson has noted (except for the matter of linguistic continuity, which is a special problem, they apply to the Greek material as well as to the Irish): the Irish language employs the same words for the incantatory lines of say, Aithirne, as for the literary satire of a later age. The makers of these lines were not mere enchanters, they were poets, *filid,* either historical or legendary, and part of their function as poets was to produce this kind of verse. They frequently attack the same vices as do the later satirists: inhospitality, stinginess, etc. Finally, and very important, their announced method, like that of later satirists, is to ridicule their victims and to shame them.[3] These lines from a fragment of Archilochus are of interest in this connection:

> "Father Lycambes, what, pray, is this thou hast imagined? Who hath perverted the wits thou wast endowed with? Thou seem'st matter for much laughter to thy fellows now."

This evidence seems adequate, at least provisionally, to establish the central point: in its early manifestations in Greece, Arabia, and Ireland satire is intimately connected with magic and the satirist hardly distinguishable from the magician.

II

The magician has always and everywhere been the focus of strong and conflicting feelings on the part of his society. In so far as he uses his great powers to enhance the well-being of society—defending it from its enemies, coercing the powers of Nature into favorable performance, enriching the inner life of society through ritualistic ceremony, etc.—he is honored and revered. Magic, according to Malinowski, "is one of the means of carrying on the established order [and] is in its turn strengthened by [that order]." But the very fact that the socially-approved practices of the magician are made possible by the exercise of supernatural power implies a complementary danger. For the powers of the magician are only in a very limited sense amenable to social control; in them is potentiality for benefit, but

[3] Ridicule, according to anthropologists, plays an enormously important role in primitive societies. Paul Radin writes: "To avoid [ridicule] a man will go to any length. He may even commit suicide in consequence of it." One thinks of Archilochus's victim, Lycambes, and of others. Radin adds: "The fear of ridicule is thus a great positive factor in the lives of primitive peoples. It is the preserver of the established order of things and more potent and tyrannous than the most restrictive and coercive of positive injunctions possibly could be." *Primitive Man as Philosopher* (New York, 1927), pp. 50-51.

also for danger, both social and personal. The magician is at once prop and threat to society and to each individual. Consequently, the relation of the magician to society is always colored by the ambivalent emotional attitudes generated by this knowledge. Clearly the situation of the satirist-magician is very similar. His satire may be incorporated into ritual, as in the Phallic Songs, and thus contribute materially to the social cohesiveness which it is one of the functions of ritual to bring about. Or it may be employed in straightforward and warlike defense of his tribe against threat from without. The satirist may even partake of a partial divinity, as did Archilochus, who was destined from birth to be immortal. The man who killed Archilochus in battle was banished from the temple of Apollo for having slain "a servitor of the Muses," and there is some evidence that at his death Archilochus became the center of a cult on his native island of Paros. In these situations the satirist unquestionably inspires emotions of honor and respect and awe. But in other, and possibly more characteristic roles, the satirist becomes the object of fear and hate; as testimony we have many legends where the fear is expressed either directly or symbolically, and we have the evidence of ancient law. Plato proposes legal measures against magical incantations (which would include magical satire); the Roman Twelve Tables invoke the death penalty for defamatory and libelous verse (which was thought to be magically efficacious); and the Irish laws are full of specific injunctions against satire. These latter, however, distinguish between lawful and unlawful satire and provide rewards for "good" satire and punishments for "bad." Here are codified, in legal formulas, the ambivalent attitudes of a society toward its satirists.

When we move from the realm of magic and blisters and incantatory death onto the more familiar ground of literary satire, we must expect some change in the relations of satirist to society. The satirist is no longer a medicine-man—half in society and half out, as he mediates between his people and higher powers; his mantic function has been pre-empted by the priest, and the focus of interest in his poetic utterance shifts from concern for its magic potency to concern for aesthetic value. Only in this way can the magic invective of an heroic folk society develop into literary art. Cassirer's statement, in the brilliant final chapter of *Language and Myth,* is precisely to this point, although he happens here to be speaking of pictorial art: "The image . . . achieves its purely representative, specifically 'aesthetic' function only as the magic circle with which mythical consciousness surrounds it is broken, and it is recognized not as a mythico-magical form, but as a particular sort of *formulation.*"4 In short, the satirist becomes, instead of a seer, a "mere" poet, writing, as he frequently confesses, in an inferior genre. The distinction is well pointed up by contrasting the magnificent confidence of power of Carpre, whose satire would render the enemy incapable of resisting warriors, with Horace's account to Augustus of the poet's function. "Though he is no hero in the field [says Horace], the poet is of use to the State, if you grant that even by small things great ends are helped." No matter how much the characteristic wry understatement discounts the literal meaning, it is a mighty falling off. But even granting the changed modes of belief and the relatively inferior status of the poet, it is still possible to see in the relationship of the satirist to a more sophisticated society some reflection of the ambiguities we have been considering.

At any rate the law continued to pay close heed to the satirist, and from Horace's day to our own the satirist has skated on the thin edge of censorship and legal retribution. It was forbidden for a time to print satires at all in Elizabethan England; and in totalitarian states today the satirists are among the first to be silenced. This relation with the law has itself been of considerable importance in determining the forms that satire will take and the methods it will use. Freud perhaps throws some light here; he notes that society has pro-

gressively stifled our hostile impulses, first by prohibiting the expression of our antagonisms in direct physical action, then by prohibiting violent personal assault in language. But the hostile feelings remain, says Freud, and in order to surmount the restrictions imposed by society, we have developed a new technique of verbal assault—a technique which employs wit. "Wit," writes Freud, "permits us to make our enemy ridiculous through that which we could not utter loudly or consciously on account of existing hindrances; in other words, wit affords us the means of surmounting restrictions and of opening up otherwise inaccessible pleasure sources."

Once wit has been brought into the service of the satiric impulse, then all the stock devices by which the literary satirist achieves his end become available: irony, burlesque, innuendo, the beast fable, the imaginary voyage, allegory —all the devices of indirection which make the study of satire so fascinating and so confusing. The Earl of Shaftesbury, writing in the eighteenth century, had some such idea in mind when he explained the prevalence of irony, raillery, and writing in disguise as resulting from the weight of censorship. " 'Tis the persecuting Spirit has raised the *bantering* one," he says. "The greater the Weight [of constraint] is, the bitterer will be the Satire. The higher the Slavery, the more exquisite the Buffoonery." We might compare this with Kenneth Burke's paradoxical notion that satire thrives best when society attempts to censor it. According to Burke, ". . . the most inventive satire arises when the artist is seeking simultaneously to take risks and escape punishment for his boldness, and is never quite certain himself whether he will be acclaimed or punished."5 The ancient ambiguity, or something very close to it, is still there.

We have an excellent opportunity to examine the satirist's claims for social approval largely by reason of the literary convention which decrees that he must justify his ungrateful art. From the times of Horace, Persius, and Juvenal down to Boileau, Swift, and Pope and into our own day with men like Wyndham Lewis, the satirist has felt compelled to write

---

4 Caricature as an art apparently did not develop until late in the sixteenth century; Ernst Kris and E. H. Gombrich account for the fact thus: "Caricature is a play with the magic power of the image, and for such a play to be licit or institutionalized the belief in the real efficacy of the spell must be firmly under control. Wherever it is not considered a joke but rather a dangerous practice to distort a man's features even on paper, caricature as an art can not develop." "The Principles of Caricature" in Kris, *Psychoanalytic Explorations in Art* (New York, 1952), pp. 189-203.

5 In a totalitarian society where control is nearly absolute, satire against the ruling regime is, of course, impossible.

an *Apologia,* whether formal or informal, in verse or prose. The Apologies are remarkably similar in their protestations (Mr. Lewis dissenting); from them we get a kind of ideal image which the satirist projects of himself and his art. According to the image the satirist is a public servant fighting the good fight against vice and folly wherever he meets it; he is honest, brave, protected by the rectitude of his motives; he attacks only the wicked and then seldom or never by name; he is, in short, a moral man appalled by the evil he sees around him, and he is forced by his conscience to write satire. Juvenal's *"facit indignatio versum"* is the prototype.

The satirist claims, with much justification, to be a true conservative. Usually (but not always—there are significant exceptions) he operates within the established framework of society, accepting its norms, appealing to reason (or to what his society accepts as rational) as the standard against which to judge the folly he sees. He is the preserver of tradition—the true tradition from which there has been grievous falling away.

Society, quite naturally, is dubious. On the most obvious level it points with outrage to the inevitable discrepancy between the ideal image, projected by rhetorical convention, and what it takes to be the actual fact. Swift, or Pope—so goes the reasoning—was a wicked man; therefore we may dismiss his satire. The *non sequitur* is comforting. But the problem on other levels is more complex. Despite society's doubts about the character of the satirist, there may develop a feeling that in its general application the satire has some truth in it—or the feeling that other people may *think* that it has some truth in it. Individuals who recognize characteristics of themselves in the objects of attack cannot afford to acknowledge the identity even to themselves. So they may reward the satirist as proof of piety, while inwardly they fear him. *"Satyr,"* says Swift, *"is a sort of Glass, wherein Beholders do generally discover every body's Face but their Own; which is the chief Reason for that kind Reception it meets in the World, and that so very few are offended with it."* "Publicly offended," one might add. Publicly the satirist may be honored, but privately he will be feared.

I think of a modern instance, perhaps trivial. Consider the high reputation in academic circles of Mary McCarthy's *Groves of Academe*. We may applaud, but many of us must feel the bite. Perhaps it would be a matter for congratulation to have Miss McCarthy on our faculties; it would hardly be a matter for comfort.

Society has even better reasons for its suspicions. No matter how conservative the rationale of the satirist may be, it is inevitable that the pressure of his art will in some ways run athwart society's efforts to maintain its equilibrium. The satirist usually claims that he does not attack institutions, he attacks perversions of institutions; when, for example, he ridicules a corrupt judge he intends no reflection on the law as such, he is attacking a corruption which has crept into the law. But it seems to be that in the hands of a powerful satirist an attack on a local phenomenon is capable of indefinite extension into an attack on the whole structure of which that phenomenon is part. It is significant, I think, that this imaginative process is essentially a magical one; it works by synechdoche which is one of the foundations of magic. In "mythico-linguistic thought"—to use Cassirer's phrase—the part does not merely represent the whole, it *is* the whole; by the magical process of identification the nail paring or the lock of hair from an enemy *is* the enemy, and it is acted on accordingly. So with our judge—for the process just described is by no means confined to a "mythically bound" society; as a different order of experience, to be sure, it is the way of the imagination when it is bound, in its own way, by the spell of the creative artist. The judge who has been ridiculed by a powerful satirist comes to stand for lawyers in general, and lawyers for the law. What starts as local attack ends up by calling the whole institution into question. Thus the satirical portraits of Chaucer, who seems to have been a thoroughly orthodox Catholic, have often been interpreted as evidence of his revolt against the Church; during the Reformation he and Langland were used for purposes doubtless far removed from their intent. Swift, attacking in *A Tale of a Tub* what he considered corruptions in the Church, unwittingly provided criticism capable of extension into an undermining action against the Church itself. I believe that Swift was deeply committed to the welfare of the Established Church as he saw it; but under the impact of his satire one of the great pillars of society rocked a bit. Swift's strength, as Empson puts it, made his instrument too strong for him. His magic, one might say, was his undoing.

The final point now, which is implicit in what has gone before. The satirist usually claims to be conservative, to be using his art to shore up the foundations of the established order. Between the claim and the reality, however, may lie a tremendous gulf. I take my last example again from Swift. The complexly simple projector of *An Argument Against Abolishing Christianity,* the "I" of the piece, argues cogently for the retention of nominal Christianity. To restore "real" Christianity, he says, "would indeed be a wild project, it would be to dig up Foundations; . . . to break the entire Frame and Constitution of Things; to ruin Trade, extinguish Arts and Sciences, with the Professors of them; in short, to turn our Courts, Exchanges, and Shops into Desarts. . . ." One reads this and one can only say, He

is right. Between Swift and the projector, of course, there is a considerable ironic remove, just as there is distance between Swift and some of the meanings set in motion by his creature. One may doubt that Swift the Tory politician, Swift the social man would have had much sympathy with breaking the "Frame and Constitution of Things." But Swift the artist is another matter. The pressure of his art works directly against the ostensibly conservative function which it is said to serve. Instead of shoring up foundations, it tears them down. It is revolutionary.

Society has doubtless been wise, in its old pragmatic way, to suspect the satirist. Whether he is an enchanter wielding the ambiguous power of magic, or whether he is a "mere" poet, his relation to society will necessarily be problematic. He is of society in the sense that his art must be grounded in his experience as social man; but he must also be apart, as he struggles to achieve proper distance. His practice is often sanative, as he proclaims; but it may be revolutionary in ways that society can not possibly approve, and in ways that may not be clear even to the satirist.

Questions

1. Discuss the two contradictory powers of satire, paying particular attention to the sources of these opposing powers in both ancient and modern satire.

2. What significance does the magical origin of satire have for an understanding of the genre as it has developed in modern times?

3. How does wit function in satire, and why did it develop?

4. Why does even the best-meaning satirist always tend to attack more than he proposes to? Provide some examples from your own reading.

5. Discuss the reasons for society's traditional suspicion of satire and the techniques the satirist has developed to lull these suspicions. Choose a political cartoon from your newspaper and show how the cartoonist has tried to protect himself from the charges that might be made against him.

NORTHROP FRYE

The Mythos of Winter: Irony and Satire

We come now to the mythical patterns of experience, the attempts to give form to the shifting ambiguities and complexities of un-idealized existence. We cannot find these patterns merely in the mimetic or representational aspect of such literature, for that aspect is one of content and not form. As structure, the central principle of ironic myth is best approached as a parody of romance: the application of romantic mythical forms to a more realistic content which fits them in unexpected ways. No one in a romance, Don Quixote protests, ever asks who pays for the hero's accommodation.

The chief distinction between irony and satire is that satire is militant irony: its moral norms are relatively clear, and it assumes standards against which the grotesque and absurd are measured. Sheer invective or name-calling ("flyting") is satire in which there is relatively little irony: on the other hand, whenever a reader is not sure what the author's attitude is or what his own is supposed to be, we have irony with relatively little satire. Fielding's *Jonathan Wild* is satiric irony: certain flat moral judgements made by the narrator (as in the description of Bagshot in chapter twelve) are in accord with the decorum of the work, but would be out of key in, say, *Madame Bovary*. Irony is consistent both with complete realism of content and with the

FROM *Anatomy of Criticism* by Northrop Frye, by permission of Princeton University Press. Copyright 1957.

suppression of attitude on the part of the author. Satire demands at least a token fantasy, a content which the reader recognizes as grotesque, and at least an implicit moral standard, the latter being essential in a militant attitude to experience. Some phenomena, such as the ravages of disease, may be called grotesque, but to make fun of them would not be very effective satire. The satirist has to select his absurdities, and the act of selection is a moral act.

The argument of Swift's *Modest Proposal* has a brain-softening plausibility about it: one is almost led to feel that the narrator is not only reasonable but even humane; yet the "almost" can never drop out of any sane man's reaction, and as long as it remains there the modest proposal will be both fantastic and immoral. When in another passage Swift suddenly says, discussing the poverty of Ireland, "But my Heart is too heavy to continue this Irony longer," he is speaking of satire, which breaks down when its content is too oppressively real to permit the maintaining of the fantastic or hypothetical tone. Hence satire is irony which is structurally close to the comic: the comic struggle of two societies, one normal and the other absurd, is reflected in its double focus of morality and fantasy. Irony with little satire is the non-heroic residue of tragedy, centering on a theme of puzzled defeat.

Two things, then, are essential to satire; one is wit or humor founded on fantasy or a sense of the grotesque or absurd, the other is an object of attack. Attack without humor, or pure denunciation, forms one of the boundaries of satire. It is a very hazy boundary, because invective is one of the most readable forms of literary art, just as panegyric is one of the dullest. It is an established datum of literature that we like hearing people cursed and are bored with hearing them praised, and almost any denunciation, if vigorous enough, is followed by a reader with the kind of pleasure that soon breaks into a smile. To attack anything, writer and audience must agree on its undesirability, which means that the content of a great deal of satire founded on national hatreds, snobbery, prejudice, and personal pique goes out of date very quickly.

But attack in literature can never be a pure expression of merely personal or even social hatred, whatever the motivation for it may be, because the words for expressing hatred, as distinct from enmity, have too limited a range. About the only ones we have are derived from the animal world, but calling a man a swine or a skunk or a woman a bitch affords a severely restricted satisfaction, as most of the unpleasant qualities of the animal are human projections. As Shakespeare's Thersites says of Menelaus, "to what form, but that he is, should wit larded with malice, and malice forced with wit, turn him to? To an ass, were nothing; he is both ass and ox; to an ox, were nothing; he is both ox and ass." For effective attack we must reach some kind of impersonal level, and that commits the attacker, if only by implication, to a moral standard. The satirist commonly takes a high moral line. Pope asserts that he is "To Virtue only and her friends a friend," suggesting that that is what he is really being when he is reflecting on the cleanliness of the underwear worn by the lady who had jilted him.

Humor, like attack, is founded on convention. The world of humor is a rigidly stylized world in which generous Scotchmen, obedient wives, beloved mothers-in-law, and professors with presence of mind are not permitted to exist. All humor demands agreement that certain things, such as a picture of a wife beating her husband in a comic strip, are conventionally funny. To introduce a comic strip in which a husband beats his wife would distress the reader, because it would mean learning a new convention. The humor of pure fantasy, the other boundary of satire, belongs to romance, though it is uneasy there, as humor perceives the incongruous, and the conventions of romance are idealized. Most fantasy is pulled back into satire by a powerful undertow often called allegory, which may be described as the implicit reference to experience in the perception of the incongruous. The White Knight in Alice who felt that one should be provided for everything, and therefore put anklets around his horse's feet to guard against the bites of sharks, may pass as pure fantasy. But when he goes on to sing an elaborate parody of Wordsworth we begin to sniff the acrid, pungent smell of satire, and when we take a second look at the White Knight we recognize a character type closely related both to Quixote and to the pedant of comedy.

As in this *mythos* we have the difficulty of two words to contend with, it may be simplest, if the reader is now accustomed to our sequence of six phases, to start with them and describe them in order, instead of abstracting a typical form and discussing it first. The first three are phases of satire, and correspond to the first three or ironic phases of comedy.

The first phase corresponds to the first phase of ironic comedy in which there is no displacement of the humorous society. The sense of absurdity about such a comedy arises as a kind of backfire or recall after the work has been seen or read. Once we have finished with it, deserts of futility open up on all sides, and we have, in spite of the humor, a sense of nightmare and a close proximity to something demonic. Even in very light-hearted comedy we may get a trace of this feeling: if the main theme of *Pride and Prejudice* had been the married life of Collins and Charlotte Lucas, one wonders how long Collins would continue to be funny. Hence it is in decorum for even a satire prevailingly light in tone, such as Pope's second Moral Essay on the characters of women, to rise to a terrifying climax of moral intensity.

The satire typical of this phase may be called the satire of the low norm. It takes for granted a world which is full of anomalies, injustices, follies, and crimes, and yet is permanent and undisplaceable. Its principle is that anyone who wishes to keep his balance in such a world must learn first of all to keep his eyes open and his mouth shut. Counsels of prudence, urging the reader in effect to adopt an *eiron* role, have been prominent in literature from Egyptian times. What is recommended is conventional life at its best: a clairvoyant knowledge of human nature in oneself and others, an avoidance of all illusion and compulsive behavior, a reliance on observation and timing rather than on aggressiveness. This is wisdom, the tried and tested way of life, which does not question the logic of social convention, but merely follows the procedures which in fact do serve to maintain one's balance from one day to the next. The *eiron* of the low norm takes an attitude of flexible pragmatism; he assumes that society will, if given any chance, behave more or less like Caliban's Setebos in Browning's poem, and he conducts himself accordingly. On all doubtful points of behavior convention is his deepest conviction. And however good or bad expertly conventional behavior may be thought to be, it is certainly the most difficult of all forms of behavior to satirize, just as anyone with a new theory of behavior, even if saint or prophet, is the easiest of all people to ridicule as a crank.

Hence the satirist may employ a plain, common-sense, conventional person as a foil for the various *alazons* of society. Such a person may be the author himself or a narrator, and he corresponds to the plain dealer in comedy or the blunt adviser in tragedy. When distinguished from the author, he is often a rustic with pastoral affinities, illustrating the connection of his role with the *agroikos* type in comedy. The kind of American satire that passes as folk humor, exemplified by the Biglow Papers, Mr. Dooley, Artemus Ward, and Will Rogers, makes a good deal of him, and this genre is closely linked with the North American development of the counsel of prudence in Poor Richard's Almanac and the Sam Slick papers. Other examples are easy enough to find, both where we expect them, as in Crabbe, whose tale *The Patron* also belongs to the counsel-of-prudence genre, and where we might not expect them, as in the Fish-Eater dialogue in Erasmus's *Colloquies*. Chaucer

represents himself as a shy, demure, inconspicuous member of his pilgrimage, agreeing politely with everybody ("And I seyde his opinion was good"), and showing to the pilgrims none of the powers of observation that he displays to his reader. We are not surprised therefore to find that one of his "own" tales is in the counsel-of-prudence tradition.

The most elaborate form of low-norm satire is the encyclopaedic form favored by the Middle Ages, closely allied to preaching, and generally based on the encyclopaedic scheme of the seven deadly sins, a form which survived as late as Elizabethan times in Nashe's *Pierce Penilesse* and Lodge's *Wits Miserie*. Erasmus's *Praise of Folly* belongs to this tradition, in which the link with the corresponding comic phase, the view of an upside-down world dominated by humors and ruling passions, can be clearly seen. When adopted by a preacher, or even an intellectual, the low-norm device is part of an implied *a fortiori* argument: if people cannot reach even ordinary common sense, or church porch virtue, there is little point in comparing them with any higher standards.

Where gaiety predominates in such satire, we have an attitude which fundamentally accepts social conventions but stresses tolerance and flexibility within their limits. Close to the conventional norm we find the lovable eccentric, the Uncle Toby or Betsey Trotwood who diversifies, without challenging, accepted codes of behavior. Such characters have much of the child about them, and a child's behavior is usually thought of as coming towards an accepted standard instead of moving away from it. Where attack predominates, we have an inconspicuous, unobtrusive *eiron* standard contrasted with the *alazons* or blocking humors who are in charge of society. This situation has for its archetype an ironic counterpart of the romance theme of giant-killing. For society to exist at all there must be a delegation of prestige and influence to organized groups such as the church, the army, the professions and the government, all of which consist of individuals given more than individual power by the institutions to which they belong. If a satirist presents, say, a clergyman as a fool or hypocrite, he is, *qua* satirist, attacking neither a man nor a church. The former has no literary or hypothetical point, and the latter carries him outside the range of satire. He is attacking an evil man protected by his church, and such a man is a gigantic monster: monstrous because not what he should be, gigantic because protected by his position and by the prestige of good clergymen. The cowl might make the monk if it were not for satire.

Milton says, "for a Satyr as it was born out of a Tragedy, so ought to resemble his parentage, to strike high, and adventure dangerously at the most eminent vices among the greatest persons." Apart from the etymology, this needs one qualification: a great vice does not need a great person to represent it. We have mentioned the gigantic size of Sir Epicure Mammon's dream in *The Alchemist:* the whole mystery of the corrupted human will is in it, yet the utter impotence of the dreamer is essential to the satire. Similarly, we miss much of the point of *Jonathan Wild* unless we take the hero seriously as a parody of greatness, or false social standards of valuation. But in general the principle may be accepted for the satirist's antagonists that the larger they come, the easier they fall. In low-norm satire the *alazon* is a Goliath encountered by a tiny David with his sudden and vicious stones, a giant prodded by a cool and observant but almost invisible enemy into a blind, stampeding fury and then polished off at leisure. This situation has run through satire from the stories of Polyphemus and Blunderbore to, in a much more ironic and equivocal context, the Chaplin films. Dryden transforms his victims into fantastic dinosaurs of bulging flesh and peanut brains; he seems genuinely impressed by the "goodly and great" bulk of Og and by the furious energy of the poet Doeg.

The figure of the low-norm *eiron* is irony's substitute for the hero, and when he is removed from satire we can see more clearly that one of the central themes of the *mythos* is the disappearance of the heroic. This is the main reason for the predominance in fictional satire of what may be called the Omphale archetype, the man bullied or dominated by women, which has been prominent in satire all through its history, and embraces a vast area of contemporary humor, both popular and sophisticated. Similarly, when the giant or monster is removed we can see that he is the mythical form of society, the hydra or fama full of tongues, Spenser's blatant beast which is still at large. And while the crank with his new idea is an obvious target for satire, still social convention is mainly fossilized dogma, and the standard appealed to by low-norm satire is a set of conventions largely invented by dead cranks. The strength of the conventional person is not in the conventions but in his common-sense way of handling them. Hence the logic of satire itself drives it on from its first phase of conventional satire on the unconventional to a second phase in which the sources and values of conventions themselves are objects of ridicule.

The simplest form of the corresponding second phase of comedy is the comedy of escape, in which a hero runs away to a more congenial society without transforming his own. The satiric counterpart of this is the picaresque novel, the story of the successful rogue who, from Reynard the Fox on, makes conventional society look foolish without setting up any positive standard. The picaresque novel is the social form of what with *Don Quixote* modulates into a more intellectualized satire, the nature of which needs some explanation.

Satire, according to Juvenal's useful if hackneyed formula, has an interest in anything men do. The philosopher, on the other hand, teaches a certain way or method of living; he stresses some things and despises others; what he recommends is carefully selected from the data of human life; he continually passes moral judgements on social behavior. His attitude is dogmatic; that of the satirist pragmatic. Hence satire may often represent the collision between a selection of standards from experience and the feeling that experience is bigger than any set of beliefs about it. The satirist demonstrates the infinite variety of what men do by showing the futility, not only of saying what they ought to do, but even of attempts to systematize or formulate a coherent scheme of what they do. Philosophies of life abstract from life, and an abstraction implies the leaving out of inconvenient data. The satirist brings up these inconvenient data, sometimes in the form of alternative and equally plausible theories, like the Erewhonian treatment of crime and disease or Swift's demonstration of the mechanical operation of spirit.

The central theme in the second or quixotic phase of satire, then, is the setting of ideas and generalizations and theories and dogmas over against the life they are supposed to explain. This theme is presented very clearly in Lucian's dialogue *The Sale of Lives*, in which a series of slave-philosophers pass in review, with all their arguments and guarantees, before a buyer who has to consider living with them. He buys a few, it is true, but as slaves, not as masters or teachers. Lucian's attitude to Greek philosophy is repeated in the attitude of Erasmus and Rabelais to the scholastics, of Swift and Samuel Butler I to Descartes and the Royal Society, of Voltaire to the Leibnitzians, of Peacock to the Romantics, of Samuel Butler II to the Darwinians, of Aldous Huxley to the behaviorists. We notice that low-norm satire often becomes *merely* anti-intellectual, a tendency that crops up in Crabbe (*vide The Learned Boy*) and even in Swift. The influence of low-norm satire in American culture has produced a popular contempt for longhairs and ivory towers, an example of what may be called a fallacy of poetic projection, or taking literary conventions to be facts of life. Anti-intellectual satire proper, however, is based on a sense of the comparative naivete of systematic thought, and should not be limited by such ready-made terms as skeptical or cynical.

Skepticism itself may be or become a dogmatic attitude, a comic humor of doubting plain evidence. Cynicism is a little closer to the satiric norm: Menippus, the founder of the Menippean satire, was a cynic, and cynics are generally associated with the role of intellectual Thersites. Lyly's play *Campaspe,* for instance, presents Plato, Aristotle, and Diogenes, but the first two are bores, and Diogenes, who is not a philosopher at all but an Elizabethan clown of the malcontent type, steals the show. But still cynicism is a philosophy, and one that may produce the strange spiritual pride of the Peregrinus of whom Lucian makes a searching and terrible analysis. In the *Sale of Lives* the cynic and the skeptic are auctioned in their turn, and the latter is the last to be sold, dragged off to have his very skepticism refuted, not by argument but by life. Erasmus and Burton called themselves Democritus Junior, followers of the philosopher who laughed at mankind, but Lucian's buyer considers that Democritus too has overdone his pose. Insofar as the satirist has a "position" of his own, it is the preference of practice to theory, experience to metaphysics. When Lucian goes to consult his master Menippus, he is told that the method of wisdom is to do the task that lies to hand, advice repeated in Voltaire's *Candide* and in the instructions given to the unborn in *Erewhon.* Thus philosophical pedantry becomes, as every target of satire eventually does, a form of romanticism or the imposing of over-simplified ideals on experience.

The satiric attitude here is neither philosophical nor anti-philosophical, but an expression of the hypothetical form of art. Satire on ideas is only the special kind of art that defends its own creative detachment. The demand for order in thought produces a supply of intellectual systems: some of these attract and convert artists, but as an equally great poet could defend any other system equally well, no one system can contain the arts as they stand. Hence a systematic reasoner, given the power, would be likely to establish hierarchies in the arts, or censor and expurgate as Plato wished to do to Homer. Satire on systems of reasoning, especially on the social effects of such systems, is art's first line of defence against all such invasions.

In the warfare of science against superstition, the satirists have done famously. Satire itself appears to have begun with the Greek *silloi* which were pro-scientific attacks on superstition. In English literature, Chaucer and Ben Jonson riddled the alchemists with a cross-fire of their own jargon; Nashe and Swift hounded astrologers into premature graves; Browning's *Sludge the Medium* annihilated the spiritualists, and a rabble of occultists, numerologists, Pythagoreans, and Rosicrucians lie sprawling in the wake of *Hudibras.* To the scientist it may seem little short of perverse that satire placidly goes on making fun of legitimate astronomers in *The Elephant in the Moon,* of experimental laboratories in *Gulliver's Travels,* of Darwinian and Malthusian cosmology in *Erewhon,* of conditioned reflexes in *Brave New World,* of technological efficiency in *1984.* Charles Fort, one of the few who have continued the tradition of intellectual satire in this century, brings the wheel full circle by mocking the scientists for their very freedom from superstition itself, a rational attitude which, like all rational attitudes, still refuses to examine all the evidence.

Similarly with religion. The satirist may feel with Lucian that the eliminating of superstition would also eliminate religion, or with Erasmus that it would restore health to religion. But whether Zeus exists or not is a question; that men who think him vicious and stupid will insist that he change the weather is a fact, accepted by scoffer and devout alike. Any really devout person would surely welcome a satirist who cauterized hypocrisy and superstition as an ally of true religion. Yet once a hypocrite who sounds exactly like a good man is sufficiently blackened, the good man also may begin to seem a little dingier than he was. Those who would agree even with the theoretical parts of *Holy Willie's Prayer* in Burns look rather like Holy Willies themselves. One feels similarly that while the personal attitudes of Erasmus, Rabelais, Swift, and Voltaire to institutional religion varied a good deal, the effect of their satire varies much less. Satire on religion includes the parody of the sacramental life in English Protestantism that runs from Milton's divorce pamphlets to *The Way of All Flesh,* and the antagonism to Christianity in Nietzsche, Yeats, and D. H. Lawrence based on the conception of Jesus as another kind of romantic idealist.

The narrator in *Erewhon* remarks that while the real religion of most of the Erewhonians was, whatever they said it was, the acceptance of low-norm conventionality (the goddess Ydgrun), there was also a small group of "high Ydgrunites" who were the best people he found in Erewhon. The attitude of these people reminds us rather of Montaigne: they had the *eiron's* sense of the value of conventions that had been long established and were now harmless; they had the *eiron's* distrust of the ability of anyone's reason, including their own, to transform society into a better structure. But they were also intellectually detached from the conventions they lived with, and were capable of seeing their anomalies and absurdities as well as their stabilizing conservatism.

The literary form that high Ydgrunism produces in second-phase satire we may call the *ingenu* form, after Voltaire's dialogue of that name. Here an outsider to the society, in this case an American Indian, is the low norm: he has no dogmatic views of his own, but he grants none of the premises which make the absurdities of society look logical to those accustomed to them. He is really a pastoral figure, and like the pastoral, a form congenial to satire, he contrasts a set of simple standards with the complex rationalizations of society. But we have just seen that it is precisely the complexity of data in experience which the satirist insists on and the simple set of standards which he distrusts. That is why the *ingenu* is an outsider; he comes from another world which is either unattainable or associated with something else undesirable. Montaigne's cannibals have all the virtues we have not, if we don't mind being cannibals. More's Utopia is an ideal state except that to enter it we must give up the idea of Christendom. The Houyhnhnms live the life of reason and nature better than we, but Gulliver finds that he is born a Yahoo, and that such a life would be nearer the capacities of gifted animals than of humans. Whenever the "other world" appears in satire, it appears as an ironic counterpart to our own, a reversal of accepted social standards. This form of satire is represented in Lucian's *Kataplous* and *Charon,* journeys to the other world in which the eminent in this one are shown doing appropriate but unaccustomed things, a form incorporated in Rabelais, and in the medieval *danse macabre.* In the last named the simple equality of death is set against the complex inequalities of life.

Intellectual satire defends the creative detachment in art, but art too tends to seek out socially accepted ideas and become in its turn a social fixation. We have spoken of the idealized art of romance as in particular the form in which an ascendant class tends to express itself, and so the rising middle class in medieval Europe naturally turned to mock-romance. Other forms of satire have a similar function, whether so intended or not. The *danse macabre* and the *kataplous* are ironic reversals of the kind of romanticism that we have in the serious vision of the other world. In Dante, for instance, the judgements of the next world usually confirm the standards of this one, and in heaven itself nearly the whole available billeting is marked for officers only. The cultural effect of such satire is not to denigrate romance, but to prevent any group of conventions from dominating the whole of literary experience. Second-phase satire shows literature assuming a special function of analysis, of breaking up the lumber of stereotypes, fossilized beliefs, superstitious terrors, crank theories, pedantic dogmatisms, oppressive fashions, and all other things that impede the free movement (not necessarily, of course, the progress) of society. Such satire is the completion of the logical process known as the *reductio ad absurdum,* which is not designed to hold one in perpetual captivity, but to bring one to the point at which one can escape from an incorrect procedure.

The romantic fixation which revolves around the beauty of perfect form, in art or elsewhere, is also a logical target for satire. The word satire is said to come from *satura,* or hash, and a kind of parody of form seems to run all through its tradition, from the mixture of prose and verse in early satire to the jerky cinematic changes of scene in Rabelais (I am thinking of a somewhat archaic type of cinema). *Tristram Shandy* and *Don Juan* illustrate very clearly the constant tendency to self-parody in satiric rhetoric which prevents even the process of writing itself from becoming an over-simplified convention or ideal. In *Don Juan* we simultaneously read the poem and watch the poet at work writing it: we eavesdrop on his associations, his struggles for rhymes, his tentative and discarded plans, the subjective preferences organizing his choice of details (e.g.: "Her stature tall—I hate a dumpy woman"), his decisions whether to be "serious" or mask himself with humor. All of this and even more is true of *Tristram Shandy.* A deliberate rambling digressiveness, which in *A Tale of a Tub* reaches the point of including a digression in praise of digressions, is endemic in the narrative technique of satire, and so is a calculated bathos or art of sinking in its suspense, such as the quizzical mock-oracular conclusions in Apuleius and Rabelais and in the refusal of Sterne for hundreds of pages even to get his hero born. An extraordinary number of great satires are fragmentary, unfinished, or anonymous. In ironic fiction a good many devices turning on the difficulty of communication, such as having a story presented through an idiot mind, serve the same purpose. Virginia Woolf's *The Waves* is made up of speeches of characters constructed precisely out of what they do *not* say, but what their behavior and attitudes say in spite of them.

This technique of disintegration brings us well into the third phase of satire, the satire of the high norm. Second-phase satire may make a tactical defence of the pragmatic against the dogmatic, but here we must let go even of ordinary common sense as a standard. For common sense too has certain implied dogmas, notably that the data of sense experience are reliable and consistent, and that our customary associations with things form a solid basis for interpreting the present and predicting the future. The satirist cannot explore all the possibilities of his form without seeing what happens if he questions these assumptions. That is why he so often gives to ordinary life a logical and self-consistent shift of perspective. He will show us society suddenly in a telescope as posturing and dignified pygmies, or in a microscope as hideous and reeking giants, or he will change his hero into an ass and show us how humanity looks from an ass's point of view. This type of fantasy breaks down customary associations, reduces sense experience to one of many possible categories, and brings out the tentative, *als ob* basis of all our thinking. Emerson says that such shifts of perspective afford "a low degree of the sublime," but actually they afford something of far greater artistic importance, a high degree of the ridiculous. And, consistently with the general basis of satire as parody-romance, they are usually adaptations of romance themes: the fairyland of little people, the land of giants, the world of enchanted animals, the wonderlands parodied in Lucian's *True History.*

When we fall back from the outworks of faith and reason to the tangible realities of the senses, satire follows us up. A slight shift of perspective, a different tinge in the emotional coloring, and the solid earth becomes an intolerable horror. *Gulliver's Travels* shows us man as a venomous rodent, man as a noisome and clumsy pachyderm, the mind of man as a bear-pit, and the body of man as a compound of filth and ferocity. But Swift is simply following where his satiric genius leads him, and genius seems to have led practically every great satirist to become what the world calls obscene. Social convention means people parading in front of each other, and the preservation of it demands that the dignity of some men and the beauty of some women should be thought of apart from excretion, copulation, and similar embarrassments. Constant reference to these latter brings us down to a bodily democracy paralleling the democracy of death in the *danse macabre*. Swift's affinity with the *danse macabre* tradition is marked in his description of the Struldbrugs, and his *Directions to Servants* and his more unquotable poems are in the tradition of the medieval preachers who painted the repulsiveness of gluttony and lechery. For here as everywhere else in satire there is a moral reference: it is all very well to eat, drink, and be merry, but one cannot always put off dying until tomorrow.

In the riotous chaos of Rabelais, Petronius, and Apuleius satire plunges through to its final victory over common sense. When we have finished with their weirdly logical fantasies of debauch, dream, and delirium we wake up wondering if Paracelsus' suggestion is right that the things seen in delirium are really there, like stars in daytime, and invisible for the same reason. Lucius becomes initiated and slips evasively out of our grasp, whether he lied or told the truth, as St. Augustine says with a touch of exasperation; Rabelais promises us a final oracle and leaves us staring at an empty bottle; Joyce's HCE struggles for pages toward wakening, but just as we seem on the point of grasping something tangible we are swung around to the first page of the book again. The *Satyricon* is a torn fragment from what seems like a history of some monstrous Atlantean race that vanished in the sea, still drunk.

The first phase of satire is dominated by the figure of the giant-killer, but in this rending of the stable universe a giant power rears up in satire itself. When the Philistine giant comes out to battle with the children of light, he naturally expects to find someone his own size ready to meet him, someone who is head and shoulders over every man in Israel. Such a Titan would have to bear down his opponent by sheer weight of words, and hence be a master of that technique of torrential abuse which we call invective. The gigantic figures in Rabelais, the awakened forms of the bound or sleeping giants that meet us in *Finnegans Wake* and the opening of *Gulliver's Travels*, are expressions of a creative exuberance of which the most typical and obvious sign is the verbal tempest, the tremendous outpouring of words in catalogues, abusive epithets and erudite technicalities which since the third chapter of Isaiah (a satire on female ornament) has been a feature, and almost a monopoly, of third-phase satire. Its golden age in English literature was the age of Burton, Nashe, Marston, and Urquhart of Cromarty, the uninhibited translator of Rabelais, who in his spare time was what Nashe would call a "scholastical squitter-book," producing books with such titles as *Trissotetras, Pantochronochanon, Ekubalauron* and *Logopandecteison*. Nobody except Joyce has in modern English made much sustained effort to carry on this tradition of verbal exuberance: even Carlyle, from this point of view, is a sad comedown after Burton and Urquhart. In American culture it is represented by the "tall talk" of the folklore boaster, which has some literary congeners in the catalogues of Whitman and *Moby Dick*.

With the fourth phase we move around to the ironic aspect of tragedy, and satire begins to recede. The fall of the tragic hero, especially in Shakespeare, is so delicately balanced emotionally that we almost exaggerate any one element in it merely by calling attention to it. One of these elements is the elegiac aspect in which irony is at a minimum, the sense of gentle and dignified pathos, often symbolized by music, which marks the desertion of Antony by Hercules, the dream of the rejected Queen Catherine in *Henry VIII*, Hamlet's "absent thee from felicity awhile," and Othello's Aleppo speech. One can of course find irony even here, as Mr. Eliot has found it in the last named, but the main emotional weight is surely thrown on the opposite side. Yet we are also aware that Hamlet dies in the middle of a frantically muddled effort at revenge which has taken eight lives instead of one, that Cleopatra fades away with great dignity after a careful search for easy ways to die, that Coriolanus is badly confused by his mother and violently resents being called a boy. Such tragic irony differs from satire in that there is no attempt to make fun of the character, but only to bring out clearly the "all too human," as distinct from the heroic, aspects of tragedy. King Lear attempts to achieve heroic dignity through his position as a king and father, and finds it instead in his suffering humanity: hence it is in *King Lear* that we find what has been called the "comedy of the grotesque," the ironic parody of the tragic situation, most elaborately developed.

As a phase of irony in its own right, the fourth phase looks at tragedy from below, from the moral and realistic perspective of the state of experience. It stresses the humanity of its heroes, minimizes the sense of ritual inevitability in tragedy, supplies social and psychological explanations for catastrophe, and makes as much as possible of human misery seem, in Thoreau's phrase, "superfluous and evitable." This is the phase of most sincere, explicit realism: it is in general Tolstoy's phase, and also that of a good deal of Hardy and Conrad. One of its central themes is Stein's answer to the problem of the "romantic" Lord Jim in Conrad: "in the destructive element immerse." This remark, without ridiculing Jim, still brings out the quixotic and romantic element in his nature and criticizes it from the point of view of experience. The chapter on watches and chronometers in Melville's *Pierre* takes a similar attitude.

The fifth phase, corresponding to fatalistic or fifth-phase tragedy, is irony in which the main emphasis is on the natural cycle, the steady unbroken turning of the wheel of fate or fortune. It sees experience, in our terms, with the point of epiphany closed up, and its motto is Browning's "there may be heaven; there must be hell." Like the corresponding phase of tragedy, it is less moral and more generalized and metaphysical in its interest, less melioristic and more stoical and resigned. The treatment of Napoleon in *War and Peace* and in *The Dynasts* affords a good contrast between the fourth and fifth phases of irony. The refrain in the Old English *Complaint of Deor:* "Thaes ofereode; thisses swa maeg" (freely translatable as "Other people got through things; maybe I can") expresses a stoicism not of the "invictus" type, which maintains a romantic dignity, but rather a sense, found also in the parallel second phase of satire, that the practical and immediate situation is likely to be worthy of more respect than the theoretical explanation of it.

The sixth phase presents human life in terms of largely unrelieved bondage. Its settings feature prisons, madhouses, lynching mobs, and places of execution, and it differs from a pure inferno mainly in the fact that in human experience suffering has an end in death. In our day the chief form of this phase is the nightmare of social tyranny, of which *1984* is perhaps the most familiar. We often find, on this boundary of the *visio malefica,* the use of parody-religious symbols suggesting some form of Satan or Antichrist worship. In Kafka's *In the Penal Colony* a parody of original sin appears in the officer's remark, "Guilt is never to be doubted." In *1984* the parody of religion in the final scenes is more elaborate: there is a parody of the atonement, for instance, when the hero is tortured into urging that the torments be inflicted on the heroine instead. The assumption is made in this story that the lust for sadistic power on the part of the ruling class is strong enough to last indefinitely, which is precisely the assumption one has to make about devils in order to accept the orthodox picture of hell. The "telescreen" device brings into irony the tragic theme of *derkou theama,* the humiliation of being constantly watched by a hostile or derisive eye.

The human figures of this phase are, of course, *desdichado* figures of misery or madness, often parodies of romantic roles. Thus the romantic theme of the helpful servant giant is parodied in *The Hairy Ape* and *Of Mice and Men,* and the romantic presenter or Prospero figure is parodied in the Benjy of *The Sound and the Fury* whose idiot mind contains, without comprehending, the whole action of the novel. Sinister parental figures naturally abound, for this is the world of the ogre and the witch, of Baudelaire's black giantess and Pope's goddess Dullness, who also has much of the parody deity about her ("Light dies before thy uncreating word!"), of the siren with the imprisoning image of shrouding hair, and, of course, of the *femme fatale* or malignant grinning female, "older than the rocks among which she sits," as Pater says of her.

This brings us around again to the point of demonic epiphany, the dark tower and prison of endless pain, the city of dreadful night in the desert, or, with a more erudite irony, the *tour abolie,* the goal of the quest that isn't there. But on the other side of this blasted world of repulsiveness and idiocy, a world without pity and without hope, satire begins again. At the bottom of Dante's hell, which is also the center of the spherical earth, Dante sees Satan standing upright in the circle of ice, and as he cautiously follows Virgil over the hip and thigh of the evil giant, letting himself down by the tufts of hair on his skin, he passes the center and finds himself no longer going down but going up, climbing out on the other side of the world to see the stars again. From this point of view, the devil is no longer upright, but standing on his head, in the same attitude in which he was hurled downward from heaven upon the other side of the earth. Tragedy and tragic irony take us into a hell of narrowing circles and culminate in some such vision of the source of all evil in a personal form. Tragedy can take us no farther; but if we persevere with the *mythos* of irony and satire, we shall pass a dead center, and finally see the gentlemanly Prince of Darkness bottom side up.

Questions

1. What distinction does Frye make between satire and irony? Provide examples of each from your reading.

2. Describe the three major kinds or "phases" of satire as Frye defines them.

3. Do you consider Frye's title for his essay on satire an appropriate one? What does it tell us about satire?

4. What does the image taken from the conclusion of Dante's "Inferno," with which Frye's essay concludes, suggest about the value and meaning of satire?

ALVIN B. KERNAN

A Theory of Satire

"There was in our time a certain parasite, Golias by name, notorious alike for his intemperance and wantonness . . . a tolerable scholar, but without morals or discipline . . . who did vomit forth against the Pope and the Roman curia a succession of famous pieces, as adroit as they were preposterous, as imprudent as they were impudent."[1] These lines, written

[1] Giraldus Cambrensis, *Speculum Ecclesiae,* in *Works,* ed. J. S. Brewer (London, 1873), *4,* 291-92. The translation is from Helen Waddell's *The Wandering Scholars* (London, John Constable, 1927), p. 160.

FROM *The Cankered Muse* by Alvin B. Kernan, copyright, 1959, Yale University Press.

in the early thirteenth century by the historian Giraldus Cambrensis, contain a fundamental error: there was no such person as "Golias." There were, however, a number of satiric poems, written in the twelfth and thirteenth centuries by anonymous poets, which were purportedly the work of one Bishop Golias, a sprightly, irreverent, devil-may-care figure who divided his time between laughing at the clergy and praising the pleasures of the flesh. But Golias himself was the purely poetic creation of those poets called the goliards or *ordo vagorum,* the wandering, witty clerics of the late medieval period, who refused to attach themselves to any benefice or to submit to any strict rule. For them Golias, whose name seems to derive from Latin *gula,* throat and gluttony, became "a kind of eponymous hero,"[2] and under the cover of this *persona* the poets flaunted their own unorthodox wit and wrote their mocking attacks on a world where people like Giraldus took themselves far too seriously.

Giraldus was a historian and he read the goliardic satires as documents, pieces of reporting, making no allowance for their pronounced artistic qualities of obliquity, exaggeration, and irony. The satiric mask of Bishop Golias was for the historian the direct reflection of an actual living person whose discreditable character, revealed by his manner of writing, explained the "preposterous," i.e. historically untrue, nature of his attacks on the church. While Giraldus' particular confusion is evident, his general approaches to satire have tenaciously remained the dominant ones down to our own time. The character who delivers the satiric attack is still identified as the author, the biographical method; and the picture of the world given in satire is taken as an attempt to portray the "actual" world, the historical method. These methods have been applied with varying degrees of sophistication, but even at their best they inevitably lead us to such unanswerable questions as, "Was first-century Rome as completely debased as Juvenal painted it?" or

"Did Swift hate mankind as extravagantly as Gulliver hated the Yahoos?" Our attention is thus directed away from the satiric work itself and toward some second object, the personality of the author or the contemporary social scene. In this way satire is denied the independence of artistic status and made a biographical and historical document, while the criticism of satire degenerates into discussion of an author's moral character and the economic and social conditions of his time.

Curiously enough, the authors of satires have encouraged this response to their works, for of all the major literary genres satire has traditionally made most pretense of being realistic. The man who after reading *Gulliver's Travels* tried to find Lilliput on the map may have been a fool, but he was led on by Swift's elaborate apparatus of verisimilitude. Elsewhere the game is not so apparent, and the satirist always assures us most seriously that he alone describes the world as it actually *is,* he deals in "deeds and language such as men do use," he has "stoop'd to truth," his subject is "quidquid agunt homines." He argues that other literary kinds—epic, romance, love poetry—are mere lies which avoid the truth about mankind, and he delights in mocking these genres and parodying them. He emphasizes his own dedication to truth by the use of straightforward language, even slang at times, and fills his work with references to contemporary customs, places, names. He will proudly call attention to the absence from his writing of the usual ornaments of poetry and raise the question, as Horace does in the fourth satire of his first book of *Sermones,* whether on the basis of realism, rough diction, and crude meter satire is even entitled to the name of poetry? Pietro Aretino's boast, which owes a good deal to Horace, is typical of the satirist's proud claim to downright truth without any fancy decoration:

> Caesar and Homer, I have stolen your bays!
> Though not a poet or an emperor;
> My style has been my star, in a manner, for
> I speak the truth, don't deal in lying praise.
> I am Aretino, censor of the ways
> Of the lofty world, prophet-ambassador
> Of truth and smiling virtue.

[2] G. F. Whicher, *The Goliard Poets* (Norfolk, Conn., New Directions, 1949), p. 3. The etymology of "Golias" is still a matter of dispute; alternate suggestions are *"guiliar,"* to deceive, and "Goliath." See J. M. Manly, "The Familia Goliae," *Modern Philology,* 5 (1907), 201-09.

In short, the satirist makes every effort to repudiate the Muse and to emphasize the down-to-earth quality of himself and his work, but the very vigor of these efforts and their continuous appearance in satire suggest that they are themselves stylistic devices used in a perfectly conventional manner to establish the character and tone traditionally thought appropriate for the satiric genre. Paradoxically, the claim to have no style is itself a trick of style employed by nearly every satirist, and his realistic touches are themselves satiric conventions. In point of fact, the claims to blunt, straightforward, and unskilled honesty made by the satirist are so patently false as to be outrageous, for in practice he is always an extremely clever poetic strategist and manipulator of language who possesses an incredibly copious and colorful vocabulary and an almost limitless arsenal of rhetorical devices. This paradox of the artless artist, innate in satire, has usually been solved either by ignoring all evidences of art and taking the satirist's word for it that he is a truthful, unskilled fellow driven to write by his indignation; or by noting his techniques of exaggeration and dismissing his presentation of himself as a plain man dedicated to truth as a mere pose designed to cover some such sinister intention as blackening the names of his enemies or passing off smut and scandal as truth in order to sell his book. Every major writer of satire has been praised by some critics for his fearless determination to tell the truth about his world and damned by others for a twisted, unstable, prurient liar whose works no careful father should allow his children to open.

This dilemma has been created by the biographical and historical methods of criticism, and to solve it we need to approach satire in the way we do other poetry—as an art; that is, not a direct report of the poet's feelings and the literal incidents which aroused those feelings, but a construct of symbols—situations, scenes, characters, language—put together to express some particular vision of the world. The individual parts must be seen in terms of their function in the total poem and not judged by reference to things outside the poem such as the medical history of the author or the social scene in which he wrote.

There have been in recent years a number of discussions of the art of satire, but these have focused somewhat narrowly on the satirist's use of linguistic devices and his ability to contrive incidental effects. We have been shown that he is a master of irony, caricature, disabling imagery, the unexpected thrust of wit, anticlimax, burlesque, and invective. He seems to be a man with an immense supply of rhetorical tools which he uses in rapid succession to belabor his victims. On the rare occasions when attempts have been made to show that the art of satire extends beyond the manipulation of language, the emphasis has still fallen on isolated effects. Mary Claire Randolph, for example, points out that within formal verse satire we find "miniature dramas, sententious proverbs and quotable maxims, beast fables (often reduced to animal metaphors), brief sermons, sharp diatribes, series of vignettes, swiftly sketched but painstakingly built up satiric 'characters' or portraits, figure-processions, little fictions and apologues, visions, apostrophes and invocations to abstractions. This bewildering array of devices suggests the diverse origins of satire and the appropriateness of its name 'satura,' or 'medley.'"[3] Demonstrations of the satirist's skillful handling of language and management of single effects have made suspect the once popular examination question, "Is Satire Art?" but we are still left with a satirist who is only an artist manqué, a contriver of farragoes rather than articulated wholes.

What is required is a more comprehensive method of describing satire which will not limit our investigations to linguistic analysis or the location of single effects but will instead include all the major elements of composition used in the form. An adequate set of terms will permit us to see individual satires as entities and thus make it possible for us to grasp the relationship of one satire to others, and ultimately to define satire with some exactitude. Historical and biographical critics have focused on what are certainly the two most striking aspects of satire, the picture of the society which is presented as a literal render-

3 "The Structural Design of Formal Verse Satire," *Philological Quarterly*, 21 (1942), 373.

ing of the *hic et nunc,* and the elusive speaker who is sometimes merely identified as "I" and sometimes given a name. In historical terms the picture of society is identified always as Rome, London, Hollywood, or some other specific place, and in biographical terms the speaker becomes Swift, Juvenal, Fielding, or some other specific author. If, however, we translate the historical and biographical terms into the dramatic terms which they readily suggest, a number of the dilemmas seemingly inherent in satire become comprehensible. Using the terms of drama, the picture of society drawn by the satirist becomes the "scene," and the voice we "hear" becomes the satiric "hero." Since the chief character of satire always lacks so signally the qualities which we associate with heroism, it will be better to refer to him simply as the "satirist," and from this point on when the word "satirist" is used it refers to the chief character—whether named, identified as "I," or the anonymous voice that tells the tale—in a satiric work. The author will be designated by other terms. The adoption of two dramatic terms, scene and satirist, entails the use of a third, "plot," for whatever we have characters in a setting there is always movement, or attempted movement, in some direction.

Satire is, like comedy and tragedy, a very ancient form which appears to have its roots in primitive ritual activities such as formulaic curses and the magical blasting of personal and tribal enemies; and just as we find tragic and comic attitudes outside art, so we find that the attitudes expressed in satire are also felt and expressed by individuals in various extraliterary ways ranging from the sneer to the street-corner tirade. But satire, although critics have always regarded it as a minor form, has long been established as a recognizable literary genre with its own traditions and conventions. The protean nature of satire has interfered with any precise definition of its conventions, but since by general agreement works as surfacely diverse as Jeremiah's bitter denunciation of his sinful people, *Gulliver's Travels, The Praise of Folly, The Clouds* and *The Threepenny Opera* have been identified as satires, then it would follow that they share some quality which we take to be character-

istic of satire. For most of us satire is synonymous with attack, particularly the savage variety, but there are attacks which are not satires —Ahab's bitter descriptions of Moby Dick, for example—and so satire must be a definite kind of attack. That is, there must be specific groupings, roles, tones, patterns, which we implicitly recognize as characteristic of satire, and these I propose to describe in terms of scene, character, and plot.

THE SCENE OF SATIRE

The scene of satire is always disorderly and crowded, packed to the very point of bursting. The deformed faces of depravity, stupidity, greed, venality, ignorance, and maliciousness group closely together for a moment, stare boldly out at us, break up, and another tight knot of figures collects, stroking full stomachs, looking vacantly into space, nervously smiling at the great, proudly displaying jewels and figures, clinking moneybags, slyly fingering new-bought fashions. The scene is equally choked with things: ostentatious buildings and statuary, chariots, sedan-chairs, clothes, books, food, horses, dildos, luxurious furnishings, gin bottles, wigs. Pick up any major satiric work and open it at random and the immediate effect is one of disorderly profusion. The sheer dirty weight, without reason or conscious purpose, of people and their vulgar possessions threatens to overwhelm the world in Trimalchio's banquet room, the streets of Juvenal's Rome, Langland's "felde ful of folke," Eleanor Rumming's Tavern, Bartholomew Fair, the City as the Dunces set off for Westminster, Don Juan's London streets that "boil over with their scum," and before the Hollywood theater where the vast mob of yokels gathers to see the "movie stars" in Nathanael West's *The Day of the Locust.* Everywhere the satirist turns he finds idiocy, foolishness, depravity, and dirt. "Auriculas asini quis non habet?" (Who is there who has not the ears of an ass?) shouts "Persius," and "Juvenal's" exclamation, "It is difficult *not* to write satire," (difficile est saturam non scribere) express the satirist's sense of a world where vice is so omnipresent and so arrant that it cannot be avoided. It is no accident that most satire is set in the city, particularly in the metropolis with a polyglot people.

In satiric painting this quality of dense, turbulent weight is even more immediately striking. The human stupidity and malice concentrated in the faces of Hieronymus Bosch's Dutch burghers crowd in a shapeless, suffocating mass which threatens to overwhelm and obliterate the face of Christ in *The Carrying of the Cross;* and in Bosch's surrealistic pictures such as *The Temptation of Saint Anthony* where human nastiness is given fantastic form, the typical density of the satiric scene finds expression in a vast multitude of small, grotesque monsters who work madly and aimlessly around the praying saint. Hogarth's satiric drawings, e.g. *Gin Lane,* are always crowded with debris and a host of rotting things, human, animal and vegetable. In Reginald Marsh's *Coney Island* vulgarity, vanity, lust, and animality combine to create a writhing mass of flesh and human litter which nearly blots out the sea, the sky, and the sand. In the occasional instances where the literary satirist uses a painting image to heighten the visual impact of his scene, the qualities of density, multiplicity, and disorder are always stressed. Henry Savile, in his "Advice to a Painter to Draw the Duke by" begins his instructions on satiric composition by saying,

> Spread a large canvass, Painter, to containe
> The great assembly and the numerous traine,
> Who all in triumph shall about him sitte
> Abhoring wisdome and dispising witt.
>
> (lines 1-4)

The chief character in Nathanael West's *The Day of the Locust* is a young painter who is attempting to get on canvas the same horrified and fearful perception of a world gone mad expressed by the book as a whole. The painter's vision is apocalyptic, and his picture, "The Burning of Los Angeles," makes concrete those forces which lie behind all satiric scenes. "Across the top, parallel with the frame, he had drawn the burning city, a great bonfire of architectural styles, ranging from Egyptian to Cape Cod colonial. Through the center, winding from left to right, was a long hill street and down it, spilling into the middle foreground, came the mob carrying baseball bats and torches. For the faces of its members he was using the innumerable sketches he had made of the people who had come to California to die. . . . In the lower foreground, men and women fled wildly before the vanguard of the crusading mob."

The men and women who flee before the mob in "The Burning of Los Angeles," while they are not morally attractive, do represent the only virtues possible in such a world: courage, vitality, intelligence. But their position on the canvas suggests that they are about to be obliterated, and this is typical of the satiric scene. Somewhere in his dense knots of ugly flesh the satiric author or painter usually inserts a hint of an ideal which is either threatened with imminent destruction or is already dead. Humanity, what man is capable of achieving, is reflected in the lovely human faces of Bosch's tortured Christ and his St. Anthony, both about to be destroyed by the monstrosities which surround and press inward on them. Far above and in the distance behind *Gin Lane* rises a church steeple, but the three balls of the pawnbroker, in the form of a cross, dominate the immediate scene of squalor and filth. In Daumier's *Articles Placed in Evidence,* one of a series of satires on the French legal system, only the feet of Christ nailed to the cross show in a picture which hangs behind three bored and stupid judges presiding at a murder trial. Juvenal manages in his satires to refer in a variety of ways to the sturdy independence and moral vigor of the old Romans of the Republic; Celia retains her virtue, somewhat woodenly, in Volpone's palace; Pope can still talk to Arbuthnot; and a copy of Shakespeare still exists and is read by one man in the desert of the *Brave New World.*

Although there is always at least a suggestion of some kind of humane ideal in satire —it may in the blackest type of satire exist only as the unnamed opposite of the idiocy and villainy portrayed—this ideal is never heavily stressed, for in the satirist's vision of the world decency is forever in a precarious position near the edge of extinction, and the world is about to pass into eternal darkness. Consequently, every effort is made to emphasize the destroying ugliness and power of vice. The author of satire always portrays the grotesque and distorted, and concentrates to an obsessive degree on the flesh. Northrop Frye remarks that "genius seems to have led practically every great satirist to become what the world calls obscene," and it is certainly true that the most unpleasant details appearing in literature are to be found in satire: Juvenal's pathic who tells us in explicit and revolting terms about his relationship with his patron, the descriptions of the excrementary functions of the Yahoos, Trimalchio's purge in *The Satyricon,* Rochester's pictures of the amorous pleasantries of King Charles and his mistresses. The satiric painter cannot be so frank, but he too seems to be fascinated by the flesh, particularly fat and the sagging, graying skin. His subjects if they are young and healthy are always gross and seem to reek of sweat, while if they are old they are either bursting the seams of their clothes or horribly cadaverous. If the satirist is more delicate than in the examples mentioned above, his characters still seem always indecently carnal; man is caught in his animal functions of eating, drinking, lusting, displaying his body, copulating, evacuating, scratching. He is riddled with hideous and deforming diseases, most often venereal: the bone-ache, falling hair, a decayed nose, ulcerous teeth, boils, scurf. Gross, sodden, rotting matter is the substance of the satiric scene and any trace of the beautiful or the spiritual is always in danger of being destroyed by the weight of this mere "stuff."

The faces peering out at us from the crowded satiric scene seldom have normal features but are grotesquely distorted by the vices they mirror. Stupidity, lust, pride, greed, hatred, and envy are revealed in exaggerated facial lineaments, gestures, bodies, and postures. We seem in satire always to be at the extreme: the bore never goes away, but prattles on without end; the flatterer says *any* outrageous thing to the vain man, who believes *all* that is said; the miser wants absolutely *all* the wealth in the world; the fop literally smothers himself under a mass of fantastic clothes; the blockhead can be persuaded to do *anything;* the politician actually sells his mother for advancement. From the "realistic" forms of satire where there is still some degree of resemblance to actual humanity and where man's bestiality, smallness of mind, and mechanistic

responses to appetite are suggested by metaphors, it is but a step to more obviously symbolic types of satire where the metaphors are given substantial form. Men *are* fantastic monsters, part rodent and part machine, in Bosch's surrealistic paintings; the ordinary worker *is* a robot in *R.U.R.;* citizens *are* horses and pigs in *Animal Farm;* and humans *are* Lilliputians and Yahoos in *Gulliver's Travels.*

The more "realistic" kinds of satire are always just on the verge of falling over into the overtly symbolic mode, despite the satiric claims to literal truthfulness, and it would be possible to classify satire according to the degree of realism to which it pretends. Working from the point of extreme realism we would begin with satires such as those of Juvenal, or Pope's *Imitations of Horace,* and pass, with the degree of realism progressively diminishing, through such works as *The Alchemist, The Adding Machine,* and *The Birds* to beast fables such as "The Nun's Priest's Tale" where literal imitation of the human scene has very nearly disappeared. Criticism has, however, traditionally distinguished, under various names, only two main types of satire: formal verse satire and Menippean satire. The term Menippean originally referred to those satires which were written in a mixture of verse and prose, but it has gradually come to include any satiric work obviously written in the third person or, to put it another way, where the attack is managed under cover of a fable. Dryden—who prefers the alternate term Varronian—cites as examples Petronius' *Satyricon,* some of Lucian's dialogues, *The Golden Ass, The Praise of Folly,* and his own *Absalom and Achitophel.*[4] In the traditional scheme all works short of extreme realism would then be classified as Menippean. Formal verse satire, a loosely defined term at best, has been used to designate those satires written in verse where the author appears to speak in his own person without the use of any continuous narrative, preferring to describe bits and pieces of the world which have stung him into writing. Works falling in our scale at the extreme realistic end would be in the category of formal verse satire: the collections

[4] "A Discourse Concerning the Original and Progress of Satire," in *Essays of John Dryden,* ed. W. P. Ker (New York, Oxford Univ. Press, 1925), 2, 66-67.

of satires of Juvenal, Hall, Marston, Boileau, Rochester, some of Horace's *Sermones*, Byron's *English Bards and Scotch Reviewers,* and Gay's *Trivia.* While I should prefer to drop the word "verse" from the term formal verse satire to allow the inclusion of works such as Philip Wylie's *Generation of Vipers* which obviously belong in this category, the terms formal and Menippean are useful because as employed today they make a meaningful differentiation of species within the genus satire. But they are confusing if used too rigidly to make something approaching an absolute distinction between two species of satire, for the scene of formal satire, despite the attempts of the author to make it appear a piece of reporting, is as much a selection of significant and interrelated details, a symbolic world, as is the scene of the beast fable where men are transformed into animals living in the forest or the barnyard. The qualities we have isolated as characteristic of the satiric scene, density, disorder, grossness, rot, and a hint of an ideal, are present in both formal and Menippean satire; they are simply made concrete in different terms.

There is, of course, a great deal of variation in the scenes of individual satires: the Rome of Horace is not identical with that of Juvenal, and the Londons of Ben Jonson and Alexander Pope are considerably different. Every author of satire is free to stress the elements of the scene which appear most important to him, but beneath the divergencies of the surface the satiric scene remains fundamentally the same picture of a dense and grotesque world of decaying matter moving without form in response only to physical forces and denying the humane ideal which once molded the crowd into a society and the collection of buildings into a city.

THE SATIRIST

Somewhere in the midst of the satiric scene or standing before it directing our attention to instances of folly and vulgarity and shaping our responses with his language, we usually find a satirist. In some cases he remains completely anonymous, merely a speaking voice who tells us nothing directly of himself, e.g., the narrator in most satiric novels. In formal satire where the satirist is usually identified as "I," or may even be given the author's name as in "An Epistle to Dr. Arbuthnot," he begins to emerge from the shadows of anonymity, and, while his back is still turned to us, he speaks of himself from time to time, giving us hints of his origins and his character. One step further and the satirist acquires a name— Colin Clout, Pierce Penilesse—and a more complete personality. At this stage it may become fairly obvious that the satirist has an unsavory character himself, and we may begin to wonder if the author is not mocking his own creation while using him to attack others, e.g., Erasmus' use of Folly in *The Praise of Folly,* or Swift's manipulation of the "Modest Proposer" and Lemuel Gulliver. Here too we must place various satirists appearing in plays who are even more unpleasant than the characters they attack: Jonson's Macilente, Shakespeare's Thersites, and Webster's Bosola. Finally, the satirist disappears altogether and we are left with only the fools and the villains who are allowed to expose and punish one another. Examples of this type of satire usually come from the theater (Jonson's *Volpone* or Aristophanes' *The Birds*), although a determined novelist may manage to keep his narration neutral enough to prevent any suggestion of a definite personality existing behind the events of the tale.

We might at this point sharpen our distinction between formal and Menippean satire somewhat and say that in formal satire the satirist is stressed and dominates the scene, while in Menippean satire the scene is stressed and absorbs the satirist, to some degree or altogether. Obviously, in the case of works occupying the middle range (such as *Gulliver's Travels*) the decision as to whether they are formal or Menippean becomes an extremely nice question: is Gulliver to be considered a part of the scene or a satirist describing and defining it? A distinction made on the basis of the extent to which the satirist is featured is useful for describing various subtypes of satire, but, again, it must not be allowed to obscure our perception of the basic unity of satire. The satirist must be regarded as but one poetic device used by the author to express his satiric vision, a device which can be dispensed with or varied to suit his purpose. We can expect, however, that if satire is a true genre then whenever the satirist does appear, whether he remains anonymous, is identified as "I," or is given a name, he will share certain basic characteristics with all other satirists. This basic character will be dictated by his function in the satiric work and established by tradition. The biographical critics of satire have insisted that each satirist is either an exact image of his creator or at least his spokesman, but, ironically enough, their writings tend to confirm the idea of a basic satiric character, for whether they are describing Juvenal, Pope, Byron, Swift or Philip Wylie they seem always to be talking about the same proud, fiery, intolerant, irascible man whom no one would want for a neighbor. There are, of course, considerable differences between the satirists created by different authors at different times, and these will be taken up in more detail shortly, but it should be possible to define in very general terms the essential satirist, those traits, attitudes, passions, which every author of satire brings together, stressing some and repressing others, and gives concrete expression to in the language, actions, and body of his particular satirist.

Every satirist is something of a Jekyll and Hyde; he has both a public and a private personality. The public personality is the one he exposes to the world, the face which he admits to and, indeed, insists on as a true image of his very nature.[5] The chief features of this personality have already been suggested in the opening pages of this chapter, and we need deal with them only briefly. Very simply, the satirist always presents himself as a blunt, honest man with no nonsense about him. This pose is established in a number of traditional ways. The satirist usually calls attention to his simple style and his preference for plain terms which express plain truth. St. Jerome, who is in fact no amateur in rhetoric, longs for "the ocean of eloquent Cicero" and the "rushing torrents of Demos-

thenes"[6] to express the absolute depravity of a priest who has used the cave where Christ was born as a place of assignation. When advised to abandon satire and "tell of the feats of Caesar," "Horace" says humbly, "Would that I could, good father, but my strength fails me. Not everyone can point ranks bristling with lances, or Gauls falling with spearheads shattered, or wounded Parthian slipping from his horse." Joseph Hall in his *Virgidemiae* tells us that his satires are "but packestaffe plaine uttring what thing they ment." Professions of this kind are one of the commonplaces of satire, but they need not always be given direct statement. The satirist may suggest that his own style is simple, and therefore truthful, simply by mocking the pretentious styles and pompous jargon of his contemporaries, as Juvenal does in his first satire; or he may employ slang and other idiomatic terms to refer to himself while using the terms of eloquence for his adversaries as Philip Wylie does in the introduction to his *Generation of Vipers*.

The pose of simplicity is frequently reinforced by references to humble but honest origins. The typical medieval satirist assumes the mask of the humble plowman working hard in the fields to support his family, close to Nature and to God. "Pope," in "An Epistle to Dr. Arbuthnot," paints a charming picture of his early years, his retirement from the busy world, his mild acceptance of insults, and his father who "held it for a rule / It was a Sin to call our Neighbour fool," while the "harmless Mother thought no Wife a Whore." Somehow the satirist seems always to come from a world of pastoral innocence and kindness: he is the prophet come down from the hills to the cities of the plain; the gawky farmboy, shepherd, or plowman come to the big city; and the scholar, nurtured at the university, abroad in the cruel world.

The satirist's moral code, which is too traditional and too straightforward to be called a philosophy, suits his rural background. "Enough for me, if I can uphold the rule our fathers have handed down, and if, so long as you need a guardian, I can keep your health

---

[5] The manner in which Pope employs this "public personality" in his satires is discussed by Maynard Mack, "The Muse of Satire," *Yale Review, 41* (1951-52), 80-92; who points out that in creating this type of persona the satiric author is following Aristotle's advice to the rhetorician to establish with his audience a character which will lend credence to what he has to say.

[6] "Calling a Lecherous Priest to Repent," in *The Satirical Letters of St. Jerome,* trans. by Paul Carroll (Chicago, Gateway, 1956), p. 115.

and name from harm," says "Horace's" father, and the words are a good description of the moral ideals of all satirists. Metaphysics, elaborate ethics, theories of redemption through suffering, these are all beyond the satirist. He views life in social terms and exhorts his audience to return to the ways of their fathers, to live with fortitude, reason, chastity, honor, justice, simplicity, the virtues which make for the good life and the good society. A Christian satirist will usually add repentance and humility before God to the list of pagan virtues, but he too takes these for granted and does not bother with speculations about their ultimate validity.

But mildness and simplicity do not suffice to make a satirist. He must not only shake his head at what he sees, he must attack it, and with vigor, if there is to be any satire. Where other men passively accept the "mortifying sight of slavery, folly and baseness" among which they are "forced to live," or rage inwardly and ineffectively, the satirist responds with that "perfect rage and resentment"[7] of which Swift speaks, and cries out with Juvenal,

Si natura negat, facit indignatio versum.
(Though nature says no, indignation forms
    my verses.)

(Satire I, line 79)

Or with Pope,

Ask you what Provocation I have had?
The strong Antipathy of Good or Bad.
(Epilogue to the Satires, Dialogue II, lines 197-98)

The degree of indignation varies with the man, and the satiric conventions of his time; it ranges from Horace's ironically mild "quid faciam" when faced with the corruption of Rome to the saeva indignatio of Juvenal and the violence of Elizabethan satire where, as John Marston puts it, with characteristic exaggeration:

Unlesse the Destin's adamantine band
Should tye my teeth, I cannot chuse but bite.
(The Scourge of Villanie, 1598-99, Satire VIII)

This violent indignation is, of course, somewhat at variance with the pose of the mild,

7 These quotations are from a passage in Swift's letter to Pope, June 1, 1728, in The Correspondence of Jonathan Swift, ed. F. E. Ball (London, G. Bell, 1910-14), 4, 34.

honest man, and the satirist always presents his raging at a wicked world as a compulsion. Things are so bad, vice so arrant, the world so overwhelmingly wicked that even a plain man like the satirist who prefers to live in peace is forced to attack the vice of mankind.

But what his passion forces him to do, his reason assents to, for the satirist views the world pessimistically and sees little hope for reform unless violent methods are used to bring mankind to its senses. His melancholy views on the prospects for the world are best understood by contrast with the situation in tragedy and comedy. Satire shares with comedy the knowledge that fools and foolishness have gotten out of hand, but it lacks the characteristic balance of comedy and the tone of amused tolerance which derive from the underlying certainty in comedy that right reason is ultimately the way of the world. Fools in comedy only need to be given enough rope and they will hang themselves, for Nature operates to restore the balance. While watching the fools in their foolishness the comic hero—Philinte, Millamant, Falstaff, or Shaw's St. Joan—can remain relatively detached and good-humored because of the deep conviction that "normality" will reassert itself.

Such consolation is denied the satirist, who typically believes that there is no pattern of reason left in the world. If Nature once operated or society functioned to maintain a reasonable world, the sheer idiocy of mankind has long since thwarted the great plan:

                         each Ape,
That can but spy the shadow of his shape,
That can no sooner ken what's vertuous,
But will avoyd it, and be vicious.

(The Scourge, IV)

The satirist's despair of man and society, which he builds up with direct statement and catalogues of human depravity, extends to the very operation of the cosmos itself. "With a goose-quill and a bottle of ink," says Aretino, "I mock myself of the universe." The powers divine and human that once kept man virtuous and society healthy seem no longer operative to the satirist, the flow of grace has been stopped by "the slime that from our soules doe flow."[8] If the satirist does not choose merely to relieve his pain by mockery, he regards himself and his satire, all other forces having withdrawn, as the only method of correction left, the last hope of mankind. Swift tells us that "the reason that satire was first introduced into the world" was to control those "whom neither religion, nor natural virtue, nor fear of punishment were able to keep within the bounds of their duty."[9] "Pope" is

> proud to see
> Men, not afraid of God, afraid of me:
> Safe from the Bar, the Pulpit, and the
> Throne,
> Yet touch'd and sham'd by *Ridicule* alone.
> (Dialogue II, lines 208-11)

The author of satire may believe, as Pope and Swift clearly did, that God still exists, but when he assumes the mask of the satirist he acts as if God and Nature were withdrawn and he stood alone in the lunatic world to stay its progressive degeneration. For this reason comic detachment and ease are impossible for the satirist. He is convinced that the fate of the world depends solely on him, and this gives rise to the heroic postures he frequently assumes. He becomes the only champion of virtue who dares to speak the truth in a world where the false insolently maintains itself as the real.

Satire shares this darkly serious view of the world with tragedy—thus the resemblance of the satiric and tragic scenes—and both satirist and tragic hero suffer an agonized compulsion to appraise the ills of the world and cure them by naming them. Every tragic hero has pronounced satiric tendencies, but he also has additional dimensions, chief among which are his ability to ponder and to change under pressure. The satirist, however, is not so complex. He sees the world as a battlefield between a definite, clearly understood good, which he represents, and an equally clear-cut evil. No ambiguities, no doubts about himself, no sense of mystery trouble him, and he retains always his monolithic certainty. Since these differences in character control the direc-

tion taken by the satiric and tragic plots, they will be discussed more fully later.

This is, very roughly, the public character of the satirist. Now it would be nonsense to argue, as the biographical critic does, that all authors of satire are straightforward, honest, pessimistic, indignant men who dislike ostentatious rhetoric, come from the country, and have simple moral codes. Each of these traditional qualities is a function of satire itself, and not primarily an attribute of the man who writes the satire. The typical satirist we have described is brought into being by the necessities of satire. If the attack on vice is to be effective, the character who delivers it must appear the moral opposite of the world he condemns; he must be fervent, he must be horrified at what he sees, and he must be able to distinguish between vice and virtue without any philosophical shillyshallying about "what is right and what is wrong?" The traditional character of the satirist enables him to perform each of these acts.

If the satirist remained as simple and coherent as his public personality, then his character would give little difficulty. He might appear too uncomplicated to deal with an extremely complicated world, but he would be fully understandable. There is always, however, a darker side to his nature, a private personality which the author may or may not allow his satirist to discuss openly, and this personality is, like the public personality, consequent upon the satirist's functions in satire. As a result of his violent attacks on vice he acquires a number of unpleasant characteristics which make suspect his pose of a simple lover of plain truth. These characteristics are best described as a series of closely related tensions. The most obvious tension results from the satirist's categorical contention that he is showing us the world and man as they actually are. Writers of epic, love poetry, or pastoral are, the satirist assures us, merely writing fiction. Only the satirist truly has for his subject "quidquid agunt homines." The lines from Joseph Hall's *Virgidemiae* (1598) are a typical instance of the satiric boast:

> For in this smoothing age who durst indite,
> Hath made his pen an hyred Parasite,

---

8 *The Scourge*, VII.

9 "The Examiner," No. 39, in *The Prose Works of Jonathan Swift*, ed. Temple Scott (London, G. Bell, 1902), *9*, 253.

To claw the back of him that beastly lives,
And pranck base men in proud Superlatives.

· · · · ·

Goe daring Muse on with thy thankless taske,
And do the ugly face of vice unmaske:

· · · · ·

Truth be thy speed, and Truth thy Patron bee.
(Book I, Prologue, lines 9-24)

But in no art form is the complexity of human existence so obviously scanted as in satire. The satirist is out to persuade us that vice is both ugly and rampant, and in order to do so he deliberately distorts, excludes, and slants. We never find characters in satire, only caricature: Swift's Yahoos, Juvenal's Romans, Pope's Dunces, Philip Wylie's Moms. The dilemma is inescapable, for the satirist is caught between the conflicting necessities of the claim to truth and the need to make vice appear as ugly and dangerous as possible. Whenever the author of satire allows his satirist to admit his inconsistency, his argument will be that distortion of literal reality is necessary in order to get at the truth. Philip Wylie tells us that he is attempting in *Generation of Vipers* to break through certain ancient dogmatic faiths, and then goes on, "The effort involves a considerable diversion of thought from normal channels and I have twirled a rather elaborate kaleidoscope, to divert it." Wylie's kaleidoscope becomes "squint-eyed sight" in Marston's satirist's attempt to explain his outrageous exaggeration:

Who would imagine that such squint-eyed
  sight
Could strike the world's deformities so right?
(*The Metamorphosis of Pigmalions Image and Certaine Satyres*, 1598, Satire II, lines 37-38)

This distortion of reality in an attempt to make vice as ugly and ridiculous as it truly is always requires a considerable amount of rhetorical skill, but, as we have seen, in order to establish his credibility the satirist must present himself as a plain, outspoken man who calls a spade a spade. In fact he then turns out to be the most cunning of rhetoricians, highly skilled in all the tricks of persuasion. As a result we have the curious spectacle of the most artful of writers pretending, like Chaucer's Franklin to whom "colours of reth-oryk been . . . queynte," to be rude and artless.

There is an old saying that "he who sups with the devil needs a long spoon," and it appears that the satirist has never had a long enough spoon. Inevitably when he dips into the devil's broth in order, he says, to show us how filthy it truly is, he gets splattered. In order to attack vice effectively, the satirist must portray it in detail and profusion, and he must explore the nastiest activities of the human animal and describe them in the revolting terms "Pope," for example, uses in the following passage:

Let Courtly Wits to Wits afford supply,
As Hog to Hog in huts of *Westphaly;*
If one, thro' Nature's Bounty or his
  Lord's,
Has what the frugal, dirty soil affords,
From him the next receives it, thick or
  thin,
As pure a Mess almost as it came in;
The blessed Benefit, not there confin'd,
Drops to the third who nuzzles close be-
  hind;
From tail to mouth, they feed, and they
  carouse;
The last, full fairly gives it to the *House.*
(Dialogue II, lines 171-80)

The *adversarius* speaks for all of us when he answers, "This filthy Similie, this beastly Line,/Quite turns my Stomach"; and "Pope's" answer is the standard defense of the satirist, "So does Flatt'ry mine." At times the satirist will go beyond mere prurience and appear pathological in his unending revelations of human nastiness and his paraded disgust with the ordure of the world. Trapped by his need for making sin appear hideous he seems always to be seeking out and thoroughly enjoying the kind of filth which he claims to be attacking. And at the same time that he opens himself to the charge of being a literary Peeping Tom, he also makes it possible to charge him with sensationalism, for the more effectively he builds up catalogues of human vice, the more it will appear that he is merely purveying salacious material to satisfy the meaner appetites of his audience.

The satirist's probity is further compromised by the necessary strength and vigor of his attack on his victims. He denounces them for being intemperate and unreasonable, and the very violence of his denunciations proclaims him equally unreasonable and intemperate. St. Jerome in his satiric letters takes his contemporaries to task for their unchristian behavior, but his own bitter attacks—as he remembers from time to time—violate the fundamental tenet of the Christian religion, charity. Juvenal's satirist adheres to some loose variety of Stoicism, but his fiery indignation stands in direct contrast to the Stoic ideals of passionless calm and stern endurance of misfortune, and he is forced to explain that though Nature, the principle of right reason operating through the universe, forbids his satiric outbursts, indignation insists upon them: "si natura negat, facit indignatio versum." But the satirist's sharp tongue involves him in even more unpleasant contradictions than mere philosophical confusion. He believes that the case of man and society is desperate, and he applies appropriate therapeutic treatments: the whip, the scalpel, the strappado, the emetic, the burning acid. But each of these cruel methods of treatment suggests that the man who uses them exclusively enjoys his work. The more powerfully the satirist swings his scourge—and he usually does so with considerable gusto—the more he will appear to have a marked sadistic tendency.

The necessary straightforwardness of his attacks on vice always opens the satirist to accusations of being proud. As the satirist passes a succession of absolute moral judgments on his fellow men, he inevitably becomes an egoistic monster bursting with his own righteousness and completely devoid of any sympathy for his victims or doubts about his own moral status. "Byron" in *English Bards and Scotch Reviewers* admits that,

> Every Brother Rake will smile to see
> That miracle, a Moralist in me.

(lines 699-700)

"Horace's" adversarius speaks to him about the same question (I.ii.25-7), "When you look over your own sins, your eyes are rheumy and daubed with ointment; why, when you view the failings of your friends, are you as keen of sight as an eagle?"

All but a few critics of satire have unerringly sought out and concentrated on these weak spots in the satirist's character, his private personality. Thomas Love Peacock, we are told, "showed himself rather obstinately blind to many of the higher aspects of life in general."[10] *Don Juan* consists of "the beastly utterances of a man who had lost all sense of decency,"[11] and William Blackwood was struck with horror by "the vile, heartless, and cold-blooded way in which this fiend [Byron] attempted to degrade every tender and sacred feeling of the human heart."[12] Another critic informs us that John Marston "exhibits an insane delight in raking the cesspits of vice . . . and feels the same pleasure in drawing attention to [evil] that boys experience in chalking up newly-discovered verbiage of obscenity."[13] Speaking of the same author, Thomas Warton pontificates: "The satirist who too freely indulges himself in the display of that licentiousness which he means to proscribe, absolutely defeats his own design. He inflames those passions which he professes to suppress, gratifies the depravations of a prurient curiosity, and seduces innocent minds to an acquaintance with ideas which they might never have known."[14] "Pope," it is argued, "finds himself unable to re-settle the equilibrium in his nervous system until he has taken out his revenge by an extra kicking administered to some old mendicant or vagrant lying in a ditch."[15]

All of the defects of character noted by these critics are unhesitatingly assigned to the authors, and while it is true that some of the greatest satiric authors have not been the most stable of men, the fact seems to have been missed that many of the characteristics con-

10 George Saintsbury, *English Prose,* ed. Henry Craik (New York, Macmillan, 1896), 5, 286.
11 Harriet Beecher Stowe, *Lady Byron Vindicated* (Boston, Fields, Osgood, 1870), p. 62.
12 From a letter quoted by Margaret Oliphant in *William Blackwood and His Sons* (New York, Scribner, 1897), *1*, 381.
13 J. Le Gay Brereton, *Writings on Elizabethan Drama* (Melbourne, Australia, Melbourne Univ. Press, 1948), p. 43.
14 *The History of English Poetry* (London, 1778-81), sec. 65.
15 Thomas DeQuincey, "Lord Carlisle on Pope" in *The Collected Writings of Thomas DeQuincey,* ed. David Masson (Edinburgh, Black, 1890), *11*, 126-27.

fidently attributed to them derive from the very nature of satire itself. Anyone who writes vigorous satire will inevitably appear to share these traits. If, however, we accept the strange, twisted, contradictory satirist as a fictitious character created in order to achieve the satiric end, the exposure of vice and depravity, then we can direct our attention to the ways in which the authors of great satire manipulate their satirists and exploit them in a thoroughly dramatic fashion. Juvenal's stern, impoverished, decayed noble who stamps about the streets of Rome suffering indignities at the hands of the nouveaux riches, and bursting with indignation and sophistic rhetoric; Skelton's crude, rustic, straightforward, unlearned countryman whose simple piety mocks the sophisticated churchmen; John Marston's biting, snarling, despairing, contradictory malcontent who noses into all the filth of Elizabethan London and becomes nearly incoherent with rage while denouncing it on the street corners; Swift's bumbling, credulous, prideful Gulliver voyaging from one misunderstood adventure to the next and finally filled with proud disdain for the human animal, the Yahoo—all these are satiric personae.

I have described in the preceding pages a basic satiric persona, and no doubt the reader has by now thought of a number of cases where some of the qualities I have called characteristic are so attenuated that they nearly cease to exist. Savagery, despair, hate, pride, intransigeance, prurience, and sadism may be innate in satire, but Horace, Chaucer, Erasmus, and, to a lesser degree, Ben Jonson, all manage to soften or find out more acceptable variations of these unpleasant traits by avoiding the extreme forms of indignation and the more shocking varieties of vice. They stress the public personality of the satirist. Their kind of satire verges on the comic, and their satirists, without losing their cutting-edge, exude good humor, easy laughter, urbanity. In Jonson's words, they "sport with human follies, not with crimes," and Horace's phrase "ridentem dicere verum" characterizes their method.

On the other hand there is an even larger group of satiric writers who seem to delight in stressing every extravagant attitude and every contradiction in the satiric character. Juvenal, Swift, Pope, Byron, Marston, Ro-chester, Marvell, all create satirists who lash out with violence, are filled with outrage, and seek out the vilest of men. When Horace goes for a walk he encounters a bore, when Juvenal walks *he* encounters a cast-off pathic. These bitter works are characterized by Juvenal's saeva indignatio, and they seem always to be on the threshold of tragedy. The works of these authors have provided a majority of my examples for the simple reason that such writers, by carrying to the extreme the private personality of the satirist, bring into relief the tendencies of all satire, tendencies which are repressed in the gentler types.

Horace and Juvenal thus provide us with the two extremes of the satirist, and while it seems likely that the personality of the author has some connection with the type of satirist he creates, other factors are more important in molding the satiric figure. The radical characteristics are always necessarily present, but just as each age forges its own typical verse forms or its architectural style, so, allowing for minor differences resulting from the different personalities of the authors involved, each age creates its own satirist who is distinguished from the satirists of the preceding age and the following. Bishop Golias, Piers Plowman, Thersites, the Pope of the *Imitations of Horace* are all related figures, but they are different in many ways, and each is a defining example of the standard satiric character of his age. Changes in satirists seem to come about in conjunction with major shifts in thought, and perhaps the best way of describing this process is to say that the satirist is always an amalgamation of the basic characteristics which develop whenever satire is written and of the ethos of a particular age. It is possible to distinguish a distinctive satiric figure in each of the major periods of our literature, and in later chapters I shall discuss in some detail the medieval satirist and the Renaissance satirist.

THE SATIRIC PLOT

If we take plot to mean, as it ordinarily does, "what happens," or to put it in a more useful way, a series of events which constitute a change, then the most striking quality of satire is the absence of plot. We seem at the conclusion of satire to be always at very nearly the same point where we began. The scenery and the faces may have changed outwardly, but fundamentally we are looking at the same world, and the same fools, and the same satirist we met at the opening of the work. Juvenal begins in his first satire by belaboring a variety of transgressors: the eunuch who has married, the matron who has exposed her breasts and entered the arena, and the former barber who has become one of the richest and most powerful men in Rome; fifteen satires later he is viciously attacking the army, and the brutality with which the soldiers treat civilians. Presumably the eunuch is still married and the barber more prosperous than ever. The scene is still as crowded with fools and villains, and the same forces of luxury, money, and foreign ideas which perverted traditional Roman virtue inside the city have infected the barracks. The satirist is still as indignant, as brave, as skillful, and as certain of himself as ever. His method is still the direct attack despite the fact that in fifteen satires he has not achieved a single result. What is true of formal satire is almost equally true of Menippean varieties, although there usually is more movement when the satire is carried by a fable. Trimalchio is as rich and gross as ever at the end of the description of his banquet; the "Big-enders" and the "Little-enders" come to no recognition of their foolishness in *Gulliver's Travels;* Colin Clout ends his song still complaining about prelates whose ease and power have not been disturbed in the slightest by an attack which Colin knows from the outset will only result in those he is attacking calling him a prating "losel . . . with a wide wesaunt!" Whenever satire does have a plot which eventuates in a shift from the original condition, it is not a true change but simply intensification of the original condition. After a number of adventures Gulliver becomes a more unpleasant kind of simpleton; during the course of *The Dunciad* dullness seeps into every part of London just as the slime from the Fleet ditch pollutes the river; absolutism stamps out the last trace of individualism in *1984,* and the hero is left drinking ersatz gin, crying maudlin tears, and adoring the face of Big Brother on the telescreen.

The normal "plot" of satire would then appear to be a stasis in which the two opposing forces, the satirist on one hand and the fools on the other, are locked in their respective attitudes without any possibility of either dialectical movement or the simple triumph of good over evil. Whatever movement there is, is not plot in the true sense of change but mere intensification of the unpleasant situation with which satire opens. It is here that one of the basic differences between satire and the other major literary genres, tragedy and comedy, becomes evident, for in both the latter kinds the developing plot is very close to being the absolute heart of the form. Perhaps the essence of comedy is that things somehow do "turn out all right." Usually they do so in a rather miraculous, unexpected, and fairly painless manner. An unknown will is discovered, a rich uncle returns from the West Indies, the boy and girl turn out not to be brother and sister after all. The deus ex machina may be anathema in tragedy, but it is a vital part of comedy. In tragedy the progression of events, both psychic and external, leads inevitably to adjustment and change, but for a time it is not unusual for the tragic hero to lock himself in the rigid attitude of the satirist and strive "in his little world of man to out-scorn/The to-and-fro-conflicting wind and rain." Both satirist and tragic hero cry out that they are men "more sinn'd against than sinning," and try to oppose the course of evil with the lash of scorn and vituperation: e.g. Oedipus' attack on superstition and prophecy which he mockingly calls "bird-lore," Hamlet's description of the world as an "unweeded garden," or Lear's magnificent explosions that relieve the unendurable pressure in his heart. But the tragic hero *learns* that evil is too powerful to be opposed in this way, and as he suffers the consequences of his stand he passes on into knowledge that evil is a part of the fabric of the world, not mere depravity or bad manners; and with this recognition he is forced on to see his own involvement in the mixed world and accept the extraordinarily heavy price he must pay to achieve an end which is only dimly perceived.

The tragic plot has been described as a continuing rhythm of "purpose, passion and perception,"[16] in which the tragic hero does

[16] The terms are Francis Fergusson's and form the basis of his discussion of drama in *The Idea of a Theater* (Princeton, N.J., Princeton Univ. Press, 1949).

something (purpose), is forced to endure the consequences of his act (passion), and then as a result of his suffering comes to a new understanding (perception), which constitutes the basis of a new purpose. The rhythm of satire, however, lacks the crucial act of perception which permits development and forward movement. Instead, the satirist alternates endlessly between his purpose and the passion which it brings on. His characteristic purpose is to cleanse society of its impurities, to heal its sicknesses; and his tools are crude ones: the surgeon's knife, the whip, the purge, the rack, the flood, and the holocaust, all typical metaphors of satire. He employs irony, sarcasm, caricature, and even plain vituperation with great vigor, determined to beat the sots into reason or cut away the infected parts of society, but the job is always too much for him. The massive weight of stupidity, bestiality, greed, and cunning, which is his scene, resists his uttermost efforts, and so he suffers frustration and the agonized sense that evil multiplies faster than it can be corrected or even catalogued. But suffering brings no change in him: his methods, his sense of his own righteousness, and his understanding of evil remain the same. His feelings of futility lead him not to revaluation of his methods and his enemies but to the belief that he simply needs to apply the lash more vigorously, and he doubles his efforts. This constant movement without change forms the basis of satire, and while we may be only half aware of the pattern as we read, it more than any other element creates the tone of pessimism inherent in the genre.

English literature contains, of course, a great many poems, plays, and novels with pronounced satiric qualities which do have a developing plot where movement results in metamorphosis. Ben Jonson's plays usually result in the unmasking and punishment of the fools; Webster's *The Duchess of Malfi* and a number of other Jacobean tragedies are heavily satiric but usually arrive at a much diminished tragic recognition; *Pride and Prejudice* has some of the deftest satire ever written—and one of the finest satirists, Mr. Bennet—but "good sense" and "warm hearts" bring an ending of tolerance and adjustment. Shaw in his plays belabors the English middle class with true satiric delight, but the "life force" works through his satire to bring about comic change in a play like *Man and Superman,* and tragic change, at least for a moment, in *Saint Joan.* Pure satire is far rarer than the mixed kinds in which after a time the satiric stasis is broken and the characters, both satirists and fools, are swept forward into the miraculous transformations of comedy or the cruel dialectic of tragedy.

CONCLUSIONS

Exact definition of any literary genre is perhaps an impossibility, but the terms I have used to describe satire are broad enough to allow for its considerable diversities without permitting the idea of the genre to disappear either in the multitude of different techniques of presentation which have been used to convey satire, or in the mass of shadowy, borderline cases where satire seems inextricably mixed with comedy or tragedy. It would seem that the basic impulse or "sense of life" which lies behind all satire finds concrete expression in a wide variety of ways. In life itself it appears without mediation in the sneer and in the sarcastic remark, or it will be sharpened and organized somewhat in the lampoon, the exposé, and the political cartoon. At this point it passes over into art where it appears in epigrams, "characters," pasquinades, "dictionaries," parodies, and a host of other minor types. But it is in the major satiric works of the literary tradition extending from classical antiquity to the present day, in the pure satires of Horace, Juvenal, Persius, the goliardic poets, Skelton, Marston, Pope, Swift, Byron, that we get the full expression of the satiric sense of life and the development of innate tendencies which are only suggested by the minor examples of the genre. These works exist in a variety of modes extending from the extreme realism of formal satire to the extreme symbolism of the beast fable, and may be presented in poem, play, essay, or novel.

But no matter what the mode of presentation, the elements of satire which I have distinguished remain fairly constant. The scene satirist, in those satires where he appears, is always indignant, dedicated to truth, pessimistic, and caught in a series of unpleasant contradictions incumbent on practicing his trade; the plot always follows the pattern of purpose followed by passion, but fails to develop beyond this point. For purposes of discussion I have treated scene, plot, and satirist as distinct from one another, while in any given satire where all are present they interact and reinforce one another to form a composite whole. Take, for example, the well-known tendency of satire to pass rapidly from one subject to another without lingering for very many lines on any single fool or particular piece of foolishness. We can consider this quality, which has earned satire the reputation of being fragmentary, as an attribute of the scene contributing to the effect of a disordered world in which there is a limitless amount of depravity. Or in formal satire, where the scene is described for us by the satirist and has no being in its own right, these rapid transitions reflect the character of the satirist and suggest his sense of urgency, his zeal, and his unwillingness to ponder any situation or investigate it thoroughly. Or we may see this same fragmentary quality as a function of the plot, demonstrating the continuous movement that never brings about change.

Questions

1. On what grounds did Giraldus attack the Goliardic satirists and why were his attacks pointless?
2. What are the biographical and historical approaches to satire?
3. Describe the "public" and "private" personalities of the satirist.
4. Distinguish between formal and Menippean satire.
5. Discuss the various ways in which the writing of satire shapes the personality of the speaker.

DAVID WORCESTER

Selections from

The Art of Satire

Satire is the most openly rhetorical of all the literary genres. We are always aware in reading it that the writer is manipulating words to produce a particular effect and to control our attitudes. Every type of writer does this, of course, but in satire this verbal manipulation stands out, even deliberately calls attention to itself. Critics have long been aware of this quality in satire and of the usefulness of rhetorical analysis in understanding how the satirists achieve their peculiar tone. The following selections from David Worcester's *The Art of Satire* (1940) provide a clear and interesting description, with examples, of some of the satirists' better-known rhetorical stocks in trade.

INVECTIVE

The Engine of Anger

In the formation of any kind of satire there are two steps. The author first evolves a criticism of conduct—ordinarily human conduct, but occasionally divine. Then he contrives ways of making his readers comprehend and remember that criticism and adopt it as their own. Without style and literary form, his message would be incomprehensible; without wit and compression it would not be memorable; without high-mindedness it would not "come home to men's business and bosoms." Juvenal's ringing words, "difficile est saturam non scribere," have given many thousands of readers the concept of a man forced by frightful wrongs to pour forth his indignation, careless of whether he has any hearers or no. In reality, Juvenal's phrase is a brilliant stroke of rhetoric. Intense suffering does not often leave a man in a literary frame of mind. Even if the sly Roman rhetorician had himself experienced the bygone ills that he denounces, he need have felt no difficulty in refraining from satire. People threatened with suffering or forced to watch others suffer are far more apt to "take pen in hand" than the man who has spent ten years in a mercury mine or who has been run down by a drunken driver. Feminine readers may find in this observation a possible explanation for the fact that no woman has ever made a mark in satire.

Curses and Epithets

Invective falls into two divisions. One lies within the province of satire, one outside it. A man who writes, "The asinine folly and loathsome immorality of the Government make decent citizens see red," is producing invective, but not satire. This gross invective, or abuse, is distinguished from satiric invective by di-

REPRINTED by permission of the publishers from David Worcester, *The Art of Satire*, Cambridge, Mass.: Harvard University Press, Copyright, 1940, by the President and Fellows of Harvard College.

rect, intense sincerity of expression. Satiric invective shows detachment, indirection, and complexity in the author's attitude.

There are exceptions to this judgment, but they are few. When an invective-piece is sublime in utterance, when it reflects the thwarted passion of a great soul for the good, when it is sincere, and when its wrath is not too long-sustained, it is satire. In such an unusual conjunction, no psychological tricks are necessary to make the reader feel that the author has risen above his subject. Ezekiel denouncing sixth-century Jerusalem, Dante committing his contemporaries to hell, Juvenal pouring vitriol into his "Legend of Bad Women," as J. W. Mackail calls the sixth satire, these achieve satirical greatness with a minimum use of wit, irony, or burlesque. If we think a trifle less respectfully of Juvenal today than our grandfathers did, it is partly owing to our growing doubts of his sincerity. Dryden, who prefers him to Horace, bears out our point about the necessary brevity of invective:

> [Juvenal] drives his reader along with him; and when he is at the end of his way, I willingly stop with him. If he went another stage, it would be too far; it would make a journey of a progress, and turn delight into fatigue.

In general, phillipic, jeremiad, and political diatribe lie outside the field of satire, because of their blunt directness. Likewise with the anathema, soberly committing its victim to hellfire. Let us glance at a portion of the prodigious curse of Ernulphus, so exhaustive that Walter Shandy remarked, "I defy a man to swear out of it."

> May the holy and eternal Virgin Mary, mother of God, curse him!—May St. Michael, the advocate of holy souls, curse him!—May all the angels, and archangels, principalities and powers, and all the heavenly armies, curse him! (Our armies swore terribly in Flanders, cried my uncle Toby, —but nothing to this.—For my own part, I could not have a heart to curse my dog so.) . . .
> May he be cursed in his brains, and in his vertex, (That is a sad curse, quoth my father)

in his temples, in his forehead, in his ears, in his eye-brows, in his cheeks, in his jaw-bones, in his nostrils, in his foreteeth and grinders, in his lips, in his throat, in his shoulders, in his wrists, in his arms, in his hands, in his fingers! . . .

May he be cursed in all the joints and articulations of his members, from the top of his head to the sole of his foot! May there be no soundness in him.

The whole excommunication, with its context, is humorous beyond any other passage in *Tristram Shandy*. The Catholic Dr. Slop beguiled into reading the curse aloud as the only fit expression of his sentiments; the discrepancy between that heroic bombination and its unheroic object, Obadiah; Uncle Toby setting off the inhuman virulence of the curse by his humane ejaculations;—a more brilliant concatenation of ironies could hardly be conceived. The keystone of the humor is the anathema itself, so sweeping, so literal, and so direct that the reader must sidestep its crushing force and escape into laughter. The serious curse is no longer satire. It was satire once, however, before men came to think it naive to invoke supernatural forces in a trivial cause. The archeology of satire and its relation to sorcery will be discussed in a later chapter.

To illustrate the curse become literature and transformed into great poetry, let us consider Job's complaint of his life:

> After this opened Job his mouth, and cursed his day.
>
> And Job spake, and said,
>
> Let the day perish wherein I was born, and the night in which it was said, There is a man child conceived.
>
> Let that day be darkness; let not God regard it from above, neither let the light shine upon it; let the blackness of the day terrify it.
>
> As for that night, let darkness seize upon it; let it not be joined unto the days of the year, let it not come into the number of the months.
>
> Lo, let that night be solitary, let no joyful voice come therein.
>
> Let them curse it that curse the day, who are ready to raise up their mourning.
>
> Let the stars of the twilight thereof be dark; let it look for light but have none; neither let it see the dawning of the day:
>
> Because it shut not up the doors of my mother's womb, nor hid sorrow from mine eyes.

Here the sincerity of the speaker is beyond question; there is no ironic duplicity or burlesque mystification in his attitude. Between his naked sentiment ("A curse on my nativity") and the reader, he has nevertheless interposed a rhetorical pattern of astonishing complexity. Seizing the profound antithesis of light and darkness, symbolic of universal creation, he builds on it with parallelism, repetition, personification, and other devices, until an organic whole emerges, worthy of being set beside such miracles of ingenuity as Bach's Ricercare from the *Musikalische Opfer* or the Beethoven quartet, Opus 131. Perhaps some hint of the balance and forward movement may be conveyed by a diagram:

Let the day perish,	and the night.
Let that day be darkness.	
Let the blackness of that day terrify it.	
	As for that night, let darkness seize upon it.
	Let that night be solitary.
Let them curse it	that curse the night.
	Let the twilight thereof be dark.
Let it not see the dawning.	

Because it shut not up the doors of my mother's womb.

The curse, in Job, has lost most of its supernatural and incantational quality. It retains just enough of that quality to provide emphasis and symbolism. The symbolism, in turn, carries the reader into the universal and introduces him to the cosmic irony upon which Job is built: that is, the revolt of the creature against the creator, the return of life to the giver. The curse of Job introduces the first and greatest example in a high tradition of satire that has endured to the present day. The problem of evil with its corollaries, the questioning of divine justice and the extravagance of human faith, has been treated in a spirit of gentle irony or bitter sarcasm or open revolt by Horace, Lucian, Chaucer, Erasmus, Rabelais, Burton, Omar Khayyam, the second James Thomson, and Hardy, to name a few.

For an example of the curse altered almost out of recognition, we draw upon the Father of Laughter.

> And therefore, to make an end of this Prologue, even as I give myselfe to an hundred Pannier-fulls of faire devils, body and soul, tripes and guts, in case that I lie so much as one single word in this whole History: After the like manner, St. Anthonies fire burne you; Mahoom's disease whirle you; the squinance with a stich in your side, and the Wolfe in your stomack trusse you, the bloody flux seize upon you, the curst sharp inflammations of wilde fire, as slender and thin as Cowes haire, strengthened with quick silver, enter into your fundament, and like those of Sodom and Gomorrha, may you fall into sulphur, fire and bottomless pits, in case you do not firmly beleeve all that I shall relate unto you in this present Chronicle.

This genial fulmination tickles the audience by an overstatement resembling that of Ernulphus's curse. The exaggeration is clearly intentional, however; it belongs to the writer's attitude of self-parody. He barks, but lets us see that he is not going to bite. The real Rabelais stands apart, smiling at the simulacrum that he presents to the audience in place of himself. The curse is thus diverted into burlesque. Three devices draw its teeth. There is first the absurd exaggeration with its implied satire on authoritarians who try to inculcate belief by bluster. Second, the reader is challenged to a game of wits by the histrionic division of the writer's personality. When the fellow's threats turn out to be so much gammon, we suspect that his professions of telling the truth are gammon likewise. We look forward to smoking him out; but he in his turn will do his best to mystify us, sometimes giving us the simulacrum and sometimes speaking in his own person. The third device is verbal luxuriance. The most deadly insult or curse is spoken in the simplest, most direct language, as witness the manner of Junius or Swift. The virulence lessens in proportion as the language grows bombastic, exotic, or sesquipedalian. Something of all these qualities appears in Rabelais's curse.

BURLESQUE

Satire by Comparison

In making the rounds of an amusement park, you can always find people "laughing like a swarm of flies" in front of the eccentric mirrors. You draw near to one of them and see a squat, obese goblin goggling at you. With a pang of surprise, you observe that the monster wears your clothes, mimics your gestures, and is, in horrid fact, you. Before the next mirror, behold yourself shot up into the wasted wreck of a giant, with pipestem arms and legs and elongated horse-face. These two experiences have introduced you to burlesque in its simplest form.

It has been shown how invective-satire, compelled to gain the sanction of society, uses wit mechanisms to circumvent mankind's prejudice against naked rage. Derision is the purpose of invective-satire. The reader has no choice in accepting the subject of condemnation, for it is held steadily before his eyes; yet he derives some sense of self-determination, for example from the simile, which permits him to make a comparison and draw his own deductions from it. The reader would sympathize with the condemnation still more, if the simile could be expanded from a brief trope into a literary vehicle capable of carrying a multiple-series of comparisons between the ideal and the real. He could then see how a man's deeds compare with his words; how the operation of a law fulfils the purpose for which it was enacted, how far a would-be hero falls short of true greatness.

Burlesque is just such a vehicle. It is a kind of extended simile. "Look here, upon this picture, and on this," says the author. The reader looks first on one, then on the other, and decides for himself whether the mirrored image faithfully reproduces the object. Of course, in satire it does not do so, for the satirist secretly aims at exposing a discrepancy in the strongest possible light. Once he has exposed it, the fewer words the better, for his insistence on pointing the moral will rob the reader of his share in the game. So long as he abstains from sermonizing, he has the reader with him. Far from using the goad of invective, he lures his audience by posing as a passive agent, letting the condemnation come home to roost by analogy. The reader then appears to himself to draw his own independent conclusions.

The reader's sense of participation is given an extra fillip by suppression of one term of the simile. We do not find a parody printed side by side with its original. It is the reader's part to supply knowledge of the model. He must hold up the model, and the author will furnish him with a distorted reflection of it. Herein lies the strength of burlesque, and its weakness. So long as the author can depend on his audience for the necessary information, he need not utter a word of reproach or obloquy; his audience will provide the curses, and he will yet "have a thank" for his good offices. And yet, knowledge that seems to one age to be graven in adamant seems to the next to have been written in the sand. The *Batrachomyomachia,* or Battle of Frogs and Mice, finds a small audience today although it parodies Homer, the Bible of the ancient world. Likewise all the machinery of the mock-heroic —the invocations, epithets, and set speeches so delicious to the eighteenth century—raises only an occasional smile today. Dryden, in writing *Absalom and Achitophel,* must have been confident that his allegory would be comprehended at sight by readers born hundreds of years to come. How many today can read it for the first time without recourse to Bible or to "Notes"? Just as invective dies when the social occasion that countenanced it passes, so burlesque withers away when the knowledge that supports it is forgotten.

Two courses are open if we wish to use the method of comparison to show up a man's shortcomings. We may draw a picture of a low fellow engaged in vicious or trivial pursuits and endow him with the features of our victim. These features, perhaps degraded and brutalized, are not altered past recognition. The first reaction of the audience on recognizing the likeness is one of pure comedy. And comic enough it is to see a hawk's bill doing duty for a human nose, or a human face translated into a fox's mask. The satiric reaction is overlaid on the comic. Comparing what we know of the real man with the caricaturist's distorted image, we single out a hawk-like rapacity in his character, or a foxy duplicity. Once this quality has been impressed on our minds, we shall find it hard to think of the man without remembering it. Thus by altering the true image, by degrading it and presenting it without dignity, the artist acts like the first of the two mirrors, the glass that reduces the spectator to a fat goblin. This process of diminishing and degrading the object is the method of low burlesque.

Low burlesque creates a standard below its victim and makes the reader measure him against that standard. Fox ethics, for example, are lower than human ethics. When the reader is led to regard a man as a fox, whatever foxy qualities the man possesses are thrown into sharp relief. In the same way, a piano with the loud pedal held down will give back whatever note is sung into it. Low burlesque calls forth these sympathetic notes or hidden affinities.

It is clear that we can obtain a second scale of comparison by placing our standard, not below the victim, but above him. Holding him up against a standard obviously too elevated for him will make his shortcomings stand out sharply. If he conceives of himself as an exalted personage, let him be invested with the trappings and dignities of a real hero, retaining only his proper features. His pretentiousness will then stand out, to the exclusion of all other qualities. The artist in this instance does the work of our second mirror. He draws us out to an unconscionable length. We seem to knock at the stars with our exalted head, until our legs, too frail to support such eminence, give way. Great then is our fall, and hugely pleasing to bystanders. It is this principle of magnification that gives us high burlesque.

IRONY, THE ALLY OF COMEDY

Verbal Irony

Irony might be defined in two words as an impractical joke. To see a top-hatted dandy slip on a banana-peel is always pleasant. But the pleasure becomes truly exquisite to the watcher who has seen the banana-peel in advance or perchance placed it where it would do the most good. While the jest of irony is played with ideas, instead of slippery or blunt objects, the distinction between the initiated and the about-to-be-initiated still remains. The little audience (Horace's *pauci lectores*) is quick-witted enough to see the trap in advance; the "many-headed vulgar" rush blindly to meet their fate. In a practical joke a single victim is enough, and comedy is the result. In literature the percipients of irony always feel themselves to be members of a small, select, secret society headed by the author. The victims, by implication, are legion. Satire enters when the few convict the many of stupidity. The implication of a large audience is not always justified by the fact. *The New Yorker* owes its success to the skill with which its editors charm five million readers into the illusion of belonging to an aloof, sophisticated, esoteric, and fastidious minority. Critics of its sometimes mastodonic irony in turn plume themselves on being the true *cognoscenti*.

> So, naturalists observe, a flea
> Has smaller fleas that on him prey;
> And these have smaller still to bite 'em,
> And so proceed *ad infinitum*.

The ironist appeals to an aristocracy of brains. It requires mental exertion to comprehend even the simplest and crudest form of irony—sarcasm. Sarcasm is derived from a Greek word that means "flesh-tearing." When someone smiles pityingly at your criticism of a novel and remarks, "Of course, we all know you could write a much better book if you only would," your flesh is torn, so to speak, but it is not the going in of the barb that wounds, but rather the pulling out. For the words build you up only to knock you down; you must perceive the intentional inversion of meaning and translate back into the original, to your own hurt, if you would not appear a blockhead and natural butt.

When we dislike a writer's irony, we call it sarcasm. The word has unpleasant connotations, and we reserve it for obvious double-dealing in words, such as appears in conversation or in written jibes and taunts. Sarcasm is irony, none the less. *The Arte of English Poesie* (1589) mentions "ironeia, or the dry-mocke," and the *New English Dictionary* cites as the earliest use of the word "irony" a passage from Wynken de Worde (1502) in which "yronye of grammar" occurs when "a man sayth one & gyveth to understande the contrarye." Sarcasm is then a form of verbal irony, produced by an inversion of meaning. It may be distinguished from the more literary kinds of irony by the fact that it never deceives its victim. It carries its sting exposed; and lest it should be misunderstood, it has established a set of non-verbal conventions to accompany it —a curl of the lip, a special intonation and falling inflection, and often a shaking or nodding of the head. Such obvious self-advertisement means that the time-lag between hearing and comprehending is much shorter than it would be in a purely ironical speech, delivered without change in voice or expression. When protracted, sarcasm quickly degenerates into "heavy sarcasm." No settled habit of speech is more wearisome and vexatious, for a long string of sarcasms is a series of jokes on the hearer which the speaker noisily explodes and relishes in advance.

As a substitute for fist-fights, corporal punishment, and invective, sarcasm has become indispensable in social intercourse. Any reader who finds this observation cynical is invited to try the experiment of living for a week, or even a day, without allowing a sarcastic utterance or intonation to cross his lips. Even the Lord found it expedient to meet Job's reasonable complaints with a crushing sarcasm:

> Canst thou draw out leviathan with an hook?
> . . . Wilt thou play with him as with a bird?
> or wilt thou bind him for thy maidens?

The existence of a double audience—an esoteric and an exoteric—is rather implied than real when sarcasm is used. There are few too dull to scent the reversed meaning. Writers, dealing with the subtleties of frozen language instead of the ephemeral spoken word, naturally produce a purer irony than do speakers, formal orators excepted. When they set down words and sentences that express the opposite of their real meaning, they have no warning flags to fly, no special intonations of the voice, no raising of the eyebrows. The reader discovers the deception for himself, unravels the contradiction, and feels happily at one with the author. Irony of inversion involves a longer timelag than invective, burlesque, or sarcasm, and it demands that the reader join more energetically with the author in the act of artistic creation.

It is scarcely necessary to give examples of irony of inversion, since every grand, artistic lie, told with a poker face, belongs to this category. My own favorites are from Chaucer. In *The Nun's Priest's Tale*, Chauntecleer, the know-it-all cock, tells his dame that, sure as Gospel,

> *Mulier est hominis confusio,—*
> Madame, the sentence of this Latyn is,
> "Womman is mannes joye and al his blis."

In *The Merchant's Tale,* the "faire, fresshe" May, after one brief interview with her husband's squire, resolves to love him though she is but a four days' bride. By way of comment, the Merchant adds a single line—Chaucer's favorite line, it has been called, from its use elsewhere:

> Lo, pitee renneth soone in gentil herte!

Earlier in the same tale is the startling observation, already noted:

> When tendre youthe hath wedded stoupyng
>   age,
> Ther is swich myrthe that it may nat be
>   writen.

Irony of inversion ordinarily compels the reader to convert apparent praise into blame. Its shocking power is greatest when it is thus used to shatter complacent truisms and unthinking optimism. Occasionally contempt and insult are to be understood as praise. Swift's disconcerting way with his friends was to address them in terms of reproach and abuse, and then, by a fine stroke of wit, to convert the whole into a compliment. In *Jonathan Wild,* Fielding represents Heartfree's simplicity and benevolence as low sentimentality and want of spirit. Stevenson in his celebrated defense of Father Damien ironically acknowledges the blemishes in Damien's character and makes them appear faint shadows that only set off the brilliance of his hero's virtues. But Swift, after all, was a virtuoso in irony, and Heartfree is only a counterpoise to Jonathan Wild, the prince of rogues, and Stevenson was answering a bill of indictment, point by point. The negative function of irony in making approval explode into dislike is more frequent and more effective than the reverse method. Irony is a form of criticism, and all irony is satirical, though not all satire is ironical. Skepticism and pessimism and melancholy are the ironist's portion, and he is content to have it so. Lucian boldly declares:

> I profess hatred of pretension and imposture, lying, and pride. . . . However, I do not neglect

the complementary branch, in which love takes the place of hate; it includes love of truth and beauty and simplicity and all that is akin to love. But the subjects for this branch of the profession are sadly few.

Swift echoes this conclusion, saying, "The materials of panegyric, being very few in number, have been long since exhausted."

It is in the mock encomium that irony of inversion reaches its greatest concentration and brilliance. Mention has been made in the preceding chapter of the *jeux d'esprit* in this kind by Lucian, Erasmus, and Rabelais. The encomiums of sponging, of folly, and of debt are orations, with classical sources in Roman *satura* and in the Greek *spoudaiogeloion* and mime-literature in general. Fielding breathed the spirit of the mock encomium into a modern form, that of the full-length novel (most burlesque novels of the eighteenth century were as long as their models). *Jonathan Wild* furnished a model for *Barry Lyndon,* although Thackeray's genius falls below Fielding's in the dexterous handling of irony and in intellectual power. In recent years Aldous Huxley has transferred the mock encomium to the field of the Utopia. Burlesque Utopias containing occasional satire existed before *Brave New World,* but Huxley's Utopia-in-reverse is in a class by itself. To the reader who satisfies the inordinate demands made upon him, it offers a carefully worked out criticism of life. In its mirror writing, every comment or surface meaning requires only to be reversed before falling into its place in Huxley's social philosophy.

IRONY, THE ALLY OF TRAGEDY

Dramatic Irony

The distinction between the world of uninitiate, common souls and the select few who share some special knowledge underlies every form of irony. This distinction must have been bitterly ruminated by Swift when he found that his defense of the Established Church in *A Tale of a Tub* had made him an object of horror in the eyes of pious Queen Anne, who thereafter refused to hear of his preferment. Defoe in the pillory must likewise have pondered the truth of the proverb, "nothing succeeds like success." And who can read the thoughts of the unfortunate man, trembling on the verge of religious conversion, to whom his mentor, Canon Ainger, innocently sent Samuel Butler's diabolical pamphlet, "In Defense of the Miraculous Element in Our Lord's Ministry upon Earth"?

The sense of belonging to a privileged minority arises from verbal irony in solving the puzzle of inversion or understatement, and from irony of manner in penetrating the disguise of the *ingénu*. When the field of observation is enlarged from words or personalities to life as a whole and the ways of Providence, the sense of esoteric knowledge is conveyed through dramatic irony. The conflict of good and evil is the central fact of intellectual experience. From age to age, man wrestles with chaos, seeks to discover universal laws, and devises orderly, uniform arrangements of the universe. Social institutions, in the Occident at least, support that search for certainty by proclaiming the benevolence and justice of God, the fairness of the moral law, or the conquest of nature by the laboratory. Religion, philosophy, and science together provide the faith that is the motive power of civilization. From this body of belief is derived the "knowledge of life" of the masses. The dangers of such a system are those that confront the *alazon* in comedy: overstatement, overconfidence, failure to preserve the inconspicuous moderation wherein safety lies. Opposed to this general, vulgar knowledge is the private knowledge of the *eiron:* the horror of becoming a Pollyanna, the realization that blind chance can destroy all that the heart holds dear, the conviction that pride goeth before destruction, the observation that knowledge brings sadness, the suspicion that the universe is indifferent, or even hostile, to man. It was not for nothing that God forbad Adam and Eve to eat the fruit of the Tree of the Knowledge of Good and Evil. In every attempt to regularize the cosmos, some allowance must be made for the Imp of the Perverse, for the jealousy of the gods, for the panurgic principle.

The spectator of a tragedy has a number of advantages over the characters of the play. He is detached from them as they strut and fret in the shadow of their own passions. So the bystander smiles ironically to see the blind men each lay hold of a different member of the elephant and each swear to his own description of the beast. Furthermore, the spectator has superior knowledge. He has come to see a tragedy, and he watches the protagonist unconsciously drawing nearer and nearer to disaster. Greek audiences were of course perfectly familiar with the traditional legends and myths to which the tragic poets restricted themselves. Their interest was not lessened by knowing the plot in advance; it was rather heightened, for they were relieved of the element of wonder. Instead of expending their energies on guessing at the outcome, as some readers impatiently flip over the pages of a detective story to get to the last chapter, they were free to concentrate on the play itself, on its meaning, and on the delicate shades of the author's art.

Besides a superiority in factual information, dramatic irony presupposes a kind of secret knowledge in the audience. Lightning never strikes the hero out of a cloudless sky, else there would be no sense of tragedy. The storm may roll up swiftly and inconspicuously, but a man with a proper respect for heaven will read the signs. Who has not seen a cat fluffed up with electricity and looked out the window to find the sky heavy with thunderclouds? On the stage, the cat is there to be seen. The hero, through egoism or a false sense of security, overlooks it; the audience, seeing it, sees through it to the oncoming catastrophe.

Questions

1. What distinguishes invective from satire?

2. Select two political cartoons from a newspaper which make use of the devices of high and low burlesque. Then write an analysis of the cartoons showing how these techniques have been employed.

3. How can we know when a statement or situation is ironic? Since Worcester is not clear on this matter, you will have to examine closely the examples of irony he provides.

III. Supplementary Material

LEWIS MUMFORD

Selections from

Technics and Civilization

Lewis Mumford is one of our most distinguished historians of culture. These pages taken from his book *Technics and Civilization* (1934) describe the nature of the belief in "Progress" which had its roots in the eighteenth century and became a commonplace in the nineteenth. This discussion is included here because it illustrates the general theory of history which the satires printed in this volume are attacking in its particular modern manifestations. But Mumford's description of progress also has another function here. While it purports to be straight historical writing, it is in fact an impassioned attack on certain beliefs and certain social and economic arrangements. No one would, I believe, call this piece of writing satire, but it approaches it, and exploring the problem of why this is not satire and why, say, *Animal Farm* is will lead to a much firmer understanding of the distinction between art and persuasive writing.

THE DOCTRINE OF PROGRESS

The mechanism that produced the conceit and the self-complacence of the paleotechnic period was in fact beautifully simple. In the eighteenth century the notion of Progress had been elevated into a cardinal doctrine of the educated classes. Man, according to the philosophers and rationalists, was climbing steadily out of the mire of superstition, ignorance, savagery, into a world that was to become ever more polished, humane and rational—the world of the Paris salons before the hailstorm of revolution broke the windowpanes and drove the talkers to the cellar. Tools and instruments and laws and institutions had all been improved: instead of being moved by in-

stincts and governed by force, men were capable of being moved and governed by reason. The student at the university had more mathematical knowledge than Euclid; and so, too, did the middle class man, surrounded by his new comforts, have more wealth than Charlemagne. In the nature of progress, the world would go on forever and forever in the same direction, becoming more humane, more comfortable, more peaceful, more smooth to travel in, and above all, much more rich.

This picture of a steady, persistent, straight-line, and almost uniform improvement throughout history had all the parochialism of the eighteenth century: for despite Rousseau's passionate conviction that the advance in the arts and sciences had depraved morals, the advocates of Progress regarded their own period—which was in fact a low one measured by almost any standard except scientific thought and raw energy—as the natural peak of humanity's ascent to date. With the rapid improvement of machines, the vague eighteenth century doctrine received new confirmation in the nineteenth century. The laws of progress became self-evident: were not new machines being invented every year? Were they not transformed by successive modifications? Did not chimneys draw better, were not houses warmer, had not railroads been invented?

Here was a convenient measuring stick for historical comparison. Assuming that progress was a reality, if the cities of the nineteenth century were dirty, the cities of the thirteenth century must have been six centuries dirtier: for had not the world become constantly cleaner? If the hospitals of the early nineteenth century were overcrowded pest-houses, then those of the fifteenth century must have been even more deadly. If the workers of the new factory towns were ignorant and superstitious, then the workers who produced Chartres and Bamberg must have been more stupid and unenlightened. If the greater part of the population were still destitute despite the prosperity of the textile trades and the hardware trades, then the workers of the handicraft period must have been more impoverished. The fact that the cities of the thirteenth century were far brighter and cleaner and better ordered than the new Victorian towns: the fact that medieval hospitals were more spacious and more sanitary than their Victorian successors: the fact that in many parts of Europe the medieval worker had demonstrably a far higher standard of living than the paleotechnic drudge, tied triumphantly to a semi-automatic machine—these facts did not even occur to the exponents of Progress as possibilities for investigation. They were ruled out automatically by the theory itself.

Plainly, by taking some low point of human development in the past, one might over a limited period of time point to a real advance. But if one began with a high point—for example, the fact that German miners in the sixteenth century frequently worked in three shifts of only eight hours each—the facts of progress, when one surveyed the mines of the nineteenth century, were non-existent. Or

if one began with the constant feudal strife of fourteenth century Europe, the peace that prevailed over great areas of Western Europe between 1815 and 1914 was a great gain. But if one compared the amount of destruction caused by a hundred years of the most murderous warfare in the Middle Ages with what took place in four short years during the World War, precisely because of such great instruments of technological progress as modern artillery, steel tanks, poison gas, bombs and flame throwers, picric acid and T.N.T., the result was a step backward.

Value, in the doctrine of progress, was reduced to a time-calculation: value was in fact *movement in time*. To be old-fashioned or to be "out of date" was to lack value. Progress was the equivalent in history of mechanical motion through space: it was after beholding a thundering railroad train that Tennyson exclaimed, with exquisite aptness, "Let the great world spin forever down the ringing grooves of change." The machine was displacing every other source of value partly because the machine was by its nature the most progressive element in the new economy.

What remained valid in the notion of progress were two things that had no essential connection with human improvement. First: the fact of life, with its birth, development, renewal, decay, which one might generalize, in such a fashion as to include the whole universe, as the fact of change, motion, transformation of energy. Second: the social fact of accumulation: that is the tendency to augment and conserve those parts of the social heritage which lend themselves to transmission through time. No society can escape the fact of change or evade the duty of selective accumulation. Unfortunately change and accumulation work in both directions: energies may be dissipated, institutions may decay, and societies may pile up evils and burdens as well as goods and benefits. To assume that a later point in development necessarily brings a higher kind of society is merely to confuse the neutral quality of complexity or maturity with improvement. To assume that a later point in time *necessarily* carries a greater accumulation of values is to forget the recurrent facts of barbarism and degradation.

Unlike the organic patterns of movement

through space and time, the cycle of growth and decay, the balanced motion of the dancer, the statement and return of the musical composition, progress was motion toward infinity, motion without completion or end, motion for motion's sake. One could not have too much progress; it could not come too rapidly; it could not spread too widely; and it could not destroy the "unprogressive" elements in society too swiftly and ruthlessly: for progress was a good in itself independent of direction or end. In the name of progress, the limited but balanced economy of the Hindu village, with its local potter, its local spinners and weavers, its local smith, was overthrown for the sake of providing a market for the potteries of the Five Towns and the textiles of Manchester and the superfluous hardware of Birmingham. The result was impoverished villages in India, hideous and destitute towns in England, and a great wastage in tonnage and man-power in plying the oceans between: but at all events a victory for progress.

Life was judged by the extent to which it ministered to progress, progress was not judged by the extent to which it ministered to life. The last possibility would have been fatal to admit: it would have transported the problem from the cosmic plane to a human one. What paleotect dared ask himself whether labor-saving, money-grubbing, power-acquiring, space-annihilating, thing-producing devices were in fact producing an equivalent expansion and enrichment of life? That question would have been the ultimate heresy. The men who asked it, the Ruskins, the Nietzsches, the Melvilles, were in fact treated as heretics and cast out of this society: in more than one case, they were condemned to an exacerbating solitude that reached the limit of madness.

THE STRUGGLE FOR EXISTENCE

But progress had an economic side: at bottom it was little less than an elaborate rationalizing of the dominant economic conditions. For Progress was possible only through increased production: production grew in volume only through larger sales: these in turn were an incentive to mechanical improvements and fresh inventions which ministered to new desires and made people conscious of new necessities. So the struggle for the market became the dominant motive in a progressive existence.

The laborer sold himself to the highest bidder in the labor market. His work was not an exhibition of personal pride and skill but a commodity, whose value varied with the quantity of other laborers who were available for performing the same task. For a while the professions, like law and medicine, still maintained a qualitative standard: but their traditions were insidiously undermined by the more general practices of the market. Similarly, the manufacturer sold his product in the commercial market. Buying cheap and selling dear, he had no other standard than that of large profits: at the height of this economy John Bright defended the adulteration of goods in the British House of Commons as a necessary incident of competitive sale.

To widen the margin between the costs of production and the return from sales in a competitive market, the manufacturer depressed wages, lengthened hours, speeded up motions, shortened the worker's period of rest, deprived him of recreation and education, robbed him in youth of the opportunities for growth, in maturity of the benefits of family life, and in old age of his security and peace. So unscrupulous was the competition that in the early part of the period, the manufacturers even defrauded their own class: the mines that used Watt's steam engine refused to pay him the royalties they owed, and Shuttle Clubs were formed by the manufacturers to assist members sued by Kay for royalties on his invention.

This struggle for the market was finally given a philosophic name: it was called the struggle for existence. Wage worker competed against wage worker for bare subsistence; the unskilled competed against the skilled; women and children competed against the male heads of families. Along with this horizontal struggle between the different elements in the working class, there was a vertical struggle that rent society in two: the class struggle, the struggle between the possessors and the dispossessed. These universal struggles served as basis for the new mythology which complimented and extended the more optimistic theory of progress.

In his essay on population the Reverend T. R. Malthus shrewdly generalized the actual state of England in the midst of the disorders that attended the new industry. He stated that population tended to expand more rapidly than the food supply, and that it avoided starvation only through a limitation by means of the positive check of continence, or the negative checks of misery, disease, and war. In the course of the struggle for food, the upper classes, with their thrift and foresight and superior mentality emerged from the ruck of mankind. With this image in mind, and with Malthus's Essay on Population as the definite stimulus to their thoughts, two British biologists, Charles Darwin and Alfred Wallace, projected the intense struggle for the market upon the world of life in general. Another philosopher of industrialism, just as characteristically a railroad engineer by profession as Spinoza had been a lens grinder, coined a phrase that touched off the whole process: to the struggle for existence and the process of natural selection Spencer appended the results: "the survival of the fittest." The phrase itself was a tautology; for survival was taken as the proof of fitness: but that did not decrease its usefulness.

This new ideology arose out of the new social order, not out of Darwin's able biological work. His scientific study of modifications, variations, and the processes of sexual selection were neither furthered nor explained by a theory which accounted not for the occurrence of new organic adaptations, but merely for a possible mechanism whereby certain forms had been weeded out after the survivors had been favorably modified. Moreover, there were the demonstrable facts of commensalism and symbiosis, to say nothing of ecological partnership, of which Darwin himself was fully conscious, to modify the Victorian nightmare of a nature red in tooth and claw.

The point is, however, that in paleotechnic society the weaker were indeed driven to the wall and mutual aid had almost disappeared. The Malthus-Darwin doctrine explained the dominance of the new bourgeoisie, people without taste, imagination, intellect, moral scruples, general culture or even elementary bowels of compassion, who rose to the surface precisely because they fitted an environment that had no place and no use for any of these humane attributes. Only anti-social qualities had survival value. Only people who valued machines more than men were capable under these conditions of governing men to their own profit and advantage.

CLASS AND NATION

The struggle between the possessing classes and the working classes during this period assumed a new form, because the system of production and exchange and the common intellectual milieu had all profoundly altered. This struggle was closely observed and for the first time accurately appraised by Friedrich Engels and Karl Marx. Just as Darwin had extended the competition of the market to the entire world of life, so did Engels and Marx extend the contemporary class struggle to the entire history of society.

But there was a significant difference between the new class struggles and the slave uprisings, the peasant rebellions, the local conflicts between masters and journeymen that had occurred previously in Europe. The new struggle was continuous, the old had been sporadic. Except for the medieval utopian movements—such as the Lollards—the earlier conflicts had been, in the main, struggles over abuses in a system which both master and worker accepted: the appeal of the worker was to an antecedent right or privilege that had been grossly violated. The new struggle was over the system itself: it was an attempt on the worker's part to modify the system of free wage competition and free contract that left the worker, a helpless atom, free to starve or cut his own throat if he did not accept the conditions the industrialists offered.

From the standpoint of the paleotechnic worker, the goal of the struggle was control of the labor market: he sought for power as a bargainer, obtaining a slightly larger share of the costs of production, or, if you will, the profits of sale. But he did not, in general, seek responsible participation as a worker in the business of production: he was not ready to be an autonomous partner in the new collective mechanism, in which the least cog was as important to the process as a whole as the engineers and scientists who had devised it and who controlled it. Here one marks the great gap between handicraft and the early machine economy. Under the first system the worker was on his way to being a journeyman; the journeyman, broadened by travel to other centers, and inducted into the mysteries of his craft, was capable, not merely of bargaining with his employer, but of *taking his place*. The class conflict was lessened by the fact that the masters could not take away the workers' tools of production, which were personal, nor could they decrease his actual pleasure of craftsmanship. Not until specialization and expropriation had given the employer a special advantage did the conflict begin to take on its paleotechnic form. Under the capitalist system the worker could achieve security and mastery only by leaving his class. The consumer's cooperative movement was a partial exception to this on the side of consumption: far more important ultimately than the spectacular wage-battles that were fought during this period; but it did not touch the organization of the factory itself.

Unfortunately, on the terms of the class struggle, there was no means of preparing the worker for the final results of his conquest. The struggle was in itself an education for warfare, not for industrial management and production. The battle was constant and bitter, and it was conducted without mercy on the part of the exploiting classes, who used the utmost brutality that the police and the soldiery were capable of, on occasion, to break the resistance of the workers. In the course of this war one or another part of the proletariat—chiefly the more skilled occupations—made definite gains in wages and hours, and they shook off the more degrading forms of wage-slavery and sweating: but the fundamental condition remained unaltered. Meanwhile, the machine process itself, with its matter-of-fact procedure, its automatism, its impersonality, its reliance upon the specialized services and intricate technological studies of the engineer, was getting further and further beyond the worker's unaided power of intellectual apprehension or political control.

Marx's original prediction that the class struggle would be fought out on strict class lines between an impoverished international proletariat and an equally coherent international bourgeoisie was falsified by two unexpected conditions. One was the growth of the middle classes and the small industries: instead of being automatically wiped out they showed unexpected resistance and staying power. In a crisis, the big industries with their vast over-capitalization and their enormous overhead, were less capable of adjusting themselves to the situation than the smaller ones. In order to make the market more secure, there were even fitful attempts to raise the standard of consumption among the workers themselves: so the sharp lines necessary for successful warfare only emerged in periods of depression. The second fact was the new alignment of forces between country and country, which tended to undermine the internationalism of capital and disrupt the unity of the proletariat. When Marx wrote in the eighteen fifties Nationalism seemed to him, as it seemed to Cobden, to be a dying movement: events showed that, on the contrary, it had taken a new lease on life.

With the massing of the population into national states which continued during the nineteenth century, the national struggle cut at right angles to the class struggle. After the French revolution war, which was once the sport of dynasties, became the major industrial occupation of whole peoples: "democratic" conscription made this possible.

The struggle for political power, always limited in the past by financial weakness, technical restrictions, the indifference and hostility of the underlying population, now became a struggle between states for the command of exploitable areas: the mines of Lorraine, the diamond fields of South Africa, the South American markets, possible sources of supply or possible outlets for products that could not be absorbed by the depressed proletariat of the industrial countries, or, finally, possible fields for investment for the surplus of capital heaped up in the "progressive" countries.

"The present," exclaimed Ure in 1835, "is distinguished from every preceding age by an universal ardor of enterprise in arts and manufactures. Nationals, convinced at length that war is always a losing game, have converted their swords and muskets into factory implements, and now contend with each other in the bloodless but still formidable strife of trade. They no longer send troops to fight on distant fields, but fabrics to drive before them those of their old adversaries in arms, to take possession of a foreign market. To impair the resources of a rival at home, by underselling his wares abroad, is the new belligerent system, in pursuance of which every nerve and sinew of the people are put upon the strain." Unfortunately the sublimation was not complete: economic rivalries added fuel to national hates and gave a pseudo-rational face to the most violently irrational motives.

Even the leading utopias of the paleotechnic phase were nationalist and militarist: Cabet's Icaria, which was contemporary with the liberal revolutions of 1848, was a masterpiece of warlike regimentation in every detail of life, whilst Bellamy, in 1888, took the organization of the army, on a basis of compulsory service, as the pattern for all industrial activities. The intensity of these nationalist struggles, aided by the more tribal instincts, somewhat weakened the effect of the class struggles. But they were alike in this respect: neither the state as conceived by the followers of Austin, nor the proletarian class as conceived by the followers of Marx, were organic entities or true social groups: they were both arbitrary collections of individuals, held together not by common functions, but by a common collective symbol of loyalty and hate. This collective symbol had a magical office: it was willed into existence by magical formulae and incantations, and kept alive by a collective ritual. So long as the ritual was piously maintained the subjective nature of its premises could be ignored. But the "nation" had this advantage over the "class": it could conjure up more primitive responses, for it played, not on material advantage, but on naïve hates and manias and death wishes. After 1850 nationalism became the drill master of the restless proletariat, and the latter worked out its sense of inferiority and defeat by identification with the all-powerful State.

THE EMPIRE OF MUDDLE

The quantity of goods produced by the machine was supposed to be automatically regulated by the law of supply and demand: commodities, like water, were supposed to seek their own level: in the long run, only so much goods would be produced as could be sold at a profit. The lessening of profits automatically, according to this theory, closed the valve of production; while the increase of profits automatically opened it and even would lead to the construction of new feeders. Producing the necessaries of life, was, however, merely a by-product of making profits. Since there was more money to be made in textiles for foreign markets than in sound workers' houses for domestic use, more profit in beer and gin than in unadulterated bread, the elementary necessities of shelter—and sometimes even food—were scandalously neglected. Ure, the lyric poet of the textile industries, readily confessed that "to the production of food and domestic accommodation not many automatic inventions have been applied, or seem to be extensively applicable." As prophecy this proved absurd; but as a description of the current limitations, it was correct.

The shortage of housing for the workers, the congestion of domestic quarters, the erection of vile insanitary barracks to serve as substitutes for decent human shelter—these were universal characteristics of the paleotechnic régime. Fortunately, the terrible incidence of disease in the poorer quarters of the cities awakened the attention of health officers, and in the name of sanitation and public health various measures were taken, dating in England to Shaftesbury's "model" housing acts in 1851, to alleviate the worst conditions by restrictive legislation, compulsory slum repair, and even an insignificant modicum of slum clearance and improved housing. Some of the best examples, from the eighteenth century on, appeared in the colliery villages of England, possibly as a result of their semi-feudal traditions, to be followed in the 1860's by Krupp's workers' housing at Essen. Slowly, a small number of the worst evils were wiped away, despite the fact that the new laws were in opposition to the holy principles of free competitive enterprise in the production of illth.

The jockeying for profits without any regard for the stable ordering of production had two unfortunate results. For one thing, it undermined agriculture. As long as food supplies and materials could be obtained cheaply from some far part of the earth, even at the expense of the speedy exhaustion of the soils that were being recklessly cropped for cotton and wheat, no effort was made to keep agriculture and industry in equipoise. The countryside, reduced in general to the margin of subsistence, was further depressed by the drift of population into the apparently thriving factory towns, with infant mortality rates that often rose as high as 300 or more per thousand live births. The application of machines to sowing, reaping, threshing, instituted on a large scale with the multitude of new reapers invented at the beginning of the century—McCormick's was merely one of many—only hastened the pace of this development.

The second effect was even more disastrous. It divided the world into areas of machine production and areas of foods and raw materials: this made the existence of the over-industrialized countries more precarious, the further they were cut off from their rural base of supplies: hence the beginning of strenuous naval competition. Not merely did the existence of the coal-agglomerations themselves depend upon their ability to command water from distant streams and lakes, and food from distant fields and farms: but continued production depended upon the ability to bribe or browbeat other parts of the earth into accepting their industrial products. The Civil War in America, by cutting off the supply of cotton, reduced to a state of extreme penury the brave and honest textile workers of Lancashire. And the fear of repeating such events, in other industries beside cotton, was responsible in good part for the panicky imperialism and armament competition that developed throughout the world after 1870. As paleotechnic industry was founded originally upon systematic child slavery, so it was dependent for its continued growth upon a forced outlet for its goods.

Unfortunately for the countries that relied upon this process to go on indefinitely, the original consuming areas—the new or the "backward" countries—speedily took possession of the common heritage in science and technics and began to produce machined goods for themselves. That tendency became universal by the eighties. It was temporarily limited by the fact that England, which long retained its technical superiority in weaving and spinning, could use 7 operatives per thousand spindles in 1837 and only 3 operatives per thousand in 1887, while Germany, its nearest competitor at the second date still used from 7½ to 9, while Bombay required 25. But in the long run neither England nor the "advanced countries" could hold the lead: for the new machine system was a universal one. Therewith one of the main props of paleotechnic industry was displaced.

The hit-or-miss tactics of the market place pervaded the entire social structure. The leaders of industry were for the most part empirics: boasting that they were "practical" men they prided themselves on their technical ignorance and naïveté. Solvay, who made a fortune out of the Solvay soda process, knew nothing about chemistry; neither did Krupp, the discoverer of cast-steel; Hancock, one of the early experimenters with India rubber was equally ignorant. Bessemer, the inventor of many things besides the Bessemer process of making steel, at first merely stumbled on his great invention through the accident of using iron with a low phosphorus content: it was only the failure of his method with the continental ores that had a high phosphorus content that led him to consider the chemistry of the process.

Within the industrial plant scientific knowledge was at a discount. The practical man, contemptuous of theory, scornful of exact training, ignorant of science, was uppermost. Trade secrets, sometimes important, sometimes merely childish empiricism, retarded the cooperative extension of knowledge which has been the basis of all our major technical advances; whilst the system of patent monopolies was used by astute business men to drive improvements out of the market, if they threatened to upset existing financial values, or to delay their introduction—as the automatic telephone was delayed—until the original rights to the patent had expired. Right down to the World War an unwillingness to avail itself of scientific knowledge or to promote scientific research characterized paleotechnic industry throughout the world. Perhaps the only large exception to this, the German dye industry, was due to its close connection with the poisons and explosives necessary for military purposes.

While free competition prevailed between individual manufacturers, planned production for industry as a whole was impossible: each manufacturer remained his own judge, on the basis of limited knowledge and information, of the amount of goods he could profitably produce and dispose of. The labor market itself was based on absence of plan: it was, in fact, by means of a constant surplus of unemployed workers, who were never systematically integrated into industry, that wages could be kept low. This excess of the unemployed in "normal and prosperous" times was essential to competitive production. The location of industries was unplanned: accident, pecuniary advantage, habit, gravitation toward the surplus labor market, were as important as the tangible advantages from a technical standpoint. The machine—the outcome of man's impulse to conquer his environment and to canalize his random impulses into orderly activities—produced during the paleotechnic phase the systematic negation of all its characteristics: nothing less than the empire of muddle. What was, indeed, the boasted "mobility of labor" but the breakdown of stable social relations and the disorganization of family life?

The state of paleotechnic society may be described, ideally, as one of wardom. Its typical organs, from mine to factory, from blastfurnace to slum, from slum to battlefield, were at the service of death. Competition: struggle for existence: domination and submission: extinction. With war at once the main stimulus, the underlying basis, and the direct destination of this society, the normal motives and reactions of human beings were narrowed down to the desire for domination and to the fear of annihilation—the fear of poverty, the fear of unemployment, the fear of losing class status, the fear of starvation, the fear of muti-

lation and death. When war finally came, it was welcomed with open arms, for it relieved the intolerable suspense: the shock of reality, however grim, was more bearable than the constant menace of spectres, worked up and paraded forth by the journalist and the politician. The mine and the battlefield underlay all the paleotechnic activities; and the practices they stimulated led to the widespread exploitation of fear.

The rich feared the poor and the poor feared the rent collector: the middle classes feared the plagues that came from the vile insanitary quarters of the industrial city and the poor feared, with justice, the dirty hospitals to which they were taken. Toward the latter part of the period religion adopted the uniform of war: singing Onward Christian Soldiers, the converted marched with defiant humility in military dress and order: imperialist salvation. The school was regimented like an army, and the army camp became the universal school: teacher and pupil feared each other, even as did capitalist and worker. Walls, barred windows, barbed wire fences surrounded the factory as well as the jail. Women feared to bear children and men feared to beget them: the fear of syphilis and gonorrhea tainted sexual intercourse: behind the diseases themselves lurked Ghosts: the spectre of locomotor ataxia, paresis, insanity, blind children, crippled legs, and the only known remedy for syphilis, till salvarsan, was itself a poison. The drab prisonlike houses, the palisades of dull streets, the treeless backyards filled with rubbish, the unbroken rooftops, with never a gap for park or playground, underlined this environment of death. A mine explosion, a railway wreck, a tenement house fire, a military assault upon a group of strikers, or finally the more potent outbreak of war—these were but appropriate punctuation marks. Exploited for power and profit, the destination of most of the goods made by the machine was either the rubbish heap or the battlefield. If the landlords and other monopolists enjoyed an unearned increment from the massing of population and the collective efficiency of the machine, the net result for society at large might be characterized as the unearned excrement.

Questions

1. Why can it be argued that what man has taken for progress is in fact regression? You will want to consider the inventions and improvements in living that permitted the optimist of the nineteenth century to believe in progress.

2. How did the theories of competition and efficient organization expand from the marketplace into other areas of life?

3. Is Mumford's view of progress an unbiased one? Is it possible even without being able to controvert his facts to argue that his report is slanted toward a particular view?

LORD BYRON

Selections from

Don Juan

Lord Byron's long mock-epic poem *Don Juan* was published between 1818 and 1823 in sixteen cantos, but was still unfinished when Byron died in Greece in 1824. The poem is the one great instance of satire written from a romantic point of view, and it tells, in a fitful and sporadic manner, the story of the great lover Don Juan. He begins his adventures in Spain, is shipwrecked on a pirate island off the Greek coast, is sold into slavery to the Turks, escapes to fight with the Russians and become the lover of Catherine the Great, and is ultimately sent as her ambassador to England. Canto XIII, here reprinted in full, describes his visit to an English country house, which provides Byron with an opportunity to satirize the English society which had ostracized him in 1816. This canto is not only an excellent example of Byron's satiric art, but it provides a picture of the same society W. H. Auden attacks in his "Letter to Lord Byron" over a hundred years later. The two excerpts from Canto I are good brief statements of Byron's basic attitude toward life and literature, and provide interesting parallels to Auden's treatments of similar topics.

CANTO I

128

Man's a strange animal, and makes strange use
  Of his own nature, and the various arts,
And likes particularly to produce
  Some new experiment to show his parts;
This is the age of oddities let loose,
  Where different talents find their different marts;

You'd best begin with truth, and when you've
    lost your
Labour, there's a sure market for imposture.

129

What opposite discoveries we have seen!
    (Signs of true genius, and of empty pockets.)
One makes new noses, one a guillotine,
    One breaks your bones, one sets them in
      their sockets;
But vaccination certainly has been
    A kind of antithesis to Congreve's rockets,
With which the Doctor paid off an old pox,
By borrowing a new one from an ox.

130

Bread has been made (indifferent) from pota-
    toes;
    And galvanism has set some corpses grin-
      ning,
But has not answer'd like the apparatus
    Of the Humane Society's beginning,
By which men are unsuffocated gratis:
    What wondrous new machines have late
      been spinning!
I said the small pox has gone out of late;
Perhaps it may be follow'd by the great.

131

'Tis said the great came from America;
    Perhaps it may set out on its return,—
The population there so spreads, they say
    'Tis grown high time to thin it in its turn,
With war, or plague, or famine, any way,
    So that civilisation they may learn;
And which in ravage the more loathsome evil
    is—
Their real lues, or our pseudo-syphilis?

132

This is the patent age of new inventions
    For killing bodies, and for saving souls,
All propagated with the best intentions;
    Sir Humphrey Davy's lantern, by which
      coals
Are safely mined for in the mode he mentions,
    Tombuctoo travels, voyages to the Poles,
Are ways to benefit mankind, as true,
Perhaps, as shooting them at Waterloo.

133

Man's a phenomenon, one knows not what,
    And wonderful beyond all wondrous meas-
      ure;

'Tis pity, though, in this sublime world, that
    Pleasure's a sin, and sometimes sin's a pleas-
      ure;
Few mortals know what end they would be
    at,
    But whether glory, power, or love, or treas-
      ure,
The path is through perplexing ways, and
    when
The goal is gain'd, we die, you know—and
    then—

200

My poem's epic, and is meant to be
    Divided in twelve books; each book con-
      taining,
With love, and war, a heavy gale at sea,
    A list of ships, and captains, and kings
      reigning,
New characters; the episodes are three:
    A panoramic view of hell's in training,
After the style of Virgil and of Homer,
So that my name of Epic's no misnomer.

201

All these things will be specified in time,
    With strict regard to Aristotle's rules,
The *Vade Mecum* of the true sublime,
    Which makes so many poets, and some fools:
Prose poets like blank-verse, I'm fond of
    rhyme,
    Good workmen never quarrel with their
      tools;
I've got new mythological machinery,
And very handsome supernatural scenery.

202

There's only one slight difference between
    Me and my epic brethren gone before,
And here the advantage is my own, I ween
    (Not that I have not several merits more,
But this will more peculiarly be seen);
    They so embellish, that 'tis quite a bore
Their labyrinth of fables to thread through,
Whereas this story's actually true.

203

If any person doubt it, I appeal
    To history, tradition, and to facts,
To newspapers, whose truth all know and
    feel,
    To plays in five, and operas in three acts;

All these confirm my statement a good deal,
    But that which more completely faith exacts
Is, that myself, and several now in Seville,
Saw Juan's last elopement with the devil.

204

If ever I should condescend to prose,
    I'll write poetical commandments, which
Shall supersede beyond all doubt all those
    That went before; in these I shall enrich
My text with many things that no one knows,
    And carry precept to the highest pitch:
I'll call the work "Longinus o'er a Bottle,
Or, Every Poet his *own* Aristotle."

205

Thou shalt believe in Milton, Dryden, Pope;
    Thou shalt not set up Wordsworth, Cole-
        ridge, Southey;
Because the first is crazed beyond all hope,
    The second drunk, the third so quaint and
        mouthy:
With Crabbe it may be difficult to cope,
    And Campbell's Hippocrene is somewhat
        drouthy:
Thou shalt not steal from Samuel Rogers, nor
Commit—flirtation with the muse of Moore.

206

Thou shalt not covet Mr. Sotheby's Muse,
    His Pegasus, nor anything that's his;
Thou shalt not bear false witness like "the
        Blues"—
    (There's one, at least, is very fond of this);
Thou shalt not write, in short, but what I
        choose:
    This is true criticism, and you may kiss—
Exactly as you please, or not,—the rod;
But if you don't, I'll lay it on, by G—d!

207

If any person should presume to assert
    This story is not moral, first, I pray,
That they will not cry out before they're hurt,
    Then that they'll read it o'er again, and say
(But, doubtless, nobody will be so pert),
    That this is not a moral tale, though gay;
Beside, in Canto Twelfth, I mean to show
The very place where wicked people go.

208

If, after all, there should be some so blind
    To their own good this warning to despise,
Led by some tortuosity of mind,

Not to believe my verse and their own eyes,
    And cry that they "the moral cannot find,"
    I tell him, if a clergyman, he lies;
Should captains the remark, or critics, make,
They also lie too—under a mistake.

209

The public approbation I expect,
    And beg they'll take my word about the
        moral,
Which I with their amusement will connect
    (So children cutting teeth receive a coral);
Meantime they'll doubtless please to recollect
    My epical pretensions to the laurel:
For fear prudish readers should grow skittish,
I've bribed my grandmother's review—the
        British.

210

I sent it in a letter to the Editor,
    Who thank'd me duly by return of post—
I'm for a handsome article his creditor;
    Yet, if my gentle Muse he please to roast,
And break a promise after having made it her,
    Denying the receipt of what it cost,
And smear his page with gall instead of honey,
All I can say is—that he had the money.

211

I think that with this holy new alliance
    I may ensure the public, and defy
All other magazines of art or science,
    Daily, or monthly or three monthly; I
Have not essay'd to multiply their clients,
    Because they tell me 'twere in vain to try,
And that the *Edinburgh Review* and *Quarterly*
Treat a dissenting author very martyrly.

212

"*Non ego hoc ferrem calida juventâ*
    Consule Planco," Horace said, and so
Say I; by which quotation there is meant a
    Hint that some six or seven good years ago
(Long ere I dreamt of dating from the Brenta)
    I was most ready to return a blow,
And would not brook at all this sort of thing
In my hot youth—when George the Third was
        King.

213

But now at thirty years my hair is grey—
    (I wonder what it will be like at forty?
I thought of a peruke the other day—)

My heart is not much greener; and, in
    short, I
Have squander'd my whole summer while
    'twas May,
    And feel no more the spirit to retort; I
Have spent my life, both interest and princi-
    pal,
And deem not, what I deem'd, my soul in-
    vincible.

214

No more—no more—Oh! never more on me
    The freshness of the heart can fall like dew,
Which out of all the lovely things we see
    Extracts emotions beautiful and new;
Hived in our bosoms like the bag o' the bee.
    Think'st thou the honey with those objects
        grew?
Alas! 'twas not in them, but in thy power
To double even the sweetness of a flower.

215

No more—no more—Oh! never more, my heart,
    Canst thou be my sole world, my universe!
Once all in all, but now a thing apart,
    Thou canst not be my blessing or my curse:
The illusion's gone for ever, and thou art
    Insensible, I trust, but none the worse,
And in thy stead I've got a deal of judgment,
Though heaven knows how it ever found a
    lodgment.

216

My days of love are over; me no more
    The charms of maid, wife, and still less of
        widow,
Can make the fool of which they made be-
    fore,—
    In short, I must not lead the life I did do;
The credulous hope of mutual minds is o'er,
    The copious use of claret is forbid too,
So for a good old-gentlemanly vice,
I think I must take up with avarice.

217

Ambition was my idol, which was broken
    Before the shrines of Sorrow, and of Pleas-
        ure;
And the two last have left me many a token
    O'er which reflection may be made at lei-
        sure;
Now, like Friar Bacon's brazen head, I've
    spoken,

"Time is, Time was, Time's past:"—a chy-
    mic treasure
Is glittering youth, which I have spent be-
    times—
My heart in passion, and my head on rhymes.

218

What is the end of fame? 'tis but to fill
    A certain portion of uncertain paper:
Some liken it to climbing up a hill,
    Whose summit, like all hills, is lost in
        vapour;
For this men write, speak, preach, and heroes
    kill,
    And bards burn what they call their "mid-
        night taper,"
To have, when the original is dust,
A name, a wretched picture, and worse bust.

219

What are the hopes of man? Old Egypt's King
    Cheops erected the first pyramid
And largest, thinking it was just the thing
    To keep his memory whole, and mummy
        hid:
But somebody or other rummaging,
    Burglariously broke his coffin's lid.
Let not a monument give you or me hopes,
Since not a pinch of dust remains of Cheops.

220

But I, being fond of true philosophy,
    Say very often to myself, "Alas!
All things that have been born were born to
    die,
    And flesh (which Death mows down to hay)
        is grass;
You've pass'd your youth not so unpleasantly.
    And if you had it o'er again—'twould pass—
So thank your stars that matters are no worse,
And read your Bible, sir, and mind your
    purse."

221

But for the present, gentle reader! and
    Still gentler purchaser! the bard—that's I—
Must, with permission, shake you by the hand,
    And so your humble servant, and good-bye!
We meet again, if we should understand
    Each other; and if not, I shall not try
Your patience further than by this short sam-
    ple—
'Twere well if others follow'd my example.

222

"Go, little book, from this my solitude!
  I cast thee on the waters—go thy ways!
And if, as I believe, thy vein be good,
  The world will find thee after many days."
When Southey's read, and Wordsworth under-
    stood,
  I can't help putting in my claim to praise—
The four first rhymes are Southey's, every line:
For God's sake, reader! take them not for
    mine!

CANTO XIII

1

I NOW mean to be serious;—it is time,
  Since laughter now-a-days is deem'd too
    serious;
A jest at Vice by Virtue's call'd a crime,
  And critically held as deleterious:
Besides, the sad's a source of the sublime,
  Although when long a little apt to weary us;
And therefore shall my lay soar high and
    solemn,
As an old temple dwindled to a column.

2

The Lady Adeline Amundeville
  ('Tis an old Norman name, and to be found
In pedigrees, by those who wander still
  Along the last fields of that Gothic ground)
Was high-born, wealthy by her father's will,
  And beauteous, even where beauties most
    abound,
In Britain—which of course true patriots find
The goodliest soil of body and of mind.

3

I'll not gainsay them; it is not my cue;
  I'll leave them to their taste, no doubt the
    best:
An eye's an eye, and whether black or blue,
  Is no great matter, so 'tis in request;
'Tis nonsense to dispute about a hue—
  The kindest may be taken as a test.
The fair sex should be always fair; and no man
Till thirty, should perceive there's a plain
    woman.

4

And after that serene and somewhat dull
  Epoch, that awkward corner turn'd for days
More quiet, when our moon's no more at full,
  We may presume to criticise or praise;
Because indifference begins to lull
  Our passions, and we walk in wisdom's ways;
Also because the figure and the face
Hint, that 'tis time to give the younger place.

5

I know that some would fain postpone this
    era,
  Reluctant as all placemen to resign
Their post, but theirs is merely a chimera,
  For they have pass'd life's equinoctial line:
But then they have their claret and Madeira
  To irrigate the dryness of decline;
And county meetings, and the parliament,
And debt, and what not, for their solace sent.

6

And is there not religion, and reform,
  Peace, war, the taxes, and what's called the
    "Nation"?
The struggle to be pilots in a storm?
  The landed and the monied speculation?
The joys of mutual hate to keep them warm,
  Instead of love, that mere hallucination?
Now hatred is by far the longest pleasure;
Men love in haste, but they detest at leisure. -

7

Rough Johnson, the great moralist, profess'd,
  Right honestly, "he liked an honest hater!"—
The only truth that yet has been confest
  Within these latest thousand years or later.
Perhaps the fine old fellow spoke in jest:—
  For my part, I am but a mere spectator,
And gaze where'er the palace or the hovel is,
Much in the mode of Goethe's Mephistoph-
    eles;

8

But neither love nor hate in much excess;
  Though 'twas not once so. If I sneer some-
    times,
It is because I cannot well do less,
  And now and then it also suits my rhymes.
I should be very willing to redress
  Men's wrongs, and rather check than punish
    crimes,
Had not Cervantes, in that too true tale
Of Quixote, shown how all such efforts fail.

9

Of all tales 'tis the saddest—and more sad,
  Because it makes us smile: his hero's right,
And still pursues the right;—to curb the bad

His only object, and 'gainst odds to fight
His guerdon: 'tis his virtue makes him mad!
  But his adventures form a sorry sight;—
A sorrier still is the great moral taught
By that real epic unto all who have thought.

10

Redressing injury, revenging wrong,
  To aid the damsel and destroy the caitiff;
Opposing singly the united strong,
  From foreign yoke to free the helpless
    native:—
Alas! must noblest views, like an old song,
  Be for mere fancy's sport a theme creative,
A jest, a riddle, Fame through thick and thin
    sought!
And Socrates himself but Wisdom's Quixote?

11

Cervantes smiled Spain's chivalry away;
  A single laugh demolish'd the right arm
Of his own country;—seldom since that day
  Has Spain had heroes. While Romance
    could charm,
The world gave ground before her bright ar-
    ray;
  And therefore have his volumes done such
    harm,
That all their glory, as a composition,
Was dearly purchased by his land's perdition.

12

I'm "at my old lunes"—digression, and forget
  The Lady Adeline Amundeville;
The fair most fatal Juan ever met,
  Although she was not evil or meant ill;
But Destiny and Passion spread the net
  (Fate is a good excuse for our own will),
And caught them;—what do they *not* catch,
    methinks?
But I'm not Œdipus, and life's a Sphinx.

13

I tell the tale as it is told, nor dare
  To venture a solution: "Davus sum!"
And now I will proceed upon the pair.
  Sweet Adeline, amidst the gay world's hum,
Was the Queen-Bee, the glass of all that's fair;
  Whose charms made all men speak, and
    women dumb.
The last's a miracle, and such was reckon'd,
And since that time there has been not a sec-
    ond.

14

Chaste was she, to detraction's desperation,
  And wedded unto one she had loved well—
A man known in the councils of the nation,
  Cool, and quite English, imperturbable,
Though apt to act with fire upon occasion,
  Proud of himself and her: the world could
    tell
Nought against either, and both seem'd se-
    cure—
She in her virtue, he in his hauteur.

15

It chanced some diplomatical relations
  Arising out of business, often brought
Himself and Juan in their mutual stations
  Into close contact. Though reserved, nor
    caught
By specious seeming, Juan's youth, and pa-
    tience,
  And talent, on his haughty spirit wrought,
And form'd a basis of esteem, which ends
In making men what courtesy calls friends.

16

And thus Lord Henry, who was cautious as
  Reserve and pride could make him, and full
    slow
In judging men—when once his judgment was
  Determined, right or wrong, on friend or
    foe,
Had all the pertinacity pride has,
  Which knows no ebb to its imperious flow,
And loves or hates, disdaining to be guided,
Because its own good pleasure hath decided.

17

His friendships, therefore, and no less aver-
    sions,
  Though oft well founded, which confirm'd
    but more
His prepossessions, like the laws of Persians
  And Medes, would ne'er revoke what went
    before.
His feelings had not those strange fits, like
    tertians,
  Of common likings, which make some de-
    plore
What they should laugh at—the mere ague still
Of men's regard, the fever or the chill.

18

" 'Tis not in mortals to command success:

But *do you more,* Sempronius—*don't* deserve it,"
And take my word, you won't have any less.
  Be wary, watch the time, and always serve it;
Give gently way, when there's too great a
    press;
  And for your conscience only learn to
    nerve it,
For, like a racer, or a boxer training,
'Twill make, if proved, vast efforts without
    paining.

19

Lord Henry also liked to be superior,
  As most men do, the little or the great;
The very lowest find out an inferior,
  At least they think so, to exert their state
Upon: for there are very few things wearier
  Than solitary Pride's oppressive weight,
Which mortals generously would divide,
By bidding others carry while they ride.

20

In birth, in rank, in fortune likewise equal,
  O'er Juan he could no distinction claim;
In years he had the advantage of time's sequel;
  And, as he thought, in country much the
    same—
Because bold Britons have a tongue and free
    quill,
  At which all modern nations vainly aim;
And the Lord Henry was a great debater,
So that few members kept the house up later.

21

These were advantages: and then he thought—
  It was his foible, but by no means sinister—
That few or none more than himself had
    caught
  Court mysteries, having been himself a
    minister:
He liked to teach that which he had been
    taught,
  And greatly shone whenever there had been
    a stir;
And reconciled all qualities which grace man,
Always a patriot, and sometimes a placeman.

22

He liked the gentle Spaniard for his gravity;
  He almost honour'd him for his docility;
Because, though young, he acquiesced with
    suavity,

Or contradicted but with proud humility.
He knew the world, and would not see depravity
  In faults which sometimes show the soil's
    fertility,
If that the weeds o'er live not the first crop—
For then they are very difficult to stop.

23

And then he talk'd with him about Madrid,
  Constantinople, and such distant places;
Where people always did as they were bid,
  Or did what they should not with foreign
    graces.
Of coursers also spake they: Henry rid
  Well, like most Englishmen, and loved the
    races;
And Juan, like a true-born Andalusian,
Could back a horse, as despots ride a Russian.

24

And thus acquaintance grew, at noble routs,
  And diplomatic dinners, or at other—
For Juan stood well with Ins and Outs,
  As in freemasonry a higher brother.
Upon his talent Henry had no doubts;
  His manner show'd him sprung from a high
    mother;
And all men like to show their hospitality
To him whose breeding matches with his
    quality.

25

A Blank-Blank Square;—for we will break no
    squares
  By naming streets: since men are so censorious,
And apt to sow an author's wheat with tares,
  Reaping allusions private and inglorious,
Where none were dreamt of, unto love's affairs,
  Which were, or are, or are to be notorious,
That therefore do I previously declare,
Lord Henry's mansion was in Blank-Blank
    Square.

26

Also there bin another pious reason
  For making squares and streets anonymous;
Which is, that there is scarce a single season
  Which doth not shake some very splendid
    house
With some slight heart-quake of domestic
    treason—
  A topic scandal doth delight to rouse:

Such I might stumble over unawares,
Unless I knew the very chastest squares.

27

'Tis true, I might have chosen Piccadilly,
　A place where peccadillos are unknown;
But I have motives, whether wise or silly,
　For letting that pure sanctuary alone.
Therefore I name not square, street, place, until I
　Find one where nothing naughty can be shown,
A vestal shrine of innocence of heart:
Such are—but I have lost the London Chart.

28

At Henry's mansion then, in Blank-Blank Square,
　Was Juan a recherché, welcome guest,
As many other noble scions were;
　And some who had but talent for their crest;
Or wealth, which is a passport everywhere;
　Or even mere fashion, which indeed's the best
Recommendation; and to be well drest
Will very often supersede the rest.

29

And since "there's safety in a multitude
　Of counsellors," as Solomon has said,
Or some one for him, in some sage, grave mood;—
　Indeed we see the daily proof display'd
In senates, at the bar, in wordy feud,
　Where'er collective wisdom can parade,
Which is the only cause that we can guess
Of Britain's present wealth and happiness;—

30

But as "there's safety" grafted in the number
　"Of counsellors" for men,—thus for the sex
A large acquaintance lets not Virtue slumber;
　Or should it shake, the choice will more perplex—
Variety itself will more encumber.
　'Midst many rocks we guard more against wrecks;
And thus with women: howsoe'er it shocks some's
Self-love, there's safety in a crowd of coxcombs.

31

But Adeline had not the least occasion

For such a shield, which leaves but little merit
To virtue proper, or good education.
　Her chief resource was in her own high spirit,
Which judged mankind at their due estimation;
　And for coquetry, she disdain'd to wear it:
Secure of admiration, its impression
Was faint as of an every-day possession.

32

To all she was polite without parade:
　To some she show'd attention of that kind
Which flatters, but is flattery convey'd
　In such a sort as cannot leave behind
A trace unworthy either wife or maid;—
　A gentle, genial courtesy of mind,
To those who were, or pass'd for meritorious,
Just to console sad glory for being glorious;

33

Which is in all respects, save now and then,
　A dull and desolate appendage. Gaze
Upon the shades of those distinguish'd men
　Who were or are the puppet-shows of praise,
The praise of persecution. Gaze again
　On the most favour'd; and amidst the blaze
Of sunset halos o'er the laurel-brow'd,
What can ye recognize?—a gilded cloud.

34

There also was of course in Adeline
　That calm patrician polish in the address,
Which ne'er can pass the equinoctial line
　Of anything which nature would express;
Just as a mandarin finds nothing fine,—
　At least his manner suffers not to guess,
That anything he views can greatly please.
Perhaps we have borrow'd this from the Chinese—

35

Perhaps from Horace: his *"Nil admirari"*
　Was what he call'd the "Art of Happiness;"
An art on which the artists greatly vary,
　And have not yet attain'd to much success.
However, 'tis expedient to be wary:
　Indifference certes don't produce distress;
And rash enthusiasm in good society
Were nothing but a moral inebriety.

36

But Adeline was not indifferent: for

(*Now* for a common-place!) beneath the
  snow,
As a volcano holds the lava more
  Within—*et cætera*. Shall I go on?—No.
I hate to hunt down a tired metaphor,
  So let the often-used volcano go,
Poor thing! How frequently, by me and others,
  It hath been stirr'd up till its smoke quite
    smothers!

37

I'll have another figure in a trice:—
  What say you to a bottle of champagne?
Frozen into a very vinous ice,
  Which leaves few drops of that immortal
    rain,
Yet in the very centre, past all price,
  About a liquid glassful will remain;
And this is stronger than the strongest grape
Could e'er express in its expanded shape:

38

'Tis the whole spirit brought to a quintessence;
  And thus the chilliest aspects may concentre
A hidden nectar under a cold presence.
  And such are many—though I only meant
    her
From whom I now deduce these moral lessons,
  On which the Muse has always sought to
    enter.
And your cold people are beyond all price,
When once you've broken their confounded
  ice.

39

But after all they are a North-West Passage
  Unto the glowing India of the soul;
And as the good ships sent upon that message
  Have not exactly ascertain'd the Pole
(Though Parry's efforts look a lucky presage),
  Thus gentlemen may run upon a shoal;
For if the Pole's not open, but all frost
(A chance still), 'tis a voyage or vessel lost.

40

And young beginners may as well commence
  With quiet cruising o'er the ocean woman;
While those who are not beginners should
    have sense
  Enough to make for port, ere Time shall
    summon
With his grey signal-flag; and the past tense,
  The dreary *"Fuimus"* of all things human,
Must be declined, while life's thin thread's
    spun out
Between the gaping heir and gnawing gout.

41

But heaven must be diverted; its diversion
  Is sometimes truculent—but never mind;
The world upon the whole is worth the asser-
    tion
  (If but for comfort) that all things are kind:
And that same devilish doctrine of the Persian,
  Of the two principles, but leaves behind
As many doubts as any other doctrine
Has ever puzzled faith withal, or yoked her in.

42

The English winter—ending in July,
  To recommence in August—now was done.
'Tis the postilion's paradise: wheels fly;
  On roads, east, south, north, west, there is
    a run.
But for post-horses who finds sympathy?
  Man's pity for himself, or for his son,
Always premising that said son at college
Has not contracted much more debt than
    knowledge.

43

The London winter's ended in July—
  Sometimes a little later. I don't err
In this: whatever other blunders lie
  Upon my shoulders, here I must aver
My Muse a glass of weatherology;
  For parliament is our barometer:
Let radicals its other acts attack,
Its sessions form our only almanack.

44

When its quicksilver's down at zero,—lo!
  Coach, chariot, luggage, baggage, equipage!
Wheels whirl from Carlton palace to Soho,
  And happiest they who horses can engage;
The turnpikes glow with dust; and Rotten
    Row
  Sleeps from the chivalry of this bright age;
And tradesmen, with long bills and longer
    faces,
Sigh—as the postboys fasten on the traces.

45

They and their bills, "Arcadians both," are
    left
  To the Greek kalends of another session.
Alas! to them of ready cash bereft,

What hope remains? Of *hope* the full possession
Or generous draft, conceded as a gift,
  At a long date—till they can get a fresh one—
Hawk'd about at a discount, small or large;
  Also the solace of an overcharge.

46

But these are trifles. Downward flies my lord,
  Nodding beside my lady in his carriage.
Away! away! "Fresh horses!" are the word,
  And changed as quickly as hearts after marriage;
The obsequious landlord hath the change restored;
  The postboys have no reason to disparage
Their fee; but ere the water'd wheels may hiss hence,
The ostler pleads too for a reminiscence.

47

'Tis granted; and the valet mounts the dickey—
  That gentleman of lords and gentlemen;
Also my lady's gentlewoman, tricky,
  Trick'd out, but modest more than poet's pen
Can paint,—*"Cosi viaggino i Ricchi!"*
  (Excuse a foreign slipslop now and then,
If but to show I've travell'd: and what's travel,
Unless it teaches one to quote and cavil?)

48

The London winter and the country summer
  Were well nigh over. 'Tis perhaps a pity,
When nature wears the gown that doth become her.
  To lose those best months in a sweaty city,
And wait until the nightingale grows dumber,
  Listening debates not very wise or witty,
Ere patriots their true *country* can remember;—
But there's no shooting (save grouse) till September.

49

I've done with my tirade. The world was gone;
  The twice two thousand, for whom earth was made,
Were vanish'd to be what they call alone—
  That is, with thirty servants for parade,
As many guests, or more; before whom groan
  As many covers, duly, daily laid.
Let none accuse old England's hospitality—
Its quantity is but condensed to quality.

50

Lord Henry and the Lady Adeline
  Departed like the rest of their compeers,
The peerage, to a mansion very fine;
  The Gothic Babel of a thousand years.
None than themselves could boast a longer line,
  Where time through heroes and through beauties steers;
And oaks as olden as their pedigree
Told of their sires, a tomb in every tree.

51

A paragraph in every paper told
  Of their departure: such is modern fame:
'Tis pity that it takes no further hold
  Than an advertisement, or much the same;
When, ere the ink be dry, the sound grows cold.
  The *Morning Post* was foremost to proclaim—
"Departure, for his country seat, to-day,
Lord H. Amundeville and Lady A."

52

"We understand the splendid host intends
  To entertain, this autumn, a select
And numerous party of his noble friends;
  'Midst whom we have heard, from sources quite correct,
The Duke of D—— the shooting season spends,
  With many more by rank and fashion deck'd;
Also a foreigner of high condition,
The envoy of the secret Russian mission."

53

And thus we see—who doubts the *Morning Post?*
  (Whose articles are like the "Thirty-nine,"
Which those most swear to who believe them most)—
  Our gay Russ Spaniard was ordain'd to shine,
Deck'd by the rays reflected from his host,
  With those who, Pope says, "greatly daring dine."—
'Tis odd, but true,—last war the News abounded
More with these dinners than the kill'd or wounded;—

54

As thus: "On Thursday there was a grand
    dinner;
    Present, Lords A.B.C."—Earls, dukes, by
      name
Announced with no less pomp than victory's
    winner:
    Then underneath, and in the very same
Column: date, "Falmouth. There has lately
    been here
    The Slap-dash regiment, so well known to
      fame,
Whose loss in the late action we regret:
The vacancies are fill'd up—see Gazette."

55

To Norman Abbey whirl'd the noble pair,—
    An old, old monastery once, and now
Still older mansion,—of a rich and rare
    Mix'd Gothic, such as artists all allow
Few specimens yet left us can compare
    Withal: it lies perhaps a little low,
Because the monks preferr'd a hill behind,
To shelter their devotion from the wind.

56

It stood embosom'd in a happy valley,
    Crown'd by high woodlands, where the
      Druid oak
Stood, like Caractacus, in act to rally
    His host, with broad arms 'gainst the thun-
      derstroke.
And from beneath his boughs were seen to
    sally
    The dappled foresters; as day awoke,
The branching stag swept down with all his
    herd,
To quaff a brook which murmur'd like a bird.

57

Before the mansion lay a lucid lake,
    Broad as transparent, deep, and freshly fed
By a river, which its soften'd way did take
    In currents through the calmer water spread
Around: the wildfowl nestled in the brake
    And sedges, brooding in their liquid bed:
The woods sloped downwards to its brink, and
    stood
With their green faces fix'd upon the flood.

58

Its outlet dash'd into a deep cascade,
    Sparkling with foam, until again subsiding,
Its shriller echoes—like an infant made
    Quiet—sank into softer ripples, gliding
Into a rivulet: and thus allay'd,
    Pursued its course, now gleaming, and now
      hiding
Its windings through the woods; now clear,
    now blue,
According as the skies their shadows threw.

59

A glorious remnant of the Gothic pile
    (While yet the church was Rome's) stood
      half apart
In a grand arch, which once screen'd many an
    aisle.
    These last had disappear'd—a loss to art:
The first yet frown'd superbly o'er the soil,
    And kindled feelings in the roughest heart,
Which mourn'd the power of time's or tem-
    pest's march,
In gazing on that venerable arch.

60

Within a niche, nigh to its pinnacle,
    Twelve saints had once stood sanctified in
      stone;
But these had fallen, not when the friars fell,
    But in the war which struck Charles from
      his throne,
When each house was a fortalice—as tell
    The annals of full many a line undone,—
The gallant cavaliers, who fought in vain
For those who knew not to resign or reign.

61

But in a higher niche, alone, but crown'd,
    The Virgin-Mother of the God-born Child,
With her Son in her blessed arms, look'd
    round;
    Spared by some chance when all beside was
      spoil'd;
She made the earth below seem holy ground.
    This may be superstition, weak or wild,
But even the faintest relics of a shrine
Of any worship wake some thoughts divine.

62

A mighty window, hollow in the centre,
    Shorn of its glass of thousand colourings,
Through which the deepen'd glories once
    could enter,
    Streaming from off the sun like seraph's
      wings,

Now yawns all desolate: now loud, now
    fainter,
      The gale sweeps through its fretwork, and
      oft sings
The owl his anthem, where the silenced quire
Lie with their hallelujahs quench'd like fire.

63

But in the noontide of the moon, and when
    The wind is winged from one point of
    heaven,
There moans a strange unearthly sound, which
    then
    Is musical—a dying accent driven
Through the huge arch, which soars and sinks
    again.
    Some deem it but the distant echo given
Back to the night wind by the waterfall,
And harmonised by the old choral wall:

64

Others, that some original shape, or form
    Shaped by decay perchance, hath given the
    power
(Though less than that of Memnon's statue,
    warm
    In Egypt's rays, to harp at a fix'd hour)
To this grey ruin, with a voice to charm;
    Sad, but serene, it sweeps o'er tree or tower;
The cause I know not, nor can solve; but such
The fact:—I've heard it,—once perhaps too
    much.

65

Amidst the court a Gothic fountain play'd,
    Symmetrical, but deck'd with carvings
    quaint—
Strange faces, like to men a masquerade,
    And here perhaps a monster, there a saint:
The spring gush'd through grim mouths of
    granite made,
    And sparkled into basins, where it spent
Its little torrent in a thousand bubbles,
Like man's vain glory, and his vainer troubles.

66

The mansion's self was vast and venerable,
    With more of the monastic than has been
Elsewhere preserved: the cloisters still were
    stable,
    The cells, too, and refectory, I ween:
An exquisite small chapel had been able,
    Still unimpair'd, to decorate the scene;

The rest had been reform'd, replaced, or sunk,
And spoke more of the baron than the monk.

67

Huge halls, long galleries, spacious chambers,
    join'd
    By no quite lawful marriage of the arts,
Might shock a connoisseur; but when com-
    bined,
    Form'd a whole which, irregular in parts,
Yet left a grand impression on the mind,
    At least of those whose eyes are in their
    hearts:
We gaze upon a giant for his stature,
Nor judge at first if all be true to nature.

68

Steel barons, molten the next generation
    To silken rows of gay and garter'd earls,
Glanced from the walls in goodly preserva-
    tion:
    And Lady Marys blooming into girls,
With fair long locks, had also kept their
    station:
    And countesses mature in robes and pearls:
Also some beauties of Sir Peter Lely,
Whose drapery hints we may admire them
    freely.

69

Judges in very formidable ermine
    Were there, with brows that did not much
    invite
The accused to think their lordships would
    determine
    His cause by leaning much from might to
    right:
Bishops, who had not left a single sermon;
    Attorneys-general, awful to the sight,
As hinting more (unless our judgments warp
    us)
Of the "Star Chamber" than of "Habeas
    Corpus."

70

Generals, some all in armour, of the old
    And iron time, ere lead had ta'en the lead;
Others in wigs of Marlborough's martial fold,
    Huger than twelve of our degenerate breed:
Lordlings, with staves of white or keys of gold:
    Nimrods, whose canvas scarce contain'd the
    steed;
And here and there some stern high patriot
    stood,

Who could not get the place for which he
  sued.

71

But ever and anon, to soothe your vision,
  Fatigued with these hereditary glories,
There rose a Carlo Dolce or a Titian,
  Or wilder group of savage Salvatore's:
Here danced Albano's boys, and here the sea
  shone
    In Vernet's ocean lights; and there the
    stories
Of martyrs awed, as Spagnoletto tainted
His brush with all the blood of all the sainted.

72

Here sweetly spread a landscape of Lorraine;
  There Rembrandt made his darkness equal
  light,
Or gloomy Caravaggio's gloomier stain
  Bronzed o'er some lean and stoic anchor-
  ite:—
But, lo! a Teniers woos, and not in vain,
  Your eyes to revel in a livelier sight:
His bell-mouth'd goblet makes me feel quite
  Danish
Or Dutch with thirst—What, ho! a flask of
  Rhenish.

73

O reader! if that thou canst read,—and know,
  'Tis not enough to spell, or even to read,
To constitute a reader; there must go
  Virtues of which both you and I have need.
Firstly, begin with the beginning—(though
  That clause is hard); and secondly, proceed:
Thirdly, commence not with the end—or, sin-
  ning
In this sort, end at last with the beginning.

74

But reader, thou hast patient been of late,
  While I, without remorse of rhyme, or fear,
Have built and laid out ground at such a rate,
  Dan Phœbus takes me for an auctioneer.
That poets were so from their earliest date,
  By Homer's "Catalogue of ships" is clear;
But a mere modern must be moderate—
I spare you then the furniture and plate.

75

The mellow autumn came, and with it came
  The promised party, to enjoy its sweets.
The corn is cut, the manor full of game;

The pointer ranges, and the sportsman beats
  In russet jacket:—lynx-like is his aim;
  Full grows his bag, and wonder*ful* his feats.
Ah, nutbrown partridges! Ah, brilliant pheas-
  ants!
And ah, ye poachers!—'Tis no sport for peas-
  ants.

76

An English autumn, though it hath no vines,
  Blushing with Bacchant coronals along
The paths, o'er which the far festoon entwines
  The red grape in the sunny lands of song,
Hath yet a purchased choice of choicest wines;
  The claret light, and the Madeira strong;
If Britain mourn her bleakness, we can tell
  her,
The very best of vineyards is the cellar.

77

Then, if she hath not that serene decline
  Which makes the southern autumn's day
  appear
As if 'twould to a second spring resign
  The season, rather than to winter drear,—
Of in-door comforts still she hath a mine,—
  The sea-coal fires, the "earliest of the year;"
Without doors, too, she may compete in mel-
  low,
As what is lost in green is gain'd in yellow.

78

And for the effeminate *villeggiatura*—
  Rife with more horns than hounds—she
  hath the chase,
So animated that it might allure a
  Saint from his beads to join the jocund race;
Even Nimrod's self might leave the plains of
  Dura,
  And wear the Melton jacket for a space:
If she hath no wild boars, she hath a tame
Preserve of bores, who ought to be made game.

79

The noble guests, assembled at the Abbey,
  Consisted of—we give the sex the *pas*—
The Duchess of Fitz-Fulke; the Countess
  Crabby;
  The Ladies Scilly, Busey;—Miss Eclat,
Miss Bombazeen, Miss Mackstay, Miss O'-
  Tabby,
  And Mrs. Rabbi, the rich banker's squaw;
Also the honourable Mrs. Sleep,

Who look'd a white lamb; yet was a black
    sheep:

80

With other Countesses of Blank—but rank;
    At once the "lie" and the "élite" of crowds;
Who pass like water filter'd in a tank,
    All purged and pious from their native
      clouds;
Or paper turn'd to money by the Bank:
    No matter how or why, the passport shrouds
The "passée" and the past; for good society
Is no less famed for tolerance than piety,—

81

That is, up to a certain point; which point
    Forms the most difficult in punctuation.
Appearances appear to form the joint
    On which it hinges in a higher station;
And so that no explosion cry "Aroint
    Thee, witch!" or each Medea has her Jason;
Or (to the point with Horace and with Pulci)
"Omne tulit punctum, quæ *miscuit utile*
    dulci."

82

I can't exactly trace their rule of right,
    Which hath a little leaning to a lottery.
I've seen a virtuous woman put down quite
    By the mere combination of a coterie;
Also a so-so matron boldly fight
    Her way back to the world by dint of plot-
      tery,
And shine the very *Siria* of the spheres,
Escaping with a few slight, scarless sneers.

83

I have seen more than I'll say:—but we will see
    How our *villeggiatura* will get on.
The party might consist of thirty-three
    Of highest caste—the Brahmins of the ton.
I have named a few, not foremost in degree,
    But ta'en at hazard as the rhyme may run.
By way of sprinkling, scatter'd amongst these
There also were some Irish absentees.

84

There was Parolles, too, the legal bully,
    Who limits all his battles to the bar
And senate: when invited elsewhere, truly,
    He shows more appetite for words than war.
There was the young bard Rackrhyme, who
      had newly
    Come out and glimmer'd as a six weeks' star.

There was Lord Pyrrho, too, the great free-
    thinker;
And Sir John Pottledeep, the mighty drinker.

85

There was the Duke of Dash, who was a—
    duke,
    "Ay, every inch a" duke; there were twelve
      peers
Like Charlemagne's—and all such peers in look
    And intellect, that neither eyes nor ears
For commoners had ever them mistook.
    There were the six Miss Rawbolds—pretty
      dears!
All song and sentiment; whose hearts were set
Less on a convent than a coronet.

86

There were four Honourable Misters, whose
    Honour was more before their names than
      after;
There was the preux Chevalier de la Ruse,
    Whom France and Fortune lately deign'd to
      waft here,
Whose chiefly harmless talent was to amuse;
    But the clubs found it rather serious laugh-
      ter,
Because—such was his magic power to please—
The dice seem'd charm'd, too, with his re-
    partees.

87

There was Dick Dubious, the metaphysician,
    Who loved philosophy and a good dinner;
Angle, the soi-disant mathematician;
    Sir Henry Silvercup, the great race-winner.
There was the Reverend Rodomont Precisian,
    Who did not hate so much the sin as sinner;
And Lord Augustus Fitz-Plantagenet,
Good at all things, but better at a bet.

88

There was Jack Jargon, the gigantic guards-
    man;
    And General Fireface, famous in the field,
A great tactician, and no less a swordsman,
    Who ate, last war, more Yankees than he
      kill'd.
There was the waggish Welsh Judge, Jefferies
    Hardsman,
    In his grave office so completely skill'd,
That when a culprit came for condemnation,
He had his judge's joke for consolation.

89

Good company's a chess-board—there are kings,
  Queens, bishops, knights, rooks, pawns; the
    world's a game;
Save that the puppets pull at their own strings,
  Methinks gay Punch hath something of the
    same.
My Muse, the butterfly hath but her wings,
  Not stings, and flits through ether without
    aim,
Alighting rarely:—were she but a hornet,
Perhaps there might be vices which would
    mourn it.

90

I had forgotten—but must not forget—
  An orator, the latest of the session,
Who had deliver'd well a very set
  Smooth speech, his first and maidenly trans-
    gression
Upon debate: the papers echoed yet
  With his début, which made a strong im-
    pression,
And rank'd with what is every day display'd—
"The best first speech that ever yet was made."

91

Proud of his "Hear hims!" proud, too, of his
    vote
  And lost virginity of oratory,
Proud of his learning (just enough to quote),
  He revell'd in his Ciceronian glory:
With memory excellent to get by rote,
  With wit to hatch a pun or tell a story,
Graced with some merit, and with more ef-
    frontery,
"His country's pride," he came down to the
    country.

92

There also were two wits by acclamation,
  Longbow from Ireland, Strongbow from the
    Tweed,
Both lawyers and both men of education:
  But Strongbow's wit was of more polish'd
    breed;
Longbow was rich in an imagination
  As beautiful and bounding as a steed,
But sometimes stumbling over a potato,—
While Strongbow's best things might have
    come from Cato.

93

Strongbow was like a new-tuned harpsichord;
  But Longbow wild as an Æolian harp,
With which the winds of heaven can claim
    accord,
  And make a music, whether flat or sharp.
Of Strongbow's talk you would not change a
    word:
  At Longbow's phrases you might sometimes
    carp:
Both wits—one born so, and the other bred,
This by his heart—his rival by his head.

94

If all these seem a heterogeneous mass
  To be assembled at a country seat,
Yet think, a specimen of every class
  Is better than a humdrum tête-à-tête.
The days of Comedy are gone, alas!
  When Congreve's fool could vie with Mo-
    lière's *bête:*
Society is smooth'd to that excess,
That manners hardly differ more than dress.

95

Our ridicules are kept in the background—
  Ridiculous enough, but also dull;
Professions, too, are no more to be found
  Professional; and there is nought to cull
Of folly's fruit; for though your fools abound,
  They're barren, and not worth the pains to
    pull.
Society is now one polish'd horde,
Form'd of two mighty tribes, the *Bores* and
    Bored.

96

But from being farmers, we turn gleaners,
    gleaning
  The scanty but right-well thresh'd ears of
    truth;
And, gentle reader! when you gather meaning,
  You may be Boaz, and I—modest Ruth.
Further I'd quote, but Scripture intervening
  Forbids. A great impression in my youth
Was made by Mrs. Adams, where she cries
"That Scriptures out of church are blas-
    phemies."

97

But what we can we glean in this vile age
  Of chaff, although our gleanings be not
    grist.
I must not quite omit the talking sage,

Kit-Cat, the famous Conversationist,
Who, in his common-place book, had a page
  Prepared each morn for evenings. "List, oh
    list!"
"Alas, poor ghost!"—What unexpected woes
Await those who have studied their bons-mots!

98

Firstly, they must allure the conversation
  By many windings to their clever clinch;
And secondly, must let slip no occasion,
  Nor *bate* (abate) their hearers of an *inch,*
But take an ell—and make a great sensation,
  If possible; and thirdly, never flinch
When some smart talker puts them to the test,
But seize the last word, which no doubt's the
  best.

99

Lord Henry and his lady were the hosts;
  The party we have touch'd on were the
    guests.
Their table was a board to tempt even ghosts
  To pass the Styx for more substantial feasts.
I will not dwell upon ragoûts or roasts,
  Albeit all human history attests
That happiness for man—the hungry sinner!—
Since Eve ate apples, much depends on dinner.

100

Witness the lands which "flow'd with milk and
  honey,"
  Held out unto the hungry Israelites:
To this we have added since, the love of
  money,
  The only sort of pleasure which requites.
Youth fades, and leaves our days no longer
  sunny;
  We tire of mistresses and parasites;
But oh, ambrosial cash! Ah! who would lose
  thee?
When we no more can use, or even abuse thee!

101

The gentlemen got up betimes to shoot,
  Or hunt: the young, because they liked the
    sport—
The first thing boys like after play and fruit;
  The middle-aged, to make the day more
    short;
For *ennui* is a growth of English root,
  Though nameless in our language:—we re-
    tort

The fact for words, and let the French translate
That awful yawn which sleep cannot abate.

102

The elderly walk'd through the library,
  And tumbled books, or criticised the pic-
    tures,
Or saunter'd through the gardens piteously,
  And made upon the hot-house several stric-
    tures,
Or rode a nag which trotted not too high,
  Or on the morning papers read their lec-
    tures,
Or on the watch their longing eyes would fix,
Longing at sixty for the hour of six.

103

But none were "gêné": the great hour of
  union
  Was rung by dinner's knell; till then all
    were
Masters of their own time—or in communion,
  Or solitary, as they chose to bear
The hours, which how to pass is but to few
  known.
  Each rose up at his own, and had to spare
What time he chose for dress, and broke his
  fast
When, where, and how he chose for that re-
  past.

104

The ladies—some rouged, some a little pale—
  Met the morn as they might. If fine, they
    rode,
Or walk'd; if foul, they read, or told a tale,
  Sung, or rehearsed the last dance from
    abroad;
Discuss'd the fashion which might next pre-
  vail,
  And settled bonnets by the newest code,
Or cramm'd twelve sheets into one little letter,
To make each correspondent a new debtor.

105

For some had absent lovers, all had friends.
  The earth has nothing like a she epistle,
And hardly heaven—because it never ends.
  I love the mystery of a female missal,
Which, like a creed, ne'er says all it intends,
  But full of cunning as Ulysses' whistle,
When he allured poor Dolon:—you had better
Take care what you reply to such a letter.

106

Then there were billiards; cards, too, but *no*
  dice;—
  Save in the clubs no man of honour plays;—
Boats when 'twas water, skating when 'twas
  ice,
  And the hard frost destroy'd the scenting
  days:
And angling, too, that solitary vice,
  Whatever Izaak Walton sings or says:
The quaint, old, cruel coxcomb, in his gullet
Should have a hook, and a small trout to
  pull it.

107

With evening came the banquet and the wine;
  The conversazione; the duet,
Attuned by voices more or less divine
  (My heart or head aches with the memory
  yet).
The four Miss Rawbolds in a glee would
  shine;
  But the two youngest loved more to be set
Down to the harp—because to music's charms
They added graceful necks, white hands and
  arms.

108

Sometimes a dance (though rarely on field
  days,
  For then the gentlemen were rather tired)
Display'd some sylph-like figures in its maze;
  Then there was small-talk ready when re-
  quired;
Flirtation—but decorous; the mere praise
  Of charms that should or should not be
  admired.
The hunters fought their fox-hunt o'er again,
And then retreated soberly—at ten.

109

The politicians, in a nook apart,
  Discuss'd the world, and settled all the
  spheres;
The wits watch'd every loophole for their art,
  To introduce a bon-mot head and ears;
Small is the rest of those who would be smart,
  A moment's good thing may have cost them
  years
Before they find an hour to introduce it;
And then, even *then,* some bore may make
  them lose it.

110

But all was gentle and aristocratic
  In this our party; polish'd, smooth, and
  cold,
As Phidian forms cut out of marble Attic.
  There now are no Squire Westerns as of
  old;
And our Sophias are not so emphatic,
  But fair as then, or fairer to behold.
We have no accomplish'd blackguards, like
  Tom Jones,
But gentlemen in stays, as stiff as stones.

111

They separated at an early hour;
  That is, ere midnight—which is London's
  noon;
But in the country ladies seek their bower
  A little earlier than the waning moon.
Peace to the slumbers of each folded flower—
  May the rose call back its true colour soon!
Good hours of fair cheeks are the fairest
  tinters,
And lower the price of rouge—at least some
  winters.

Questions

1. Investigate the ways in which Byron uses off-rhymes and jingling meters to mock certain ideas.

2. The stanzaic form in *Don Juan* is called *ottava rima* (*abababcc*). Choose one stanza and analyze the way in which Byron uses this form. For example, is there a shift in tone and attitude in the concluding couplet?

3. How does Byron view the poetry of the past? What are his own literary principles?

4. What are the common characteristics of the Amundeville guests? Are there any contrasting characters?

5. Describe the setting, the architecture, and the history of the Amundeville castle. Do these details contribute anything to Byron's meaning?

6. Write an essay on the imagery of stagnation and containment in Canto XIII. Take into account the opposing imagery of flow and freedom.

ELLEN DOUGLASS LEYBURN

Animal Stories

Ellen Douglass Leyburn is Professor of English at Agnes Scott College. "Animal Stories" is Chapter 4 of her book, *Satiric Allegory: Mirror of Man* (1956). The beast fable is one of the oldest and most frequently used satiric devices, and the description printed here provides both a concise history of the device and a skillful analysis of how it works. This material raises some interesting questions about the example of animal satire included in this book, *Animal Farm*.

prettie Allegories stealing under the formall Tales of beastes, makes many more beastly then beastes: begin to heare the sound of vertue from these dumb speakers.

SIR PHILIP SIDNEY

Brute creation seems sometimes to exist as a satire on mankind. All that the allegorist needs to do is to point the parallel. Moralists have used man's likeness to the animals for instruction in a variety of ways ranging from the strange edification of the medieval bestiary to the reproof of the newspaper political cartoon. There has never been a time when men were not trying to teach each other the lessons to be learned from the creatures. The Bible is full of such teaching; and the stories spread under the name of Aesop are probably more widely known than any other classical literature. The

FROM *Satiric Allegory: Mirror of Man* by Ellen Douglass Leyburn, by permission of Yale University Press. Copyright 1956.

Orient is as rich as the Occident in this lore; and the African folk tales, many of which reappear with a new set of animal characters in the Uncle Remus stories, attest the vitality of the genre without dependence on a written language.

Sometimes the teaching is so explicit that the resulting work cannot be called allegory. This is true of many of the fables of Aesop and his successors; but it is a significant proof of the value of indirection in art, even the art of pedagogy, that the best and best known of the Aesopic fables label the moral and leave it as something distinct and outside the story instead of making it explicit within the narrative. The ones that do point the lesson within the tale are the least effective of the group. When the mother of the wayward thrush explains to her son, who wants to make a companion of the swallow, that friendship between those who cannot bear the same climate is folly, we have the feeling that the bird would have learned more by making the experiment and we by watching its outcome. In this fable, the moral is at least dramatized to the extent of being explained to a character within the action. The reader is even more dismayed when the point is simply explained directly to him, as in the fable of Jupiter's not granting horns to the camel because the prayer was for something nature had not intended. The more artistic fables tell the story and stop like true allegories, allowing the reader the pleasure of drawing his own conclusion before he reaches the labeled moral, which remains outside the story.

When the cock tells the fox who has been preaching a general peace among the animals in order to make the cock come down out of the tree, that the dogs are coming, the story is complete with the dramatic ending of the fox's running off. When the fox who has refused to visit the sick lion says that he notices tracks of other animals going to the lion's palace, but none coming away, we know what to think without having the moral further pointed. The moral is left suspended within the tale in all the most familiar of Aesop's fables: The Fox and the Grapes, The Dog in the Manger, The Hare and the Tortoise, The Fox and the Stork, The Dog and His Shadow, and the Country Mouse and the City Mouse. And when any of these reappear in the writings of sophisticated artists, as when Horace retells the last named story, the same rule holds. The artist respects the integrity of the story and the intelligence of the reader and lets the tale make its own point. Perhaps L'Estrange is right in the preface to his edition of the Fables when he says that we are all like children and prefer the pill of moral teaching sweetened with the pleasure of the tale.[1] Nor do we want the pleasure of the allegory spoiled by being told that it is really moral medicine after all. The moral labeled and separated from the tale as is customary in Aesop's stories, we accept without protest because no disguise is presented, and there is therefore no violation of conception; but having the moral stated within the story, where we expect to get

it only through the images, destroys the imaginative effect which it has been the whole object of the story to produce. The case is somewhat altered in a work like Swift's "Beasts' Confession," where the application is longer than the tale, and the animal allegory serves just as introduction to the classes of mankind who mistake their talents. But even here Swift announces the pointing of the moral as distinct from the tale.

A different sort of problem is created by the animal story which is instruction about man observed from the point of view of the animals. A highly effective example of this use of the beasts is Johnson's *Idler*, 22[2] in which the old vulture gives instruction to her young about the order of the universe in which man is created as the "natural food of a vulture." The mother bird, in response to the puzzled inquiry as to how man is to be killed if he is so much bigger and stronger than the vulture, replies:

"We have not the strength of man . . . and I am sometimes in doubt whether we have the subtilty; and the vultures would seldom feast upon his flesh, had not nature, that devoted him to our uses, infused into him a strange ferocity, which I have never observed in any other being that feeds upon the earth. Two herds of men will often meet and shake the earth with noise, and fill the air with fire. When you hear noise, and see fire, with flashes along the ground, hasten to the place with your swiftest wing, for men are surely destroying one another; you will then find the ground smoking with blood, and covered with carcasses, of which many are dismembered, and mangled for the convenience of the vulture."—"But when men have killed their prey," said the pupil, "Why do they not eat it?" "When the wolf has killed a sheep, he suffers not the vulture to touch it till he has satisfied himself. Is not man another kind of wolf?"—"Man," said the mother, "is the only beast who kills that which he does not devour, and this quality makes him so much a benefactor to our species."

In the effort to explain the mystery of human behavior, the mother quotes a wise old vulture of the Carpathian rocks:

[1] *Fables of Aesop and Other Eminent Mythologists with Morals and Reflexions* by Sir Roger L'Estrange (London, 1692), A₂.

[2] Johnson omitted this essay from collected editions of the *Idler;* but it is reprinted at the end of Chalmers's edition. The quotations are from *British Essayists*, ed. by A. Chalmers (Boston, 1864), 27, 400-02.

"His opinion was, that man had only the appearance of animal life, being really vegetables with a power of motion; and that as the boughs of an oak are dashed together by the storm, that swine may fatten upon the falling acorns, so men are, by some unaccountable power, driven one against another, till they lose their motion, that vultures may be fed. Others think they have observed something of contrivance and policy among these mischievous beings; and those that hover more closely round them, pretend, that there is, in every herd, one that gives directions to the rest, and seems to be more eminently delighted with a wide carnage. What it is that entitles him to such preëminence we know not; he is seldom the biggest or the swiftest, but he shows by his eagerness and diligence that he is, more than any of the others, a friend to vultures."

The impact of the satire here comes from the ironic point of view. At first the essay seems not allegorical at all since the animals are not acting in a way that parallels man's actions. But it turns out that the point of view itself is an allegory of man's assumption that he is the center of the universe, with all other beings created for his benefit. This attitude of the vultures, which is perfectly sustained once Johnson leaves the awkward introduction of the shepherd for the story itself, contributes an extra level to the irony of the analysis of the reasons why men kill each other for the "convenience of the vulture."

In addition to the large body of assorted kinds of fables, there are a great many more strictly allegorical satires with animal characters. The very universality and obviousness of the relation of animals to man makes at once the appeal of this sort of satiric story and its special difficulty. Both sides of the parallel are so familiar that it is hard to keep them in proper balance, and every reader feels himself competent from his own observation to judge what the writer is doing with the material. But beyond this recognition of the familiar, there are certain criteria by which to judge success in the form.

One gift essential to the teller of satiric animal tales is the power to keep his reader conscious simultaneously of the human traits satirized and of the animals as animals. The moment he loses hold on resemblance and lets his protagonists become merely animals or merely people, his instrument has slipped in his hands and deflected his material away from satiric allegory into something like *Black Beauty* or *The Three Bears*. But if the writer of animal allegory can successfully sustain and play upon two levels of perception, making us feel that his animals are really animals and yet as human as ourselves, he can control the imaginative response. This doubleness of effect is the central power of great animal stories as different as the *Nun's Priest's Tale* and *The Tar Baby*. We delight in Chaunticleer and Pertelote and Brer Rabbit because they are at once real as people and real as animals. The climax of the Tar Baby story, "Bred en bawn in a brier-patch, Brer Fox—bred en bawn in a brier-patch!" reminds us inescapably that this creature is a rabbit exactly while it reminds us of his resemblance to the human being who by his wit can extricate himself from any difficulty. Uncle Remus concludes, "en wid dat he skip out des ez lively ez a cricket in de embers," and we find his liveliness irresistible because we see a real rabbit skipping off in a mood that we know as human. So with Chaucer's masterpiece: Pertelote's "Pekke hem up right as they growe and ete hem yn" is often cited as one of Chaucer's wittiest reductions to the animal level in all his mock-heroic scheme. Yet this remark, which reminds the reader with humorous felicity that a hen is speaking, conveys also the quintessence of Pertolote's wifely solicitude. It seems that when she is most a chicken, she is most full of the particular sort of femininity that Chaucer is placing beside masculine roosterishness for amused scrutiny.

Indeed, it is belief in these creatures as animals that accentuates and isolates the human trait singled out for laughing observation. The animal make-up from which the human characteristic emerges throws it into high light and sharpens perception, acting as a proper vehicle for the tenor. Thus the true animal allegory fulfills I. A. Richards' requirement: "the vehicle is not . . . a mere embellishment of a tenor which is otherwise unchanged but the vehicle and tenor in co-operation give a meaning of more varied powers than can be ascribed to either."[3]

Since the whole point of animal satire is to

[3] *The Philosophy of Rhetoric* (New York, 1936), p. 100.

show up humanity by revealing human traits in nonhuman characters, it follows that the few human beings who appear must not be characterized at all lest they break into the allegorical scheme. At the end of the Uncle Remus stories we know no more about "Miss Meadows en de gals" than does the little boy when he first asks, "Who was Miss Meadows, Uncle Remus?" and gets the unenlightening response: "Don't ax me, honey. She wuz in de tale, Miss Meadows en de gals wuz, en de tale I give you like hi't wer' gun ter me." The characterization of Mr. Man is if possible even vaguer: "Des a man, honey. Dat's all." In George Orwell's *Animal Farm,* where the notion of man as tyrannical master is necessary to the imaginative plan, the only human character who really figures after the ousting of Mr. Jones is Whymper, who as his name suggests has no personality at all, and he is never seen by the nonporcine animals from whose point of view the story is told. The *Nun's Priest's Tale* may seem an exception to this rule, for there is a good deal of circumstantial detail in the depicting of the widow who owns the fowls. But when we come to examine the treatment of her "sooty bower" and her "attempree diete," we find that all the attention is given to externals. As a person, the widow has no more identity than do the peasants who own Chaunticleer in Chaucer's sources. The realistic detail of her few possessions and her meager life is all used to sharpen the humor of the elaborate mock-heroic treatment of the cock and his lady. It seems safe to say that there does not exist anywhere a successful animal allegory which includes a vivid human character.

Another outgrowth of the choice of animal characters to throw human traits into bold relief is the concentration upon isolated human characteristics. The successful writer of animal allegory rarely gives his characters more than one human trait at a time. This concentrated singleness of attack might almost be laid down as a second law of the genre, as binding as the first that the animals shall stay both animal and human. It removes the possibility of very complex characterization. The complexity comes from the double consciousness of animal and human attributes; and the force of the tale is almost in proportion to the singleness and simplicity on the human level. This is true even of a fairly sustained piece such as Munro Leaf's *Ferdinand.* The increasingly funny repetition of the comment that Ferdinand just sat down quietly and smelled the flowers whenever he was expected to fight not only endears the bull to us in our belligerent world, but leaves the essence of his character indelibly fixed in our minds. This is all we know of him and all we need to know except that "He is very happy."

The same practice holds in aggregations of stories centered around one character such as the medieval beast epic of *Reynard the Fox,* where Reynard is always cruelly taking advantage of his neighbors, and the Uncle Remus stories, where Brer Rabbit always mischievously turns the tables on his stronger enemies. As Uncle Remus puts it, "Eve'y time I run over in my min' 'bout the pranks er Brer Rabbit . . . hit make me laugh mo' en mo'. He mos' allers come out on top, yit dey wuz times w'en he hatter be mighty spry." His invention is boundless, but he is always himself.

The essence of his character revealed in story after story Uncle Remus summarizes: "dey w'a'n't no man 'mungs de creeturs w'at kin stan' right flat-footed en wuk he min' quick lak Brer Rabbit." What most stimulates his intelligence is being in a tight place: "Brer Rabbit 'gun ter git skeer'd, en w'en dat creetur git skeer'd, he min' wuk lak one er deze yer flutter-mills."

A corollary of the focus upon single human traits in animal tales is brevity. The swiftness with which the narrative reaches its climax sharpens the concentrated effect of the flashing out of the human motive. Uncle Remus's comment on his hero's character gives the clue to the simple plot of most of his stories, which without ever seeming monotonous repeatedly show Brer Rabbit "monst'us busy . . . sailin' 'roun' fixin' up his tricks" to outdo the other animals who have it in for him: "dem t'er creeturs. Dey wuz allers a-layin' traps fer Brer Rabbit en gittin' cotch in um deyse'f." Though he is usually extricating himself from a difficulty, he sometimes initiates pranks from sheer love of mischief. He is always alert for fun. "Brer Rabbit, he one er deze yer kinder mens w'at sleep wid der eye wide open." The illustrations of his ingenuity as it makes the plots for the tales are endless: he gets Mr. Fox, who has come to fetch him for revenge to serve as his "ridin' hoss" by pretending to be too ill to accompany Brer Fox on foot; he gets Miss Cow stuck fast by the horns in the persimmon tree so that he and all his family can milk her by promising her a feast of persimmons that she is to shake down by butting the tree; he scalds Mr. Wolf, who runs into his chest for protection from the dogs; he gets the bag after Mr. Fox's hunt by playing dead and tempting Brer Fox to add the rabbit to his game; on two occasions he nibbles up the butter and manages to let the 'possum and the weasel have the blame; he saves the meat of his own cow, takes Mr. Man's cow from Brer Fox, and steals Mr. Man's meat and money by a series of ruses; he often persuades other animals to take his place in traps by appealing to their greed; he escapes from the hawk by begging to be allowed to grow big enough to make a full meal and from the embrace of the wildcat by offering to tell him how to get turkey meat; he turns the tables on other enemies by appealing to their perversity in many variations on the Tar Baby story. Always Brer Rabbit is equal to the emergency. His own ruses succeed and those to outwit him fail. Only the Terrapin and the Crow ever best him, never any of the stronger animals like the Fox, the Bear, and the Lion. After the account of his exploits, Uncle Remus's judgment seems a model of understatement: "Bless yo' soul, honey, Brer Rabbit mought er bin kinder fibble in de legs, but he w'a'n't no ways cripple und' de hat."

Just as the hero of these stories represents always mischievous fooling, so he confronts only one trait in his antagonist in each story. The singleness of impression, which enforces the sharpness, is never violated. But one source of variety from story to story is the range of human traits singled out in the other creatures for Brer Rabbit's laughter. To be sure, laughter is the quality of his prankish intelligence. "Well . . . you know w'at kinder man Brer Rabbit is. He des went off some'ers by he own-alone se'f en tuck a big laugh." Uncle Remus's adjective for him is "sassy." But the very story of his Laughing Place is another illustration that the weaknesses of the other creatures give him ample scope to exercise

his ingenuity in besting them for his own amusement.

In Caxton's version of the medieval stories of Reynard, on the other hand, the hero is the bully. Surely from the folklorist's viewpoint one of the most interesting aspects of animal stories is the relationships among the various groups. The story of Brer Rabbit's rising from the well by getting the fox to leap into the other well bucket, for instance, is identical with the story that Erswynd, wife of Isegrim the Wulf, tells of her being tricked into the well bucket by Reynard. A plot that is repeated with different characters in both sets of stories is that of the creature delivered and turning on his deliverer, only to be reimprisoned by the judgment of a third party. Rukenaw tells in Caxton the story of the man's freeing the serpent, who then turns on the man, with Reynard as the judge who refuses advice until he sees the contestants in their original positions. In the Uncle Remus version, the creature under the rock is the wolf, who is freed by Brer Rabbit, and the judge is Brer Tarrypin (always Brer Rabbit's ally except when he outruns his speedier friend in the Uncle Remus variant of the story of the Tortoise and the Hare) who says: "I hates might'ly fer ter put you all gents ter so much trouble; yit, dey aint no two ways, I'll hatter see des how Brer Wolf was kotch, en des how de rock wuz layin' 'pun top un 'im." Then of course the wolf is left pinned under the rock just as is the snake in the other story.

The intricate ramifications of interrelations of sources for both sets of stories lie beyond the scope of this study, which is concerned with the artistry of the telling. But the subject of the representation of the heroes is an aesthetic problem which is curiously linked with the larger anthropological relation. It is hard to resist the impression that somewhere in the course of the development of the two groups of tales, one hero was set up in deliberate response to the other. Both are extremely clever; and both triumph over the other animals by deceits. But the feeling created by the two is totally different. When Uncle Remus says, "dat seetful Brer Rabbit done fool ole Brer Fox" we laugh with the rabbit. When Erswynd says, "Ache felle reynart/noman can kepe hym self fro the[e]/thou canst so wel vttre thy wordes and thy falsenes and reson sette forth," our sympathy is all with the duped she-wolf. Instead of rejoicing at Reynard's triumphs, the reader shudders at the cruelty of his tricks, which grow in evil from his making Bruin lose "his scalp, ears, and forepaws," in his bloody escape "nearly dead" from the cloven tree, through his preparing for his false pilgrimage by securing a square foot of Bruin's hide for his scrip and two shoes from each by ripping off the pawskins of Isegrim and Erswynd, through his cold-blooded devouring of Cuwart, the Hare, to the horrors of the final fight in which he slips his shaved and oiled body always out of Isegrim's grasp while he blinds the wolf by slapping his face with the tail befouled according to Rukenaw's suggestion, kicking sand into Isegrim's eyes, and treating him with every sort of indignity until he wins with his ugly stratagem leaving Isegrim mutilated and half dead. Parallel to the mounting cruelty of his deeds is the increasing baseness of his false speeches. His deceits instead of tickling the fancy like those of Brer Rabbit make their treachery abhorrent. There is serious hatred of Reynard and serious reason for it:

> Alle the beestis both poure and riche were alle stylle when the foxe spak so stoutly / the cony laprel and the roek were so sore aferde that they durste not speke but pyked and stryked them out of the court bothe two. and whan they were a room fer in the playne they saide. god graunte that this felle murderare may fare euyl. he can bywrappe and couere his falshede. that his wordes seme as trewe as the gospel herof knoweth noman than we. how shold we brynge wytnesse. it is better that we wyke and departe. than we sholde holde a felde and fyghte with hym. he is so shrewde. ye [a] thaugh ther of vs were fyue we coude not defende vs. but he shold sle vs alle.

While the narrative management in *Reynard the Fox*, as in other groups of animal stories is episodic, Caxton's version of the epic has decided organization toward a climax. The increasing tension is craftily arranged. Reynard's first false defense is filled with consummate treachery; but his villainy is greater in his second hoodwinking of the king. When honors are finally heaped upon him after his foul play to Isegrim, perfidy is left triumphant. If we turn from such a spectacle of evil to the merry pranks of Brer Rabbit, we are bound to feel some slight restoring of poetic justice in the fact that Brer Fox is always defeated in his efforts to outwit Brer Rabbit. Nothing can bring to life the hens and pigeons and other helpless creatures, even Cuwart the Hare himself, whom Reynard has foully murdered; but it is hard to resist the feeling that the sly Brer Fox is suffering some retribution for the sins of Reynard.

This strong difference in response to the two protagonists suggests a third criterion by which to judge the satirist using animal tales for his allegory. The kinds of smartness displayed by Reynard and Brer Rabbit are, of course, different; but much of the difference in the feeling about them is determined by the attitude toward them displayed in the stories. The establishing of a clear point of view toward the animal characters seems as important a requisite for the successful animal tale as does the focusing on a single dominant trait in the animal. The rejoicing of Uncle Remus and his various hearers in the exploits of Brer Rabbit is an incalculable aid to Harris in communicating the same attitude to the reader; but as he repeatedly says in the introductions to his various volumes, he did not create Uncle Remus's point of view. Brer Rabbit is the hero, in the full admiring sense of the word, of the stories as Harris heard them told by Negro after Negro. To be sure, he is a hero that can be laughed at; but the gay satire is directed at the human foibles of the other animals which lead them into Brer Rabbit's traps. In the stories of Reynard, on the other hand, while there is some mockery of the animals who are Reynard's dupes, the appalling comment on human character comes in Reynard himself. Modern experience of the rise of tyrants through cruelty and lies must intensify response to the revelation of iniquity in Reynard; but there can be no doubt that Caxton intends Reynard to be regarded as a villain. We see that Isegrim is as simpleminded as Brer Wolf; but instead of feeling that his stupidity is mocked, we resent the violence done him. We are conscious of the greed of Bruin and Tybert which helps make them prey to Reynard's wiles; Bellin's desire for importance is directly responsible for his being killed as Cuwart's murderer; and Nobel seems a very unsuspecting monarch indeed to be taken in by Reynard's flattery. But many of the fox's victims have no other weakness than physical helplessness. The revealing light of the allegorical satire is turned most searchingly upon the villainous hero himself; and when he is allowed to go off triumphant in the end, the feeling is that the wicked ways of the world have been convincingly displayed.

There is obviously a good deal of social satire, especially of abuses in the church, in *Reynard the Fox*. This would be in a measure true of any group of stories presenting a number of animals together. The mere assembling of individuals suggests some comment on social structure. Even the fables of La Fontaine display the classes of society, as does the assembly of birds alone in *The Parlement of Foules*. But in some animal stories, the central purpose is clearly comment on society rather than on individual human traits. In such stories the same artistic criteria hold. The sustaining of the animal disguise is still the first requisite; the absence of strong human characters and the presence of sharply individualized animal characters with a single dominant human trait seem as important for the social satire couched in animal terms as for the story whose object is simply laughter at a human foible; a clear viewpoint again must control the response. The failure to meet these tests of the successful writer of animal allegory explains the ineptitudes of so great an allegorist as Spenser when he tries to tell an animal story.

Mother Hubberds Tale, for all its vivid picture of abuses in church and court, is not a successful animal satire. The Fox and the Ape are specious rogues indeed, but we never believe in them as animals except possibly for the moment of their stealing the Lion's skin. Many similarities have been shown between Spenser's material and that of the medieval stories of Reynard, including the basic one of alliance in trickery of these two animals. But Spenser never succeeds in giving them the life of their prototypes. Part of his difficulty in giving his characters reality as animals may

come from his being unable to transmute the images of real men. It seems clear that the animals stand for actual individuals at Elizabeth's court, though scholars dispute about the identification of the Ape. The result of their not becoming convincing animal characters is that the poem affords none of the pleasure of using the imagination at two levels, which is the chief reason for being of allegory. When Spenser's protagonists trick the husbandman into hiring them as shepherd and dog, they are simply thieves who enjoy stealing and slaying the sheep. They do eat the flock; but there is no distinction between the eating done by Ape and Fox, for they are both all the while simply deceitful men. In the final episode when they come to rule, with the Ape in the stolen skin of the Lion, we forget altogether that it is a lion's throne they have usurped and are given almost a lecture on the abuses of false human courtiers and the pitiful plight of suitors at court, with the lesson pointed by the contrasting picture of the man who truly loves honor. Spenser is writing here with too much passion of personal disillusion to achieve artistic detachment and the indirection of allegory. Animals are forgotten in lines like these:

Most miserable man, whom wicked fate
Hath brought to Court, to sue for had ywist,
That few haue found, and manie one hath mist;
Full little knowest thou that hast not tride,
What hell it is, in suing long to bide:
To loose good dayes, that might be better spent;
To wast long nights in pensiue discontent;
To speed to day, to be put back to morrow;
To feed on hope, to pine with feare and sorrow;
To haue thy Princes grace, yet want her Peeres;
To haue thy asking, yet waite manie yeeres;
To fret thy soule with crosses and with cares;
To eate thy heart through comfortlesse dispaires;
To fawne, to crowche, to waite, to ride, to ronne,
To spend, to giue, to want, to be vndonne.
Vnhappie wight, borne to desastrous end,
That doth his life in so long tendance spend.
                    (ll. 892-908, Variorum ed.)

It is, in fact, startling to return to the story of the sleeping Lion by the awkward device of having Jove send Mercury to awaken him and spur him back to his kingdom to drive out the usurpers. The encounter with the priest whom the Fox and the Ape meet between their tricks as shepherds and as courtiers is a sharply ironic indictment of the worldly practices of churchmen. But the account of the proper way to make a priest's life a soft one is put into the mouth of a real priest, who is all too convincingly human. Consequently, we almost nowhere feel that we are in an animal world; and when Sir Mule or the sheep whose lamb the wolf has killed does appear as an actual animal, we are startled and jarred. *Mother Hubberds Tale* is almost as far from being true animal allegory as is *The Hind and the Panther*. The force of Spenser's satiric feeling and the variety of his poetic power carry us along; but the poem does not succeed as a work of art.

George Orwell, a writer of much less stature than Spenser, has written in *Animal Farm* a more effective social satire than *Mother Hubberds Tale*. His animals are absolutely real as animals from the first meeting in the big barn to hear Old Major's dream of a world in which the animals are equal and free of their human masters to their frightened approach to the farmhouse window at the end of the book when only those animals who are tall enough can peep in. The horses are always horses who pull loads; the cows are cows who must be milked, however, awkwardly, by the pigs, "their trotters being well adapted to this task"; the hens are hens who lay eggs and want to keep them; even the bureaucratic pigs remain pigs, hard as they try to be human—which gives its overwhelming force to the denouément of the story when the terrified subject animals creep back to the window of the farmhouse and look "from pig to man, and from man to pig, and from pig to man again; but already it [is] impossible to say which [is] which."

The point of view is always that of the animals who are being duped. Their plight is deepened for the reader by his being allowed to discover the successive machinations of the pigs only as they are borne in upon the stupider animals. Orwell never forgets and lets us inside the consciousness of Napoleon and Squealer. We simply see the one strutting and lording it over his victims and hear the other giving specious explanations of why the pigs must live in luxury. We see and hear what the subject animals see and hear.

While they are consistently animals, each reveals a predominant human trait. Clover is a "stout motherly mare" from the time when at the opening meeting she makes a protecting wall around the motherless ducklings with her great foreleg, through the time after the purge when the desolate survivors huddle around her, and through her efforts to keep Boxer from overworking and then to rescue him from the knacker, until she leads her fearful fellow creatures up to the farmhouse at the end, to witness the full extent of their betrayal.

Boxer "was not of first-rate intelligence, but he was universally respected for his steadiness of character and tremendous powers of work." His inability to learn the alphabet is linked with his unswerving devotion to his two mottoes: "I will work harder" and "Comrade Napoleon is always right," for there is something stupid in his letting his great strength be used up to serve the interests of the oppressors in the totalitarian state. Yet his loyalty is intensely moving, especially as his strength fails and he still works harder than ever: "Sometimes on the slope leading to the top of the quarry, when he braced his muscles against the weight of some vast boulder, it seemed that nothing kept him on his feet except the will to continue. At such times his lips were seen to form the words, 'I will worker harder'; he had no voice left." And when in the knacker's van the drumming of his hoofs grows fainter and dies away, we feel all the force of human goodness traduced so that after the faithful horse has been made into glue and dog meat, there is all the greater sense of outrage at Squealer's fraudulent speech to the Comrades distorting all the circumstances of Boxer's life and death (for which he makes up a sentimental deathbed scene in a beautifully tended hospital instead of the actual slaughter house one) to make the other animals more servile slaves than ever.

The delineation of a single human trait is just as vivid in the other animals: the boar Snowball, the impetuous, inventive leader who is ousted; the other boar Napoleon the dictator, who starts out by taking the milk and apples for the pigs and goes on to the creating of a slave state; Squealer, the pig propagandist, who shifts the commandments to suit the leaders' actions and explains all their oppressions as to the advantage of the comrades; the donkey Benjamin, who is a cynic; Mollie, the pretty white mare who loves ribbons more than principle; and all the others. Even the animals who are not named and appear in groups show up human crowds in single moods. The silly sheep always bleat at the pigs' command, whether their tune is "Four legs good, two legs bad" or "Four legs good, two legs better." The terrible dogs trained as Napoleon's bodyguard are always the ferocious, bloodthirsty instruments of terror. They are the police of the police state.

Since Orwell has succeeded in his underlining of separate human characteristics in his individual animals, his comment on society is convincing. It is because the imaginative scheme of the animal allegory is sustained that the revelation of the ease with which well-meaning citizens can be duped into serving the masters of a totalitarian state achieves its power. Orwell's keeping the point of view consistently that of the helpless animals and letting us make only the discoveries that they make forces us to interpret for ourselves not just the misfortunes of the renamed Manor Farm, but also those of our own world. We are compelled to participate imaginatively. *Animal Farm* is successful social satire because it is successful allegory.

Questions

1. What does Ellen Leyburn mean by the term *allegory?*
2. What criteria for judging the effectiveness of animal satire are suggested in this article?

CHRISTOPHER HOLLIS

Animal Farm

This discussion of *Animal Farm* provides the necessary information about the political scene in which the book was written and opens a number of questions about its form, its style, and its meaning. Christopher Hollis is a distinguished contemporary of Orwell's—they were classmates at Eton—who has had a most successful political career. His book *A Study of George Orwell* (1956), from which this selection is taken, was written, Hollis explains in the preface, as an extension of a "continuing friendly argument" with Orwell about his political views.

Whatever the advantages or disadvantages of the German invasion of Russia, at least it saved Britain from the risk of immediate invasion and defeat, and thus such a man as Orwell, who was alarmed at the ultimate consequences of the Russian alliance, was able to live his life under a lesser strain in the last years of the war than in the first. He was able to give his mind once more to creative writing. Yet the problem what to write was not simple. The crying need to his mind was to arouse public opinion to the dangers of the Russian alliance. Yet the mood of the country at the time when Stalingrad was being defended was not such that it would tolerate a straightforward and bitter attack on Russia—the kind of attack which he had already launched in his essay in the composite volume, the *Betrayal of the Left,* which he had published in 1941, when of course public opinion in Britain was willing to tolerate it because Russia was still bound in hostility to us by the Nazi-Soviet Pact. Now direction could only be found out by indirection. The consequence, immediately and apparently inconvenient to Orwell as a writer, turned out in the event to be brilliantly fortunate. For it caused Orwell to make his point by the indirect, roundabout, whimsical road of an animal fairy-story and thus led him to experiment with a new form of writing of which he proved himself magnificently the master. Whereas his previous books had never had more than small and struggling sales, *Animal Farm* at once caught the public fancy in almost every country of the world— particularly in the United States—was translated into every one of the leading languages, established him as one of the best-selling authors of the day and incidentally gave him for the first time in life a tolerable income.

Fortune favoured him in the timing of the publication which it imposed upon him. *Animal Farm,* a short book of less than a hundred pages, was written between November 1943 and February 1944. It was, said Orwell, "the only one of my books I really sweated over." What would have been its fate had it immediately found a publisher and appeared in the winter of 1944, when Russia was still fighting

FROM *A Study of George Orwell* by Christopher Hollis, by permission of Henry Regnery Company and Hollis and Carter Ltd. Copyright 1956.

and Western statesmen were full of optimism about the possibility of just arrangements with her, it is hard to say. Influences and the climate of opinion might well have prevented it from gaining any but a small and eccentric market. Happily for Orwell four publishers in succession rejected it on the ground that it would be against public policy at such a time to put on the market a book attacking our Russian ally. As a result it only appeared through Messrs. Secker and Warburg in the early summer of 1945, in the month of the German surrender, when fighting had come to an end, and its first circulation exactly coincided with the beginnings of popular disillusionment with Russian policy, as people in the West saw to their dismay the ugly methods by which the Russians were establishing themselves in the East. By chance it exactly struck the public mood and was the first book to strike it.

The story of *Animal Farm* is so familiar that it hardly needs detailed recapitulation. An old boar, of the name of Major, on the brink of death summons to the barn all the animals on the farm of a broken-down drunkard, called Jones, and gives to them his farewell message —the result of his long meditation on life. It is that the enemy of all animals is Man. Man lives by exploiting his animals. The animals produce their food of one sort or another, but they are not allowed to draw for themselves any benefit from their increased production. Man seizes it all for his own need, allows to the animals only sufficient to keep them alive and able to work, cynically and ruthlessly exploits them in their lives and as cynically and ruthlessly destroys them as soon as their days of work are done. Let the animals rise up, expel the enemy Man and run the farm as a co-operative farm of animals in the animals' own interest.

Three days later Major dies, but he has left behind him his message of revolt. The animals are, it is true, not as yet clear how to carry into practice this gospel of revolt. They meet and sing together their new hymn "Beasts of England." An unpremeditated accident eventually brings on the revolt. On midsummer eve Jones gets drunk in the neighbouring village of Wilmington. The hired men milk the cows and then go off for a day's rabbiting, leaving the animals unfed. In the afternoon, when the animals can stand their hunger no longer, one of the cows breaks in the door of the store-shed with her horn and all the animals rush in and start helping themselves from the bin. Jones wakes up from his drunken slumber. He and the men rush out with whips in their hands and start laying about them. Though there had been no plan of resistance, the animals turn on Jones and the men, attack them and, before they know where they are, have driven them helter-skelter from the farm.

Thus the animals established themselves with unexpected ease as the masters of the farm. It is Orwell's humour to show no great difficulty in the task in which they had expected their main difficulty—in the seizure of power—but enormous and finally fatal difficulty in the task which they hardly expected to present a problem at all—in the exercise of power when seized. With the death of Major the leadership of the animals falls into the hands of the two leading pigs, Snowball and Napoleon—for Orwell throughout represents the pigs as far more intelligent than any of the other animals. Of these he explains with delicious mock solemnity that Napoleon was "not much of a talker" but had "a reputation for getting his own way." Snowball was quicker, but "was not considered to have the same depth of character." There is a full and vivid portrait gallery of other animals of which the most notable are Boxer, the good, stupid, unsuspicious horse, of immense physical strength, to whose unquestioning mind the remedy for all problems was to work harder— Squealer, another pig, who was, as it were, the P.R.O. to Napoleon—Benjamin, the donkey, the only cynic among the animals, who knows that life has always been hard, believes that it always will be hard and is sceptical of all promises of improvement, and Moses, the raven, who does no work but continually tells to the other animals his tale of the Sugar Candy Mountains above the sky where "it was Sunday seven days a week, clover was in season all the year round and lump-sugar and linseed oil grew on the hedges."

In the early days of Animal Farm the animals have to prepare themselves for the inevitable counter-attack when Jones and his fellow men will attempt to recapture the farm. The rivalry between Snowball and Napoleon is becoming increasingly evident and they differ and quarrel on every point of policy, but in face of the threat of Man's attack they do not dare to let things come to an open breach. Then in October Jones attacks and, owing to the heroism and strategy of Snowball, he is driven off in rout at the Battle of the Cowshed.

After the defeat of Jones there is no longer any reason why Snowball and Napoleon should preserve even an appearance of amity. The fundamental difference between them is that Snowball thinks that the animals should "send out more pigeons and stir up rebellion among the animals on other farms," while Napoleon thinks that "what the animals must do was to produce firearms and train themselves to the use of them." They also differ over Snowball's ambition to build a windmill to which Napoleon is opposed.

Napoleon bides his time. He has made himself the master of a litter of young puppies which he is secretly training up as his gendarmerie. Then when the day comes, he suddenly introduces these dogs, as they have by then become, into the assembly and lets them loose on Snowball, whom they chase from the farm. It is then that the pace of the degradation increases. More and more Napoleon and the pigs who are faithful to him seize for themselves almost all the food of the farm. The other animals are forced down to a standard of living lower than that which they had in Jones's time. They have to work harder. Whenever anything goes wrong on the farm, the fault is ascribed to Snowball, who is supposed to be lurking in a near-by farm and making nocturnal raids into Animal Farm. He was, the animals are told, in league with Jones from the first. Documents had proved it. The history of Animal Farm is unblushingly falsified. The animals are told, first, that Snowball's part in the Battle of the Cowshed was greatly exaggerated, then that he had in fact fought in it on Jones's side. The windmill is built, but the animals are now told that it was Napoleon who was in favour of it all along and Snowball who was against it. To all complaints that the animals may make at their hard lot the invariable and crushing reply is,

"Do you want Jones back?" They must put up with all hardships as the only alternative to this more awful fate.

In the original constitution the animals had sworn to have no dealings with Man, but the next summer Napoleon announces the new policy by which the Farm is to trade with neighbouring men in order to obtain certain essential materials of life. The trade is of course to be kept entirely in Napoleon's own hands. No other animals than he are to have any contact with the surrounding men. Then he moves into Jones's house and establishes it as his palace. He lives a life increasingly remote from the other animals by whom he is rarely seen. In the autumn a storm blows down the windmill, but of course it is explained that its destruction is not at all due to defects in building but to the sabotage of Snowball. The winter is a hard one and there is a situation bordering on rebellion—particularly among the hens who object to the seizure of their eggs for the purpose of trade with men. Napoleon deals with it in characteristically unhesitating and terrible fashion [see p. 129, pars. 4 and 5].

After that the old song "Beasts of England" is suppressed, and there is substituted for it Minimus's new song,

> Animal Farm, Animal Farm,
> Never through me shalt thou come to harm.

One after another the commandments on which Animal Farm was built are found to have been secretly altered. For "No animal shall kill another animal," the animals now find the commandment to read, "No animal shall kill another animal without cause." "No animal shall sleep in a bed" is now "No animal shall sleep in a bed with sheets." It had been Napoleon's plan to sell a load of timber to their neighbouring human farmer, Frederick, with the money for which he will buy machinery for the windmill. The timber is delivered and five-pound notes are paid to the animals in exchange. It is only when through their agent the animals attempt to use the five-pound notes for purchases that they find that Frederick has cheated them and that the notes are forgeries. Napoleon attempts to enlist the alliance of the animals' other neighbour, Pilkington, against Frederick,

but Pilkington is unsympathetic. "Serves you right," he says. The humans determine on a second attack on Animal Farm. They come this time armed with guns. They destroy the windmill but are driven off in a second defeat.

It is a few days later that the pigs discover a case of whiskey in Jones's cellar, and it is, naturally enough, at the same time that the commandment "No animal shall drink alcohol" is found now to read "No animal shall drink alcohol to excess."

All comes to a climax when the faithful Boxer one day falls down between the shafts and is no longer strong enough to work. Under the pretence that they are sending him to the vet to be cured, the pigs sell him to a knacker, tell the other animals that he has died at the vet's, in spite of having received every attention, and that his last words were "Forward, Comrades!! Forward in the name of Rebellion! Long live Animal Farm! Long live Comrade Napoleon! Napoleon is always right!" With the money that they have received from Boxer's carcass the pigs buy a case of whiskey and hold a banquet in Jones's house.

The great mark of Animal Farm had been its hostility to everything that went on two legs. "Four legs good, two legs bad" had been the continual bleat of the sheep and four legs had been the great mark of animalism, of animal solidarity. But now the pigs set themselves to learning how to walk on two legs. The motto of the Farm is changed into "All animals are equal, but some animals are more equal than others," and one day the pigs emerge from Jones's house walking on two legs and with whips in their hands. They take out subscriptions to *John Bull, Tit-Bits* and the *Daily Mirror*. The obedient sheep, trained in secret by Squealer, change their bleat of "Four legs good, two legs bad" into "Four legs good, two legs better."

After their second defeat in the Battle of the Windmill the neighbouring men had given up all hope of defeating and destroying the animals, nor indeed once the pigs had shown themselves as ready to impose discipline on their animals as was any human farmer, was there any longer any need, from their point of view, for them to do so. A policy of peaceful co-existence in every way suited them better. Parties of men used to come on visits to the farm and were taken round on conducted tours. At last there comes the night of the great banquet of alliance between the human Pilkington and Napoleon. The animals, looking in through the windows, see pigs and men sitting together and hear the exchange of congratulatory speeches. Mr. Pilkington "believed that he was right in saying that the lower animals on Animal Farm did more work and received less food than any animals in the country. . . . If you have your lower animals to contend with, we have our lower classes." As the celebrations proceed, the pigs, the animals notice, come to look more and more like men and the men more and more like pigs. "The creatures outside looked from pig to man and from man to pig, and from pig to man again, but already it was impossible to say which was which." But assimilation cannot bring harmony. They fall to playing cards, and the banquet breaks up into chaos as Mr. Pilkington and Napoleon each play the ace of spades simultaneously.

The interpretation of the fable is plain enough. Major, Napoleon, Snowball—Lenin, Stalin and Trotzky—Pilkington and Frederick, the two groups of non-Communist powers—the Marxian thesis, as expounded by Major, that society is divided into exploiters and exploited and that all the exploited need to do is to rise up, to expel the exploiters and seize the "surplus value" which the exploiters have previously annexed to themselves—the Actonian thesis that power corrupts and the Burnhamian thesis that the leaders of the exploited, having used the rhetoric of equality to get rid of the old exploiters, establish in their place not a classless society but themselves as a new governing class—the greed and unprincipled opportunism of the non-Communist states, which are ready enough to overthrow the Communists by force so long as they imagine that their overthrow will be easy but begin to talk of peace when they find the task difficult and when they think that they can use the Communists to satisfy their greed—the dishonour among total thugs, as a result of which, though greed may make original ideology irrelevant, turning pigs into men and men into pigs, the thugs fall out among themselves, as the Nazis and the Communists fell out, not through difference of ideology but because in a society of utter baseness and insincerity there is no motive of confidence. The interpretation is so plain that no serious critic can dispute it. Those Russian critics who have professed to see in it merely a general satire on bureaucracy without any special reference to any particular country can hardly be taken seriously.

Yet even a total acceptance of Orwell's political opinions would not in itself make *Animal Farm* a great work of art. The world is full of animal fables in which this or that country is symbolized by this or that animal, and very tedious affairs the greater number of them are—and that, irrespective of whether we agree or disagree with their opinions. To be a great book, a book of animal fables requires literary greatness as well as good cause. Such greatness *Animal Farm* surely possesses. As Orwell fairly claimed, *Animal Farm* "was the first book in which I tried, with full consciousness of what I was doing, to fuse political purpose and artistic purpose into one whole"—and he succeeded.

The problems that are set by this peculiar form of art, which makes animals behave like human beings, are clear. The writer must throughout be successful in preserving a delicate and whimsical balance. As Johnson truly says in his criticism of Dryden's *Hind and the Panther,* there is an initial absurdity in making animals discuss complicated intellectual problems—the nature of the Church's authority in Dryden's case, the communist ideology in Orwell's. The absurdity can only be saved from ridicule if the author is able to couch his argument in very simple terms and to draw his illustrations from the facts of animal life. In this Orwell is as successful as he could be—a great deal more successful incidentally than Dryden, who in the excitement of the argument often forgets that it is animals who are supposed to be putting it forward. The practical difficulties of the conceit must either be ignored or apparently solved in some simple and striking—if possible, amusing—fashion. Since obviously they could not in reality be solved at all, the author merely makes himself ridiculous if he allows himself to get bogged down in tedious and detailed explanations which at the end of all cannot in the nature of things explain anything. Thus

Orwell is quite right merely to ignore the difficulties of language, to assume that the animals can communicate with one another by speech—or to assume that the new ordinance which forbids any animal to take another animal's life could be applied with only the comparatively mild consequence of gradual increase in animal population. He is justified in telling us the stories of the two attacks by men for the recapture of the Farm but in refusing to spoil his story by allowing the men to take the full measures which obviously men would take if they found themselves in such an impossible situation. The means by which the animals rout the men are inevitably signally unconvincing if we are to consider them seriously at all. It would as obviously be ridiculous to delay for pages to describe how animals build windmills or how they write up commandments on a wall. It heightens the comedy to give a passing sentence of description to their hauling the stone up a hill so that it may be broken into manageable fractions when it falls over the precipice, or to Squealer, climbing a ladder to paint up his message.

The animal fable, if it is to succeed at all, ought clearly to carry with it a gay and light-hearted message. It must be full of comedy and laughter. The form is too far removed from reality to tolerate sustained bitterness. Both Chaucer and La Fontaine discovered this in their times, and the trouble with Orwell was that the lesson which he wished to teach was not ultimately a gay lesson. It was not the lesson that mankind had its foibles and its follies but that all would be well in the end. It was more nearly a lesson of despair—the lesson that anarchy was intolerable, that mankind could not be ruled without entrusting power somewhere or other and, to whomsoever power was entrusted, it was almost certain to be abused. For power was itself corrupting. But it was Orwell's twisted triumph that in the relief of the months immediately after the war mankind was probably not prepared to take such dark medicine if it had been offered to it undiluted. It accepted it because it came in this gay and coloured and fanciful form.

The film version gives to *Animal Farm* a happy ending. The animals all the world over, hearing how Napoleon has betrayed the animal cause, rise up against him at the end and in a second revolution expel him. After this second revolution, we are left to believe, a rule of freedom and equality is established and survives. But of course this ending makes nonsense of the whole thesis. It was the Orwellian thesis, right or wrong, that power inevitably corrupts and that revolutions therefore inevitably fail of their purpose. The new masters are necessarily corrupted by their new power. The second revolution would necessarily have failed of its purpose just as the first had failed. It would merely have set up a second vicious circle.

Animal Farm possesses two essential qualities of a successful animal fable. On the one hand the author of such a fable must have the Swift-like capacity of ascribing with solemn face to the animals idiotic but easily recognized human qualities, decking them out in aptly changed phraseology to suit the animal life—ascribe the quality and then pass quickly on before the reader has begun to find the point overlaboured. This Orwell has to perfection [see p. 115, par. 1, and p. 136, par. 6].
. . .

But what is also essential—and this is often overlooked—is that the writer should have himself a genuine love of animals—should be able to create here and there, in the midst of all his absurdity, scenes of animal life, in themselves realistic and lovable. In that Chaucer, the first and greatest of Orwell's masters in this form of art, pre-eminently excelled. It was in that that Orwell himself excelled. He had always been himself a lover of animals, intimate with their ways. "Most of the good memories of my childhood, and up to the age of about twenty," he wrote in *Such, Such Were the Joys,* "are in some way connected with animals," and it was the work with animals which attracted him in maturer years to agricultural life. There is a real poetic quality, mixed whimsically in with absurdity, in his picture of the first meeting of the animals in the barn with which the book opens.

As I say, there is no difficulty in interpreting the symbolism of the story. But it is not quite so certain what is the total moral that we are supposed to draw from it. Is it that there is some special evil and fraud in Communism which makes it inevitable that all communist movements will turn only into a new and worse tyranny? or is it rather that power is in itself, to whatever ideology it may nominally be allied, inevitably corrupting? that all promises of equality and liberty will prove inevitably to be deceptions? and that history does not, and cannot, consist of anything other than the overthrow of old tyrants in order that new tyrants may be put in their place? It is obvious that the second alternative was much more natural to Orwell's mind than the first and that Conservatives who hailed *Animal Farm* as an attack simply on Communism interpreted it too narrowly and too much to suit their own convenience. Orwell's whole record from Spanish days onwards shows his impartial hatred of all tyrannies and of all totalitarian claims, and as a matter of history, it was against what he thought of as a fascist tyranny that he first enlisted to fight. In *Animal Farm* itself we must not be diverted by the satire on the animals from noticing how utterly worthless are without exception the parts played by men, who represent the conservative principle. He complained of Mr. Rayner Heppenstall's radio version of it for "casting a sop to those stinking Catholics." There is no hint of a suggestion that Jones, a drunken brute, who was letting the farm down, did not deserve all that he got. The parts that he played both when he had the farm and after he lost it were alike discreditable. His men were no better. When Jones was away drunk they took advantage of his absence not to feed the animals. The two neighbouring farmers—Pilkington, "an easy-going gentleman farmer who spent most of his time in fishing or hunting according to the season"—and Frederick, "a tough, shrewd man, perpetually involved in lawsuits and with a name for driving hard bargains"—are equally worthless. Their sole motive is greed. They are willing to destroy the animals, if possible, and, if it is not possible, to make out of them what they can, and they are incapable of honouring their bargains. The lesson of *Animal Farm* is clearly not merely the corrupting effect of power when exercised by Communists, but the corrupting effect of power when exercised by anybody. As for the Communists being worse than other people—clearly, rightly or wrongly,

Orwell did not think that Communists were worse than Fascists. By Fascists he really meant Nazis, for he never bothered much about Mussolini one way or the other and, although in Catalonia he called the followers of Franco Fascists, he specifically recognized that they were something different. But Fascists, if Fascists means Nazis, he thought to be worse than Communists. It was of no great moment what were the nominal creeds either of the one party or the other, for absolute power tends to corrupt absolutely, and the totalitarian is in practice, whatever he may profess, solely concerned with maintaining and extending his power. It is power politics and nothing but power politics.

But was there then no remedy and no hope? There was certainly no hope in anything like the modern circumstances of life that we should see anything of the nature of free and equal society. From time to time Orwell expresses a hope that we may be moving "eventually" to such a consummation, but with no great confidence and for no very clear reason. "Of course no honest person claims that happiness is *now* a normal condition among adult human beings," he writes, "but perhaps it *could* be made normal, and it is upon this question that all serious political controversy really turns." All the evidence is, he admits, that we are moving away from it. All that we can really say is that time has a certain mollifying influence and that, though all governments are tyrannies, old tyrannies are less ruthless than new. The rule of law is a great deal better than the rule of public opinion or of an arbitrary tyrant. "In a society in which there is no law, and in theory no compulsion, the only arbiter of behaviour is public opinion. But public opinion, because of the tremendous urge to conformity in gregarious animals, is less tolerant than any system of law." Therefore it might appear that the conclusion that ought to follow is that no régime would be very good but that the least bad would be a moderate conservative régime—a régime which preserved the traditional structure of society and at the same time preserved the liberal principles so that those parts of it that in the development of events showed signs of collapse might be at necessity modified—indeed something of the nature of what we in the West call free institutions. The clean choice of Socialist theory between production for profit and production for social use, which Orwell had himself to some extent offered in "England, Your England," belongs to the lecture room rather than to real life. In the real world of the years after 1945, with the Socialists leaving so many industries under private enterprise and the Conservatives leaving so many industries nationalized, nationalization was clearly a matter of the balance of advantage and disadvantage in each particular case rather than of absolute good and evil. It was not a stark choice of one sort of society against another sort. The policy which Orwell believed that Dickens recommended to the nineteenth century should, it would seem on this argument, be the sort of policy which he should recommend to the twentieth century.

I should myself be prepared to argue that this was the conclusion which Orwell ought to have drawn from his own writings in general and from *Animal Farm* in particular. But it must be admitted that it was not a conclusion which Orwell ever did explicitly draw. As a reporter of fact Mr. Brander is substantially accurate when he writes, "Orwell wrote very little about the Church in his criticism of society. He classed it with Conservatism as no longer serious enough to be considered." Orwell's complaint was not so much against an ideal philosophy of Conservatism, for which, when he found it, he had a reasonable respect, as against those who called themselves Conservatives and had captured the Conservative machine. His complaint against them was that they were at once too arrogant and too compromising. They were too arrogant in so far as they tended to claim their privileges as something which they had deserved and to arrogate to themselves the airs of superior people. These very claims obscured the true case for Conservatism which was that society

had to be arranged, that there was little reason to think that it would ever be arranged ideally well, that it was fatally easy for men to fritter away all their energies in agitation and scheming for its rearrangement and that therefore there was always something to be said, within limits, for accepting society broadly as it is and getting on with the business of living. It may very well turn out that there would be more liberty that way than down a more revolutionary, more ideally perfectionist, road —and liberty was what really mattered. Even in his most revolutionary moods—as in "England, Your England"—he was, if we analyse his argument, primarily concerned with the proclamation of a libertarian and egalitarian purpose. Once the purpose was proclaimed he was quite content in practice to let things move forward at a slow and conservative pace. Willing to impose drastic sufferings upon himself, he never, save in moments of special exaltation, imagined that it would be possible to impose such drastic sufferings on society at large and to preserve freedom.

But a more important complaint against the Conservatives was that they were too compromising. While the case for Conservatism was that it stood for traditional ways and ancient liberties against the menace of the new philosophies, the Conservatives in practice, he complained, had shown themselves always only too ready to do a deal with the new philosophies and "the stream-lined men," as Pilkington did his deal with Napoleon, as soon as the "stream-lined men" had shown themselves to be in the least tough and strong. They did a deal with the Fascists before the war and with the Communists in the Anglo-Russian alliance during the war. Orwell despaired of the Conservatives because the Conservatives despaired of Conservatism. They were without principle.

Questions

1. According to Hollis, what are the problems of writing animal satire, and how does Orwell solve them?

2. How does the end of the film *Animal Farm* make nonsense of the book?

3. Do you believe, as Hollis states, that the writer of animal satire should have "a genuine love of animals"?

4. Discuss the problems that Hollis raises about the ultimate meaning of *Animal Farm*.

Why I Write

Since Orwell is frequently accused by his enemies of being a "mere pamphleteer" who never disciplined his feelings or marshaled his observations, this essay, written in 1947, is of particular interest for readers of his books. He raises here, in his usual honest, clear fashion, the fundamental artistic problem of the relation between life and art, personality and style, which is of crucial importance for a writer like Orwell whose books are often frankly political and polemical.

From a very early age, perhaps the age of five or six, I knew that when I grew up I should be a writer. Between the ages of about seventeen and twenty-four I tried to abandon this idea, but I did so with the consciousness that I was outraging my true nature and that sooner or later I should have to settle down and write books.

I was the middle child of three, but there was a gap of five years on either side, and I barely saw my father before I was eight. For this and other reasons I was somewhat lonely, and I soon developed disagreeable mannerisms which made me unpopular throughout my schooldays. I had the lonely child's habit of making up stories and holding conversations with imaginary persons, and I think from the very start my literary ambitions were mixed up with the feeling of being isolated and undervalued. I knew that I had a facility with words and a power of facing unpleasant facts, and I felt that this created a sort of private

world in which I could get my own back for my failure in everyday life. Nevertheless the volume of serious—*i.e.* seriously intended—writing which I produced all through my childhood and boyhood would not amount to half a dozen pages. I wrote my first poem at the age of four or five, my mother taking it down to dictation. I cannot remember anything about it except that it was about a tiger and the tiger had "chair-like teeth"—a good enough phrase, but I fancy the poem was a plagiarism of Blake's "Tiger, Tiger." At eleven, when the war of 1914-18 broke out, I wrote a patriotic poem which was printed in the local newspaper, as was another, two years later, on the death of Kitchener. From time to time, when I was a bit older, I wrote bad and usually unfinished "nature poems" in the Georgian style. I also, about twice, attempted a short story which was a ghastly failure. That was the total of the would-be serious work that I actually set down on paper during all those years.

However, throughout this time I did in a sense engage in literary activities. To begin with there was the made-to-order stuff which

I produced quickly, easily and without much pleasure to myself. Apart from school work, I wrote *vers d'occasion,* semi-comic poems which I could turn out at what now seems to me astonishing speed—at fourteen I wrote a whole rhyming play, in imitation of Aristophanes, in about a week—and helped to edit school magazines, both printed and in manuscript. These magazines were the most pitiful burlesque stuff that you could imagine, and I took far less trouble with them than I now would with the cheapest journalism. But side by side with all this, for fifteen years or more, I was carrying out a literary exercise of a quite different kind: this was the making up of a continuous "story" about myself, a sort of diary existing only in the mind. I believe this is a common habit of children and adolescents. As a very small child I used to imagine that I was, say, Robin Hood, and picture myself as the hero of thrilling adventures, but quite soon my "story" ceased to be narcissistic in a crude way and became more and more a mere description of what I was doing and the things I saw. For minutes at a time this kind of thing would be running through my head: "He pushed the door open and entered the room. A yellow beam of sunlight, filtering through the muslin curtains, slanted on to the table, where a matchbox, half open, lay beside the inkpot. With his right hand in his pocket he moved across to the window. Down in the street a tortoiseshell cat was chasing a dead leaf," etc., etc. This habit continued till I was about twenty-five, right through my non-literary years. Although I had to search, and did search, for the right words, I seemed to be making this descriptive effort almost against my will, under a kind of compulsion from outside. The "story" must, I suppose, have reflected the styles of the various writers I admired at different ages, but so far as I remember it always had the same meticulous descriptive quality.

When I was about sixteen I suddenly discovered the joy of mere words, *i.e.* the sounds and associations of words. The lines from *Paradise Lost*—

So hee with difficulty and labour hard
Moved on: with difficulty and labour hee,

which do not now seem to me so very wonderful, sent shivers down my backbone; and the spelling "hee" for "he" was an added pleasure. As for the need to describe things, I knew all about it already. So it is clear what kind of books I wanted to write, in so far as I could be said to want to write books at that time. I wanted to write enormous naturalistic novels with unhappy endings, full of detailed descriptions and arresting similes, and also full of purple passages in which words were used partly for the sake of their sound. And in fact my first completed novel, *Burmese Days,* which I wrote when I was thirty but projected much earlier, is rather that kind of book.

I give all this background information because I do not think one can assess a writer's motives without knowing something of his early development. His subject matter will be determined by the age he lives in—at least this is true in tumultuous, revolutionary ages like our own—but before he ever begins to write he will have acquired an emotional attitude from which he will never completely escape. It is his job, no doubt, to discipline his temperament and avoid getting stuck at some immature stage, or in some perverse mood: but if he escapes from his early influences altogether, he will have killed his impulse to write. Putting aside the need to earn a living, I think there are four great motives for writing, at any rate for writing prose. They exist in different degrees in every writer, and in any one writer the proportions will vary from time to time, according to the atmosphere in which he is living. They are:

1. Sheer egoism. Desire to seem clever, to be talked about, to be remembered after death, to get your own back on grownups who snubbed you in childhood, etc., etc. It is humbug to pretend that this is not a motive, and a strong one. Writers share this characteristic with scientists, artists, politicians, lawyers, soldiers, successful businessmen—in short, with the whole top crust of humanity. The great mass of human beings are not acutely selfish. After the age of about thirty they abandon individual ambition—in many cases, indeed, they almost abandon the sense of being individuals at all—and live chiefly for others, or are simply smothered under drudgery. But there is also the minority of gifted, wilful people who are determined to live their own lives

to the end, and writers belong in this class. Serious writers, I should say, are on the whole more vain and self-centred than journalists, though less interested in money.

2. Esthetic enthusiasm. Perception of beauty in the external world, or, on the other hand, in words and their right arrangement. Pleasure in the impact of one sound on another, in the firmness of good prose or the rhythm of a good story. Desire to share an experience which one feels is valuable and ought not to be missed. The esthetic motive is very feeble in a lot of writers, but even a pamphleteer or a writer of textbooks will have pet words and phrases which appeal to him for non-utilitarian reasons; or he may feels strongly about typography, width of margins, etc. Above the level of a railway guide, no book is quite free from esthetic considerations.

3. Historical impulse. Desire to see things as they are, to find out true facts and store them up for the use of posterity.

4. Political purpose—using the word "political" in the widest possible sense. Desire to push the world in a certain direction, to alter other people's idea of the kind of society that they should strive after. Once again, no book is genuinely free from political bias. The opinion that art should have nothing to do with politics is itself a political attitude.

It can be seen how these various impulses must war against one another, and how they must fluctuate from person to person and from time to time. By nature—taking your "nature" to be the state you have attained when you are first adult—I am a person in whom the first three motives would outweigh the fourth. In a peaceful age I might have written ornate or merely descriptive books, and might have remained almost unaware of my political loyalties. As it is I have been forced into becoming a sort of pamphleteer. First I spent five years in an unsuitable profession (the Indian Imperial Police, in Burma), and then I underwent poverty and the sense of failure. This increased my natural hatred of authority and made me for the first time fully aware of the existence of the working classes, and the job in Burma had given me some understanding of the nature of imperialism: but these experiences were not enough to give me an accurate political orientation. Then came Hitler, the Spanish civil war, etc. By the end of 1935 I had still failed to reach a firm decision. I remember a little poem that I wrote at that date, expressing my dilemma:

A happy vicar I might have been
Two hundred years ago,
To preach upon eternal doom
And watch my walnuts grow;

But born, alas, in an evil time,
I missed that pleasant haven,
For the hair has grown on my upper lip
And the clergy are all clean-shaven.

And later still the times were good,
We were so easy to please,
We rocked our troubled thoughts to sleep
On the bosoms of the trees.

All ignorant we dared to own
The joys we now dissemble;
The greenfinch on the apple bough
Could make my enemies tremble.

But girls' bellies and apricots,
Roach in a shaded stream,
Horses, ducks in flight at dawn,
All these are a dream.

It is forbidden to dream again;
We maim our joys or hide them;
Horses are made of chromium steel
And little fat men shall ride them.

I am the worm who never turned,
The eunuch without a harem;
Between the priest and the commissar
I walk like Eugene Aram;

And the commissar is telling my fortune
While the radio plays,
But the priest has promised an Austin Seven
For Duggie always pays.

I dreamed I dwelt in marble halls,
And woke to find it true;
I wasn't born for an age like this;
Was Smith? Was Jones? Were you?

The Spanish war and other events in 1936-7 turned the scale and thereafter I knew where I stood. Every line of serious work that I have written since 1936 has been written, directly or indirectly, *against* totalitarianism and *for* democratic socialism, as I understand it. It seems to me nonsense, in a period like our own, to think that one can avoid writing of such subjects. Everyone writes of them in one guise or another. It is simply a question of which side one takes and what approach one follows. And the more one is conscious of one's political bias, the more chance one has of acting politically without sacrificing one's esthetic and intellectual integrity.

What I have most wanted to do throughout the past ten years is to make political writing into an art. My starting point is always a feeling of partisanship, a sense of injustice. When I sit down to write a book, I do not say to myself, "I am going to produce a work of art." I write it because there is some lie that I want to expose, some fact to which I want to draw attention, and my initial concern is to get a hearing. But I could not do the work of writing a book, or even a long magazine article, if it were not also an esthetic experience. Anyone who cares to examine my work will see that even when it is downright propaganda it contains much that a full-time politician would consider irrelevant. I am not able, and I do not want, completely to abandon the world-view that I acquired in childhood. So long as I remain alive and well I shall continue to feel strongly about prose style, to love the surface of the earth, and to take a pleasure in solid objects and scraps of useless information. It is no use trying to suppress that side of myself. The job is to reconcile my ingrained likes and dislikes with the essentially public, non-individual activities that this age forces on all of us.

It is not easy. It raises problems of construction and of language, and it raises in a new way the problem of truthfulness. Let me give just one example of the cruder kind of difficulty that arises. My book about the Spanish civil war, *Homage to Catalonia,* is, of course, a frankly political book, but in the main it is written with a certain detachment and regard for form. I did try very hard in it to tell the whole truth without violating my literary instincts. But among other things it contains a long chapter, full of newspaper quotations and the like, defending the Trotskyists who were accused of plotting with Franco. Clearly such a chapter, which after a year or two would lose its interest for any ordinary reader, must ruin the book. A critic whom I respect read me a lecture about it. "Why did you put

in all that stuff?" he said. "You've turned what might have been a good book into journalism." What he said was true, but I could not have done otherwise. I happened to know, what very few people in England had been allowed to know, that innocent men were being falsely accused. If I had not been angry about that I should never have written the book.

In one form or another this problem comes up again. The problem of language is subtler and would take too long to discuss. I will only say that of late years I have tried to write less picturesquely and more exactly. In any case I find that by the time you have perfected any style of writing, you have always outgrown it. *Animal Farm* was the first book in which I tried, with full consciousness of what I was doing, to fuse political purpose and artistic purpose into one whole. I have not written a novel for seven years, but I hope to write another fairly soon. It is bound to be a failure, every book is a failure, but I do know with some clarity what kind of book I want to write.

Looking back through the last page or two, I see that I have made it appear as though my motives in writing were wholly public-spirited. I don't want to leave that as the final impression. All writers are vain, selfish and lazy, and at the very bottom of their motives there lies a mystery. Writing a book is a horrible, exhausting struggle, like a long bout of some painful illness. One would never undertake such a thing if one were not driven on by some demon whom one can neither resist nor understand. For all one knows that demon is simply the same instinct that makes a baby squall for attention. And yet it is also true that one can write nothing readable unless one constantly struggles to efface one's own personality. Good prose is like a window pane. I cannot say with certainty which of my motives are the strongest, but I know which of them deserve to be followed. And looking back through my work, I see that it is invariably where I lacked a *political* purpose that I wrote lifeless books and was betrayed into purple passages, sentences without meaning, decorative adjectives and humbug generally.

Questions

1. How did Orwell's natural talents combine with his situation in life to make a writer of him?

2. Of the four reasons Orwell gives for writing, which is the most prominent in his own work, and what reason does he give for this fact? Is it possible that he selected the wrong motive?

3. What is Orwell's view of the proper relation between propaganda and "art" in a piece of writing? What does Orwell seem to mean by the vague term "artistic purpose"?

SUGGESTED PAPER TOPICS

Papers of Medium Length
Based on a Comparison of the Satires

1. Philip Wylie and Mark Twain are both attacking contemporary abuses, but they deliver their attacks in very different ways. Contrast the two methods. Which is more effective and why?

2. It has been said that the basis of every satire is a particular view of the nature of man. Compare the views of human nature in two or more of the satires.

3. Working from the statement in Question 2, see if you can find any correlation in several of the satires between the view of human nature and the particular method used to display human foolishness.

4. Contrast Auden's and Wylie's attitudes toward the world.

5. Discuss the ways in which several of the satirists contrive to bring up the awkward, even terrible, realities of existence which make a mockery of overoptimistic views of history, society, and human nature.

6. Describe in straightforward, expository prose an ideal society on which several or all of the satirists in this volume would agree.

7. Picking examples from the selections, discuss whether any literary form represented here—essay, poem, play, or story—is more suitable for satire than the others are.

Papers of Medium Length
Applying the Criticism to the Satires

1. Apply Elliott's theory about our habitual distrust of satire to one or more of the satires.

2. Which of the satires in this volume is the most "primitive" by Elliott's definition? Which is the most sophisticated? Why?

3. Take one or more satires and show which of Frye's three major "phases" of satire it fits into.

4. Using Frye's and Kernan's articles, write an essay to demonstrate which of the satires is closest to comedy and which is closest to tragedy.

5. Does Wylie's character as revealed in his essay fit the picture of the typical satirist in "A Theory of Satire"?

6. Apply the description of the typical scene of satire (or the typical plot) given in "A Theory of Satire" to several of the satires.

7. Are the conclusions of the satires similar in any way?

8. Describe several instances of invective, high burlesque, low burlesque, and verbal and situational irony in the satires.

9. Is Wylie's essay invective or satire?

10. What are the principal qualities of the satiric scene and the satiric plot in "Love Among the Ruins"?

Papers of Medium Length Using
the Supplementary Material and the Satires

1. Can Mumford's "Doctrine of Progress" be called a satire? How is it similar to the satires and how is it different from them?

2. Using Mumford, write an essay discussing the various aspects of "progress" which are ridiculed in several of the satires.

3. How does Auden adapt Byron's stanzaic form, ottave rima, and what effect on his meaning does the adaptation have?

4. Compare the society of Byron's *Don Juan* with that of Auden's *Letter to Lord Byron*. Could we say that one is the ancestor of the other?

5. Using Leyburn's criteria, consider whether *Animal Farm* is effective animal satire.

6. Can "Inflexible Logic" also be termed animal satire? If so, what are the implications for the meaning of the story?

7. Which of the satires can be termed allegory?

8. Read Hollis' chapter on *Animal Farm* and then discuss whether you think his interpretation of the book is correct.

9. Does Orwell's line "Between the priest and the commissar" accurately describe his position in *Animal Farm*?

Long Papers

1. Satire, because it deals with contemporary problems, is apt to be ephemeral. But lasting satire always manages, even while focusing on the immediate present, to transcend the here and now and to present a picture of society and man which is always true. Determine which of the satires have the best chance of being read by future generations.

2. One of the chief problems of the satirist is getting his readers to take his criticism to heart. We always look around and say, "How true—of the other fellow." Which of the satires in this volume manages to trick us into condemning ourselves, and how does it achieve this most difficult of all tasks?

3. Do the satires in this volume support Orwell's contention that nothing of value can be written unless "one constantly struggles to efface one's own personality"?

4. One of the standard charges leveled against satire is that while it pretends to be true to life it grossly exaggerates human failings and is extremely partial in its selection of details. Is this true of these satires, and if so can you defend satire against this charge? Would the best satire be the one which exaggerated least?

5. Trace the history of the "mock Utopia" from More's *Utopia* to the present. Then discuss the suitability of this device for satire.

6. Select several reviews of *Generation of Vipers* that were written early in 1943 and attempt to catalogue the types of criticisms made. Do they fit the pattern described in "A Theory of Satire"?

7. Construct a defense for science which will answer the charges made against it by some of the satires in this volume.